THE BEST

POP

PUB QUIZ BOOK

Ever!

THE BEST **pop** PUB QUIZ BOOK *Ever!*

CARLTON

Contents

INTRODUCTION

Over the past decade snugs and lounges in pubs the length and breadth of the country have become if not seats of learning, at least seats of intellect – which makes a change from seats of worn leatherette (although these still prevail in some areas). The pub quiz has transformed the bar into an arena of knowledge where beery brethren battle to the final bell. The format is simple; some friends, acquaintances even complete strangers will do, a questioner, some paper, a collection of ragged Biros and a surfeit of beer and questions are all that is needed to create the perfect evening's entertainment. Wits are challenged, heads are huddled and patience is tested as teams attempt to outdo each other in their show of trivia retention. At these events you will learn that no fact is too small, no pop star too obscure and no record too insignificant to test the pub crowd's grey matter. In fact, the more obscure and wide-ranging the questions, the greater the chance of involving the entire barroom – nothing will gain the pub idiot greater respect than showing that they know every Cliff Richard song off by heart, except perhaps their switching from slip-ons to lace ups. So take heart, and a copy of *The Best Pop Pub Quiz Book Ever!* to the boozer and have a few warm up sessions and see if you can't organise your own pub quiz. You know it makes sense; it's the only way you'll know all the answers.

The main aim of *The Best Pop Pub Quiz Book Ever!* is to entertain, so it is important that you retain a sense of humour and good sportsmanship as you play along, whether you are testing friends at home or setting a quiz for your local hostelry. That aside you also have to ensure that you are fully in control of your questions and players; remain calm, speak in a steady voice and be constantly unflapped when challenged by any of the more heavily imbibed, as indeed you will be.

If the locals do get testy your best bet is to head for the door while throwing beer nuts in the air to confuse them, though this should happen in only the roughest pubs or on outings with the extended family – in which case you should attempt to rescue your spouse, if you can do so without spilling your drink and it isn't them causing the trouble.

The Best Pop Pub Quiz Book Ever! is divided into Easy, Medium and Hard questions, which are all subdivided by specialist and Pot Luck rounds. The former can be chosen either to help or hinder your players, giving Easy questions to some is bound to reveal some interesting answers, but it is possibly more challenging to tailor your questions so that the experts receive the brain-wracking Hard questions and the novices the stupefyingly simple Easy questions. Nothing hurts a fanatic more than being beaten on their specialist subject and the division of questions gives you the chance to employ a handicap system. Other handicap systems will also become apparent as you continue as quiz master, the team that wins the Sunday afternoon quiz will doubtless fail when it comes to Sunday night although if you want to set a quiz on Friday night you should check pupil dilation first, as on that evening of great relaxation you may find your teams asleep or brawling before calling the whole thing quits and joining them in a drink... or three.

In the interest of further clarification there follows a brief run down of each section:

Easy
In this primary round the main objective is to keep breathing and keep a pen in your hand. These questions are so easy that even the most docile pub idiot could gurgle his way through them in the time it takes to down a pint and still have time left to knock over the stack of pennies on the bar. If you know what shape a guitar is, you shouldn't have too much difficulty.

Medium
On your toes people, things are getting tricky. By now the ringers on the out-of-towner's team will no longer be looking smug. These questions make for a challenge but you are bound to get the odd pop nut who will fancy his chances, for which you should continue on to section three.

Hard
Ask a full 20 of these questions and only the shrill wail of the pub cat fighting in the yard will be heard. Brows will be furrowed, glances exchanged and beer stared into.

All that is left to say is good luck with your testing and if you can't keep your spirits up at least try to keep them down.

The Easy Questions

If you don't know the difference between Van Halen and Van Morrison, then you will no doubt struggle through the next few questions. For the rest of us though these are the EASY questions, so called because if the quizzee falters on these they are either three sheets to the wind or far too young to be in the pub – either state rendering them toddling buffoons whose social graces will equal their breadth of knowledge.

These questions are perfect when used in the first round of an open entry quiz as they lull everyone into a false sense of security – although you must beware that contestants don't shout answers out which creates a problematic precedent for the later, harder questions. Another way of placing these questions is to dot them about throughout your quiz, thus making sure that on every team everyone should know the answer to at least one question despite their age.

If you are running a league quiz then some of your team members may heap derision on such obvious questions but don't worry, even the cleverest quiz team member can come a cropper.

Quiz 1 Pot Luck 1

Answers – see page 11

LEVEL 1

1 How is Reg Dwight better known?

2 Which Bryan's first hit was "Run To You"?

3 What is the home country of Celine Dion?

4 What was Blondie's Heart made of in 1979?

5 In 1985 Talking Heads were taking the Road to where?

6 Who was lead singer with the Police?

7 Who joined Bennie on a 1976 hit by Elton John?

8 Which surname is shared by Carly and Paul?

9 How many members of the Carpenters were there?

10 What did Bill Haley sing after "See you later, alligator"?

11 Which musical instrument does Eric Clapton play?

12 Which David appeared on TV with the Partridge Family?

13 Which legendary dancer called Fred described Michael Jackson as "a wonderful mover"?

14 In which Queen No. 1 will you hear Beelzebub and Galileo?

15 Who led the Dreamers?

16 Who hit the top with "What Becomes of the Broken Hearted?" in 1996?

17 What was the Spice Girls' No. 1 album in late 1996?

18 What type of dance goes with Spandau in the charts?

19 Which Damon takes lead vocals with Blur?

20 Which London duo sang "you've got more rabbit than Sainsbury's"?

Answers

Pot Luck 2 (see Quiz 3)
1 Collins. 2 Piano. 3 Banshees. 4 Norway. 5 Crickets.
6 Marley. 7 Jesus. 8 Roll. 9 Gerry. 10 "The Power of Love".
11 Kenny Everett. 12 Football. 13 Hillbilly Roll. 14 Ball.
15 Sue. 16 Hotel. 17 Diana Ross. 18 Baker. 19 Cilla Black.
20 Abba.

Quiz 2 The 50s

LEVEL 1

1　What did Bill Haley and the Comets do after "Shake and Rattle"?

2　What rhymes with "Cupid" on the title of the Connie Francis No. 1?

3　Where did Fats Domino find his thrill in 1956?

4　Which Eddie had the Summertime Blues?

5　According to the Everly Brothers in 1959 All I Have to Do Is what?

6　What did Jerry Lee Lewis sing about Great Balls of in 1958?

7　What Gets in your Eyes according to the Platters?

8　Which musical instrument did Russ Conway play?

9　What colour pink went with Apple Blossom White according to Perez Prado and Eddie Calvert in 1955?

10　Which Doris said "Whatever will be, will be" in 1956?

11　What were Guy Mitchell and Tommy Steele each singing for the first month of 1957 at the top of the charts?

12　Which Perry hit the top with "Don't Let the Stars Get in Your Eyes"?

13　How many Everly Brothers were there?

14　Which Adam hit the No. 1 spot with "What Do You Want"?

15　Which Craig was Only Sixteen in 1959?

16　Which Dickie's special day was possibly February 14?

17　Which British Frankie was behind the Green Door and in The Garden of Eden in the 50s?

18　What was the first name of the vocalist Mr Twitty?

19　In Eddie Cochran's "Three Steps to Heaven" at which step does she "Fall in love with you"?

20　How was the Richard described who sang "Long Tall Sally" and "Lucille"?

Quiz 3 Pot Luck 2

Answers – see page 9

1   Which Phil had an album called *No Jacket Required*?

2   Which musical instrument does Elton John play?

3   Who was Siouxsie's group?

4   What is the home country of A-ha?

5   Which Buddy Holly group shares its name with insects?

6   Which Bob sang with the Wailers ?

7   Which part did David Essex play in the musical *Godspell*?

8   What goes with Shake and Rattle in the 50s song?

9   Who led the Pacemakers?

10   Which song title gave No. 1 hits to Jennifer Rush and Frankie Goes to Hollywood?

11   Which late zany DJ was born Maurice Cole?

12   For which sport was "Nessun Dorma" used as a theme in 1990?

13   What goes after Hillbilly Rock in the title of the Woolpackers' hit?

14   Which surname is shared by the singer Michael and bandleader Kenny?

15   What was A Boy Named according to Johnny Cash in 1969?

16   Which Heartbreak place did Elvis stay at in 1956?

17   Who was the original lead singer with the Supremes?

18   In 1978 Gerry Rafferty was in which London Street?

19   How is Priscilla White better known?

20   Whose first hit was "Waterloo"?

Quiz 4 The 60s

Answers – see page 10

1 Who was the drummer with the Dave Clark Five?

2 Which Small mod group were all under five foot six tall?

3 Who completed the line-up of Dave Dee, Dozy, Beaky and Mick?

4 In 1965 the Kinks sang about a Dedicated Follower of what?

5 What did Marvin Gaye Hear it Through in 1969?

6 What did the Beatles Want to Hold on their first US No. 1?

7 Which Corner had Andy Fairweather-Low as lead singer?

8 Which Little girl sang "The Locomotion" in 1962?

9 Which head of the Diddymen shed Tears in 1965?

10 What Is Over according to the Seekers in 1965?

11 Which Engelbert Humperdinck song's second line is "Let me go"?

12 Which 60s dance was popularized by Chubby Checker?

13 Which country were the Bachelors from?

14 What sort of Vibrations did the Beach Boys have in 1966?

15 Which Australian had the last No. 1 of the 60s with "Two Little Boys"?

16 What follows "Ob-La-Di" in the Marmalade No. 1?

17 Which lover of Romeo was a hit for the Four Pennies?

18 In 1960 what was the profession of Lonnie Donegan's dad?

19 Which Pretty pink bird was a No. 1 for Manfred Mann?

20 How old was the Sweet person Neil Sedaka wished Happy Birthday to in 1961?

1 What is the home country of Bryan Adams?

2 Who did Dexy's Midnight Runners tell to Come On in 1982?

3 Which surname is shared by the musical star Darren and the 50s singer Doris?

4 Which Supply's first hit was "All Out of Love"?

5 Which Sheena was a Modern Girl in 1980?

6 What was the first name of the rock star Zappa?

7 In which US state are music towns Memphis and Nashville?

8 Were the Isley Brothers really brothers?

9 Who had a 1994 No. 1 with "Doop"?

10 Who is Vic Reeves's backing band?

11 What do the letters HMV stand for?

12 Which trio of record producers are credited on the 1989 "Ferry 'Cross the Mersey"?

13 What was the Bangles' Flame like in 1989?

14 How is Mark Feld better known?

15 Which "Doctor Who" machine were the Timelords Doctorin' in 1988?

16 Right Said Fred were Deeply what in 1992?

17 How many members of Abba were there?

18 Who is lead singer with Simply Red?

19 In 1967 the Beatles were in which Lane?

20 Which Hearts did Elton John sing about in 1985?

Pot Luck 4 (see Quiz 7)

Answers

1 Cilla Black. 2 Debbie Harry. 3 Mae. 4 Roxy Music.
5 Shapiro. 6 Paul Anka. 7 Cockney Rebel. 8 Neil Diamond.
9 Australia. 10 Guitar. 11 Joseph. 12 k.d. 13 Greece.
14 Turner. 15 Yates. 16 Newcastle. 17 Softly. 18 Starr.
19 Miss Molly. 20 Abbey Road.

Quiz 6 The 70s

Answers – see page 16

1 Which People were with the "YMCA" in 1979?

2 Who was the lead singer with Wings?

3 Which seasonal Nights did John Travolta and Olivia Newton-John sing about?

4 Which country did the Eurovision winner Dana come from?

5 Who had a single called "Killer Queen"?

6 Who were Stayin' Alive?

7 Which birds of prey stayed at the Hotel California?

8 Which glam group had an album called Sweet Fanny Adams?

9 Who had hits with "Close to You" and "We've Only Just Begun"?

10 What colour ribbons did Dawn tie round the Old Oak Tree?

11 Which Ms Knight was backed by the Pips?

12 Which Roberta was "Killing Me Softly With His Song"?

13 Which Gary was "Leader of the Gang"?

14 Whose single and album Bridge Over Troubled Water went to No. 1?

15 Which former Supreme was Still Waiting in 1971?

16 What did the New Seekers say They'd Like to Teach the World to do in 1972?

17 What did Tyrannosaurus Rex change their name to?

18 Which Tubular sounds were a hit for Mike Oldfield?

19 What type of Loaf had a Bat Out of Hell?

20 Which Zeppelin had a string of No. 1 albums during the 70s?

The 80s (see Quiz 8)
1 Newton-John. 2 Two. 3 George. 4 Diana Ross. 5 Whisper.
6 Rogers, Parton. 7 The Gang. 8 Africa. 9 Slade. 10 Wake
Me Up. 11 Dire Straits. 12 U2. 13 Pet Shop. 14 Le Bon.
15 Stand and Deliver. 16 House of Fun. 17 Michael Jackson.
18 Springsteen. 19 *Whitney Houston*. 20 Rain.

14

Quiz 7 Pot Luck 4

Answers – see page 13

 LEVEL 1

1 Which Liverpool lady had a No. 1 with "Anyone Who Had a Heart" in 1963?

2 Who was lead singer with Blondie?

3 Which Vanessa's album was called *The Violin Player*?

4 Which Music group was Bryan Ferry lead singer with?

5 Which Helen was Walking Back to Happiness in 1961?

6 Whose first hit was "Diana" in 1957?

7 Who was Steve Harley's backing group?

8 How is Noah Kaminsky better known?

9 What is the home country of Kylie Minogue?

10 Which musical instrument does Queen's Brian May play?

11 Which character with a Technicolor Dreamcoat did Jason Donovan play on the London stage?

12 What are the initials of the Canadian Ms lang?

13 Which country is Nana Mouskouri from?

14 Which Tina's life story was in the film What's Love Got to Do With It??

15 Which Paula was Mrs Bob Geldof?

16 Which north-east city did the Animals come from?

17 How were the Fugees Killing Me in 1996?

18 Which surname is shared by Edwin and Ringo?

19 Who did Little Richard say Good Golly to back in 1958?

20 Which Road famous for its recording studios is the title of a Beatles album?

Pot Luck 3 (see Quiz 5)
1 Canada. 2 Eileen. 3 Day. 4 Air Supply. 5 Easton. 6 Frank. 7 Tennessee. 8 Yes. 9 Doop. 10 The Wonder Stuff. 11 His Master's Voice. 12 Stock, Aitken and Waterman. 13 Eternal. 14 Marc Bolan. 15 The TARDIS. 16 Dippy. 17 Four. 18 Mick Hucknall. 19 Penny. 20 Breaking.

Quiz 8 The 80s

LEVEL 1

1 Which Olivia got Physical in 1981?

2 How many Tribes were a big hit for Frankie Goes to Hollywood?

3 Which Boy was a Karma Chameleon?

4 Which ex-Supreme joined Lionel Richie on "Endless Love"?

5 Which Careless sound was a hit for George Michael?

6 Which Kenny and Dolly recorded "Islands in the Stream"?

7 Who had a Celebration with Kool?

8 What were the USA for on "We Are the World"?

9 Noddy Holder was the lead singer with which band?

10 What did Wham! say to do Before You Go Go?

11 Which Sultans of Swing took the Walk of Life?

12 Which Irish group's name is made up of one letter and a number?

13 Which Boys had a No. 1 with "West End Girls"?

14 Which Simon sang with Duran Duran?

15 Which highwayman demand did Adam and the Ants give in 1981?

16 Which House provided Madness with their first No. 1?

17 Who had huge album success with *Thriller*?

18 Which Bruce was "Born in the USA"?

19 What was Whitney Houston's first album called?

20 Which Purple weather was a film soundtrack album for Prince?

Quiz 9 Pot Luck 5

Answers – see page 19

LEVEL 1

1   Which song was a No. 1 for the Equals and Pato Banton?

2   Who formed a duo with Lyle?

3   How many c.c. were in the group which sang "I'm Not in Love"?

4   Which Yorkshire town's Fair was the subject of a Simon and Garfunkel song?

5   What Killed the Radio Star according to the Buggles?

6   What is the home country of Björk?

7   Which Elvis song has the line "I gave a letter to the postman, He put it in his sack"?

8   Where did the Police find a Message in 1979?

9   Which Orchestra joined Olivia Newton-John on "Xanadu"?

10 Which Bob wrote "Knockin' on Heaven's Door"?

11 Which instrument does Acker Bilk play?

12 Who took "Sloop John B" into the 60s charts?

13 Who was Alone Again (Naturally) in 1972?

14 How many members of the Thompson Twins were there?

15 Which surname is shared by Cat and Shakin'?

16 Which country star pleaded for Jolene not to take her man in 1976?

17 Whose first hit was "Love and Affection"?

18 How is Robert Zimmerman better known?

19 Who was lead singer with the Mechanics?

20 Which Yellow Brick thoroughfare did Elton John say Goodbye to in 1973?

Answers

Pot Luck 6 (see Quiz 11)

1 USA. 2 Mick Jagger. 3 Sue. 4 Young. 5 South America.
6 Trumpet. 7 Gore. 8 Cardiff. 9 Donny. 10 Three Degrees.
11 The Dock of the Bay. 12 George Martin. 13 The Faces.
14 Parton. 15 Margaret Thatcher. 16 Michael Ball.
17 M People. 18 The Vandellas. 19 Sting. 20 Warwick.

Quiz 10 The 90s

Answers – see page 20

1 Which Melody took Robson and Jerome to No. 1?

2 How long were Take That Back For in 1995?

3 Which Paradise was a hit for Coolio featuring LV?

4 Which Night was special for Whigfield?

5 What is the nationality of chart-topper Alanis Morissette?

6 Whose *Immaculate Collection* was a 1991 bestseller?

7 What was Oasis's first album called?

8 Which opera singer had a hit with "Nessun Dorma" in 1990?

9 Which Ms O'Connor had a No. 1 with "Nothing Compares 2 U"?

10 How many Spice Girls are there?

11 Which superstar's first solo No. 1 was "Sacrifice" in 1990 after more than 50 hit singles?

12 Which Jimmy was famous for his Crocodile Shoes?

13 Which Tasmin reached No. 1 with her first single "Sleeping Satellite" in 1992?

14 Which group named themselves after the hit record "Boys to Men"?

15 Which Mariah had a hit with "Without You" in 1994?

16 What Is All Around according to Wet Wet Wet in 1994?

17 Where was Celine Dion Falling Into in 1996?

18 Which country do Boyzone come from?

19 Which former Wham! member released an album called *Older*?

20 Which Peter chose the right Flava to get to No. 1?

Quiz 11 Pot Luck 6

Answers – see page 17

1   What is the home country of Michael Bolton?

2   Who is lead singer with the Rolling Stones?

3   Which Peggy was a classic 50s hit for Buddy Holly?

4   Which surname is shared by Neil and Paul?

5   Which continent is famous for its Pan Pipes?

6   Which brass instrument did Louis Armstrong play?

7   Which Lesley had the original hit with "It's My Party"?

8   Which Welsh city was Shirley Bassey born in?

9   Which Osmond had a hit with "Young Love"?

10 Which trio was made up of Sheila Ferguson, Valerie Thompson and Fayette Pickney?

11 What was Otis Redding Sittin' On in 1968?

12 Which record producer was known as the Fifth Beatle?

13 Which group was formed when the Small Faces disbanded?

14 What name is shared by Dolly and Stella?

15 Which politician did the Spice Girls say was an original Spice Girl?

16 Whose first hit was "Love Changes Everything"?

17 Which People was Heather Small lead singer of?

18 Who was Martha Reeves's backing group?

19 Which ex-Police man sang "Fields of Gold" in 1993?

20 Which Dionne was a Heartbreaker in 1982?

Quiz 12 The Rolling Stones

Answers – see page 18

LEVEL 1

1 How many members made up the Rolling Stones when they first charted?

2 Which musical instrument does Charlie Watts play?

3 Which Rolling Stones real name is William Perks?

4 Which words go in brackets before the 1965 No. 1 "Satisfaction"?

5 Which two words describe the Rooster in the Stones' No. 1 in November 1964?

6 Which Merseysiders, later seen as Stones' rivals, wrote the Stones' first Top Twenty hit "I Wanna Be Your Man"?

7 The Stones' first album was called *The Rolling Stones*. What was the second album called?

8 Which Nervous Breakdown features in the title of the 1966 hit?

9 In which part of his home was Brian Jones found dead in July 1969?

10 Which controversial song was on the other side of "Ruby Tuesday"?

11 Who did Bianca Rose Perez Moreno de Macias marry in 1970?

12 Complete the title of the 70s album *Goat's Head____*.

13 Which record label signed the Stones in the early 1990s?

14 Who was Jagger Dancin' in the Street with at the Live Aid concert?

15 Who quit the Stones in 1992?

16 Which Stones guitarist sang with the X-pensive Winos?

17 What colour did the Rolling Stones Paint It in 1966?

18 What was Tumbling for the Stones in their Top Five hit in 1972?

19 Which record label did the Stones record on throughout the Sixties?

20 What was the Stones' own record label called?

Answers

The 90s (see Quiz 10)
1 Unchained. 2 Good. 3 Gangsta's. 4 Saturday. 5 Canadian.
6 Madonna. 7 *Oasis*. 8 Pavarotti. 9 Sinead. 10 Five.
11 Elton John. 12 Nail. 13 Archer. 14 Boyz II Men.
15 Carey. 16 Love. 17 You. 18 Ireland. 19 George Michael.
20 André.

Quiz 13 Pot Luck 7

Answers – see page 23

LEVEL 1

1 Which surname is shared by Chuck, Dave and Nick?

2 How many members of the Bee Gees are there?

3 Which Livin' object was Cliff Richard's first No. 1?

4 Which Andrew wrote the music for *Jesus Christ Superstar*?

5 Which Miss Clark had a 60s hit with "Downtown"?

6 Procul Harum sang about a Whiter Shade of what?

7 Which Mungo sang "In the Summertime" in 1970?

8 Which part of East London had the 1994 Christmas No. 1 "Stay Another Day"?

9 Which 90s band sounds like a fertile part of a desert?

10 Whose first hit was "Surfin' USA"?

11 Which initials went with Duncan on "Let's Get Ready to Rhumble" in 1994?

12 What sort of Rampage did Sweet go on in 1974?

13 Which Alvin originally charted as Shane Fenton?

14 Which relative was seen to Swing Out with "Breakout" and "Surrender" in the 80s?

15 "Mandy" gave which Barry his first UK hit?

16 Who was lead singer with Genesis?

17 Martha Reeves, David Bowie and Mick Jagger have all been Dancing where?

18 Which Stewart sang "You're In My Heart" in 1977?

19 Who makes up the trio with Emerson and Lake?

20 What is the home country of Tom Jones?

Pot Luck 8 (see Quiz 15)
1 Cher. 2 Hand. 3 My Love. 4 Guitar. 5 Essex.
6 Matchstalk cats and dogs. 7 The Pacemakers. 8 Four Tops.
9 Greece. 10 The Beatles. 11 Scotland. 12 Sonny.
13 The World. 14 Atlantic. 15 USA. 16 Tyler. 17 Stewart.
18 Delilah. 19 Bob Geldof. 20 Strawberry.

Answers

21

Quiz 14 Karaoke

Answers – see page 24

Answers – see page 24

LEVEL 1

1 Which karaoke classic begins "First I was afraid, I was petrified"?

2 Which song starts "And now the end is near"?

3 What are the first three words of "Unchained Melody"?

4 Which Rhapsody begins "Is this the real life? Is this just fantasy?"?

5 Which Boyzone hit begins "Smile an everlasting smile"?

6 How many times is "Yeah" sung in the chorus of the Beatles' "She Loves You"?

7 Which soccer anthem begins "When you walk through a storm"?

8 Which words follow "Wake up Maggie" in Rod Stewart's "Maggie May"?

9 Which words from the Abba hit go before "It's a rich man's world"?

10 What five words does Stevie Wonder sing after "I just called…"?

11 How many times are the words "We are the champions" sung in the chorus of the song?

12 Which line follows "If I said you had a beautiful body"?

13 Which Cliff Richard classic begins, "When I was young my father said"?

14 Which Slade Christmas hit includes the line "Does your grandma always tell ya, That the old songs are the best?"?

15 What did Carly Simon sing before "I bet you think this song is about you"?

16 Which Robson and Jerome hit included the lines "for every drop of rain that falls, A flower grows"?

17 Which Wet Wet Wet hit begins "I feel it in my fingers, I feel it in my toes"?

18 Which Cher No. 1 includes the lines "If you want to know if he loves you so, It's in his kiss"?

19 Which Don McLean song asks "Do you believe in rock 'n' roll?"?

20 Which song begins "Never seen you looking so gorgeous as you did tonight"?

Answers

Groups (see Quiz 16)

1 Oasis. 2 Take That. 3 Hollywood. 4 Beach Boys. 5 Bay. 6 Culture. 7 Electric Light Orchestra. 8 Genesis. 9 Papas. 10 Wet Wet Wet. 11 Bee Gees. 12 Paul McCartney. 13 Pink Floyd. 14 Jacksons. 15 Fire. 16 South. 17 Abba. 18 Supremes. 19 East 17. 20 Dire Straits.

Quiz 15 Pot Luck 8

Answers – see page 21

LEVEL 1

1 How is Cherilyn Sarkasian LaPier better known?

2 What part of her did Kylie Minogue put on her Heart in 1989?

3 The Colour of what was Celine Dion's top selling album of 1995?

4 Which instrument did Suzi Quatro play?

5 Which singer called David played Che in the original stage production of *Evita*?

6 What did the painter paint along with Matchstalk Men?

7 Who was Gerry's backing group?

8 Which quartet's only UK No. 1 was "Reach Out I'll Be There"?

9 Which country does Demis Roussos come from?

10 Whose first hit was "Love Me Do"?

11 What is the home country of Lulu?

12 Who was Cher's husband when she recorded her first singles?

13 In 1985 Tears For Fears said Everyone Wants to Rule what?

14 Which record label shares its name with an ocean?

15 Which country were the Three Degrees from?

16 Which Bonnie had a 1984 hit with Shakin' Stevens?

17 Which surname is shared by Rod and Dave, formerly of the Eurythmics?

18 Which temptress provided Tom Jones with a 60s hit?

19 Who was lead singer with the Boomtown Rats?

20 Which fruity Fields were the Beatles in in 1967, 1976 and 1987?

Pot Luck 7 (see Quiz 13)
1 Berry. 2 Three. 3 Doll. 4 Lloyd Webber. 5 Petula. 6 Pale.
7 Jerry. 8 17. 9 Oasis. 10 The Beach Boys. 11 P.J.
12 Teenage. 13 Stardust. 14 Sister. 15 Manilow. 16 Phil
Collins. 17 In the Street. 18 Rod. 19 Palmer. 20 Wales.

Quiz 16 Groups

Answers – see page 22

1 Which group includes the two Gallagher brothers?

2 Which group did Robbie Williams leave in 1995?

3 Frankie Goes to where in the name of the 80s group?

4 Which Boys were famous for their surfing sound in the 60s and 70s?

5 Which City Rollers were teen idols in the 70s?

6 Which Club was fronted by Boy George?

7 What was the ELO's full name?

8 Which group shares its name with the first book of the Bible?

9 Who were the other half of the Mamas?

10 Which band's three-word name describes the British weather?

11 Which group is made up of the Gibb brothers?

12 Which ex-Beatle formed Wings?

13 Which group had albums called *The Wall* and *Dark Side of the Moon*?

14 Which group were 5 until they lost Michael?

15 What follows Earth and Wind in the group of the 70s?

16 Which point of the compass is Beautiful?

17 Which group was Sweden's biggest export?

18 Which group did Diana Ross leave to go solo?

19 Which 90s group shares its name with a district of London?

20 Which band with Mark Knopfler had the album *Brothers in Arms*?

Answers

Karaoke (see Quiz 14)
1 "I Will Survive". 2 "My Way". 3 "Oh my love". 4 Bohemian.
5 "Words". 6 Ten. 7 "You'll Never Walk Alone". 8 "I think I got somethin' to say to you". 9 "Money Money Money". 10 "...to say I love you". 11 Four. 12 "Would you hold it against me". 13 "Bachelor Boy". 14 "Merry Xmas Everybody". 15 "You're So Vain". 16 "I Believe". 17 "Love is All Around". 18 "The Shoop Shoop Song". 19 "American Pie". 20 "Lady in Red".

Quiz 17 Pot Luck 9

Answers – see page 27

LEVEL 1

1 Which surname is shared by Elkie and Garth?

2 According to Kirsty MacColl There's A Guy Works Down the Chipshop Swears he's who?

3 What Can't Barry Manilow do Without You according to his 1978 hit?

4 How many members of the Beach Boys were there?

5 What is the home country of Clannad?

6 Which Belinda sang "Heaven is a Place on Earth" in 1987?

7 Which Captain took "Happy Talk" to No. 1 in 1982?

8 What was In the Window when the 50s star Lita Roza asked How Much it was?

9 In which musical, revived on the West End in the 90s, does Fagin appear?

10 Which Moody group sang "Nights in White Satin"?

11 Which Dina pleaded "Don't Be A Stranger" in 1993?

12 What did Chaka Demus and Pliers do as well as Twist at No. 1 in 1993?

13 What was the middle name of Natalie Cole's father Nat?

14 Which musical instrument did the 50s chart-topper Russ Conway play?

15 Roger Daltrey was lead singer of which 60s wild group?

16 Which Cyndi proved Girls Just Want to Have Fun in 1984?

17 Which Sweet girl was a 1971 hit for Neil Diamond?

18 Who was lead singer with Duran Duran?

19 Which London thoroughfares was Ralph McTell in 1974?

20 What's Gotten Hold of My Heart according to Gene Pitney in 1967?

Answers

Pot Luck 10 (see Quiz 19)
1 Freddie Mercury. 2 Susie. 3 Marvin. 4 Collins. 5 Robson and Jerome. 6 Australia. 7 Status Quo. 8 Midler. 9 Midge Ure. 10 Boyzone. 11 New. 12 Numan. 13 Prince. 14 Rat. 15 Four. 16 Tom Jones. 17 The Gang. 18 Wooden. 19 USA. 20 "He Ain't Heavy He's My Brother".

Quiz 18 Space Oddity

Answers – see page 28

 LEVEL 1

1 Which 90s group had a hit with "Female of the Species"?

2 Which Alvin had a No. 1 with "Jealous Mind"?

3 Which Way were OMD Walking on in 1996?

4 Which Man did Elton John sing about in 1972?

5 Which star was in the title of the hit Elton John had with George Michael?

6 Which space puppets Are Go in the Fab hit of 1990?

7 Which David sang "Space Oddity" back in 1969?

8 What was in the Sky according to Doctor and the Medics in 1986?

9 What Always Shines on TV according to A-ha in 1985?

10 The Dark Side of which celestial body was a classic album for Pink Floyd?

11 Which all-girl group sang "Venus" in 1986?

12 Which Song was a 1995 No. 1 for Michael Jackson?

13 What was the Satellite doing on Tasmin Archer's No. 1?

14 What did M/A/R/R/S Pump Up in 1987?

15 Who did Sarah Brightman Lose Her Heart To in 1978?

16 What was David Essex Gonna Make You in 1974?

17 What sort of Craft were the Carpenters Calling All Occupants of in 1977?

18 Where were the Police Walking on in 1979?

19 What sort of Star did gravel-voiced Lee Marvin sing about in 1970?

20 Which intergalactic Wars theme got into the Top Ten in 1977?

Answers

No. 1s (see Quiz 20)
1 Spice Girls. 2 G. 3 Abba. 4 Elvis Presley. 5 Jason Donovan.
6 Three. 7 The Tough Get Going. 8 Manchester United.
9 The Beatles. 10 Mr Blobby. 11 Lulu. 12 Whitney Houston.
13 The Simpsons. 14 Elton John. 15 On the Block. 16 Adams.
17 The Street. 18 The Broken Hearted. 19 I Love You.
20 Dexy's.

Quiz 19 Pot Luck 10

Answers – see page 25

LEVEL 1

1 Who was lead singer with Queen?

2 Which Little girl did the Everly Brothers tell to Wake Up in 1957?

3 Which Hank was part of the Shadows and has had solo success?

4 Which surname is shared by the singer/drummer Phil and singer Judy?

5 Which military duo were the top-selling album artists of 1995?

6 What is the home country of Men at Work, who had a No. 1 with "Down Under"?

7 In which band does Francis Rossi play guitar and take lead vocals?

8 Which Bette is known as "The Divine Miss M"?

9 How is Ultravox's James Ure better known?

10 Which Irish group had a hit with the Osmonds' "Love Me For A Reason" in 1994?

11 What goes before Order and Model Army in the names of groups of the 80s and 90s?

12 Which Gary took "Cars" to the top in 1979?

13 In 1993 which performer asked to be known by a symbol rather than a name?

14 Which animal links the performer Roland and the subject of the song Ben?

15 How many Tops were in the group that sang "Reach Out I'll Be There"?

16 How is Thomas Woodward better known?

17 Who was Kool's backing group?

18 Elvis sang about what kind of Heart in 1961?

19 What is the home country of Mariah Carey?

20 Which Hollies hit begins "The road is long, with many a winding turn"?

Answers

Pot Luck 9 (see Quiz 17)
1 Brooks. 2 Elvis. 3 Smile. 4 Five. 5 Ireland. 6 Carlisle.
7 Sensible. 8 Doggie. 9 *Oliver!*. 10 Blues. 11 Carroll.
12 Shout. 13 King. 14 Piano. 15 The Who. 16 Lauper.
17 Caroline. 18 Simon Le Bon. 19 Streets. 20 Something.

27

Quiz 20 No. 1s

Answers – see page 26

LEVEL 1

1 Who managed the rare double of Christmas single and album in 1996?

2 Which Gina sang "Ooh Aah Just a Little Bit" in May '96?

3 Who had three consecutive No. 1s with "Knowing Me, Knowing You", "The Name of the Game" and "Take A Chance on Me"?

4 Which American solo singer has had the most No. 1 hits?

5 Who did Kylie Minogue share the top spot with in 1988?

6 How many Lions topped the charts in June 1996?

7 What did Billy Ocean say happened When the Going Gets Tough?

8 Which football side were the first to have a No. 1 in 1994 with "Come On You Reds"?

9 Which Liverpool group has had a record-breaking 17 No. 1 hits?

10 Which No. 1 artist was pink with yellow spots?

11 Which Scottish female singer had her first hit "Shout" in 1964, before any of Take That were born, but topped the charts with them in 1993?

12 Which star of *The Bodyguard* took "I Will Always Love You" to the No. 1 spot making it the best selling CD single at that time?

13 Which cartoon group did "The Bartman" in 1991?

14 Whose first solo No. 1 was in 1990, 14 years after hitting the top spot with Kiki Dee and "Don't Go Breaking My Heart"?

15 Which New Kids had their first No. 1 in 1989?

16 Which Canadian Bryan was at No. 1 for 16 weeks in 1991?

17 Where were David Bowie and Mick Jagger Dancing in 1985?

18 According to Robson and Jerome, who have had love that's now departed?

19 In 1984 Stevie Wonder Just Called to Say what?

20 Whose Midnight Runners sang "Come On Eileen" in 1982?

Answers

Space Oddity (see Quiz 18)

1 Space. 2 Stardust. 3 Milky Way. 4 Rocket. 5 Sun. "Don't Let the Sun Go Down on Me". 6 Thunderbirds. 7 Bowie. 8 Spirit. 9 Sun. 10 The Moon. 11 Bananarama. 12 "Earth". 13 Sleeping. 14 The volume. 15 A Starship Trooper. 16 A Star. 17 Interplanetary. 18 The Moon. 19 Wand'rin'. 20 "Star Wars".

Quiz 21 Pot Luck 11

Answers – see page 31

LEVEL 1

1 Who was lead singer with the Sex Pistols?

2 Which Olivia had a 70s hit with "Sam"?

3 Which surname is shared by brothers Don and Phil?

4 How many members of Bucks Fizz were there?

5 What is the home country of Chris de Burgh?

6 Which instrument did the Who's Keith Moon play?

7 Which country does Bonnie Tyler come from?

8 Which birthday did Shirley Bassey celebrate in January 1997?

9 Which group did Dusty leave to go solo?

10 Which hostel did the Village People stay at?

11 How does the country singer Whitman describe his physique?

12 How many times did Dawn say to knock on the ceiling in their 1971 hit?

13 Who was the shortest Beatle?

14 Which Roy was lead singer with Wizzard?

15 Which record label shares its name with a fruit?

16 Which Deep colour is the name of a band who first found fame in the 70s?

17 What goes with Parsley and Sage in the Simon and Garfunkel song?

18 What do the letters R and B stand for?

19 Who is Tom Jones singing about when he sings "My, my, my" then "Why why why"?

20 Which soul singer Heard It Through The Grapevine?

Answers

Pot Luck 12 (see Quiz 23)
1 The Aces. 2 Gibb. 3 Cyndi Lauper. 4 Tamla Motown.
5 Of Man. 6 SOS. 7 Boy George. 8 Pat. 9 USA. 10 Jim Reeves. 11 Prison. 12 Simply Red. 13 King. 14 Relax.
15 The Monkees. 16 Australia. 17 "Vogue". 18 The Roof.
19 Jack Flash. 20 Bono.

29

Quiz 22 Instrumentals

Answers – see page 32

LEVEL 1

1 Which Nigel took Vivaldi's *The Four Seasons* into the album charts?

2 Which country does the bandleader James Last come from?

3 Which film about the Olympics won a music Oscar for the composer Vangelis?

4 Which musical instrument does Vanessa-Mae play?

5 What relation is the album-chart cellist Julian Lloyd Webber to the composer Andrew?

6 Which Herb had a Tijuana Brass?

7 Which Perez had chart success in 1994 with "Guaglione"?

8 In '96 Hank Marvin released an album of which late 50s star's songs?

9 Which song from *Evita* did the Shadows release in 1978?

10 The *Riverdance* album has music from which country?

11 Which musical instrument features most strongly on the Royals Scots Dragoon Guards' recording of "Amazing Grace"?

12 Who played lead guitar on *Tubular Bells*?

13 On which Richard Branson label was it first released?

14 Who left the Shadows with Jet Harris and took "Diamonds" to No. 1?

15 What is the nationality of Jean Michel Jarre?

16 Which classical guitarist John was a member of Sky?

17 Who joined the Good on the orchestral No. 1 film theme for Ennio Morricone?

18 Which TV cop show gave Jan Hammer chart success with "Crockett's Theme"?

19 What is Steve Harley's instrumental backing group?

20 Which anthem did Queen play as an instrumental?

Answers

Solo Singers (see Quiz 24)
1 Manilow. 2 Essex. 3 Joel. 4 Sting. 5 Phil Collins.
6 Aretha. 7 Björk. 8 Whitney Houston. 9 Rea. 10 Costello.
11 Streisand. 12 Time. 13 Just a Little Bit. 14 Corner.
15 Prince. 16 Stansfield. 17 Tina Turner. 18 Carlisle.
19 Rick. 20 Billy.

Quiz 23 Pot Luck 12

Answers – see page 29

LEVEL 1

1 Who was Desmond Dekker's backing group?

2 Which surname is shared by the brothers Barry, Maurice and Robin?

3 Who had an album called *Seven Deadly Cyns ... And Then Some*?

4 Which record label did the Four Tops record their 60s hits on?

5 Which Brotherhood won the Eurovision Song Contest for the UK in 1976?

6 Which Abba single is a distress signal?

7 Who was Culture Club's singer?

8 What is the first name of the US vocalist Ms Benatar?

9 Which country do R.E.M. come from?

10 Which late country singer recorded "I Love You Because"?

11 What type of institution is Johnny Cash performing in on Johnny Cash at San Quentin?

12 Whose albums have been Simply called *Stars* and *Life*?

13 Which Carole had a best-selling 70s album called Tapestry?

14 How did Frankie Goes to Hollywood tell us to unwind in 1984?

15 Which animal-sounding US group had a British lead singer, Davy Jones?

16 What is the home country of Jason Donovan?

17 Which 90s Madonna hit shares its name with a glossy magazine?

18 Robson and Jerome were Up On what part of the house in 1995?

19 Which Jumpin' character was a hit for the Rolling Stones and Aretha Franklin?

20 Who is U2's lead singer ?

Quiz 24 Solo Singers

Answers – see page 30

Answers – see page 30

LEVEL 1

1 Which Barry sang about the Copacabana?

2 Which David's hits include "I'm Gonna Make You a Star" and "Hold Me Close"?

3 Which Billy sang about his Uptown Girl in 1983?

4 Which ex-Police man Spread a Little Happiness in 1982?

5 Which Genesis drummer went solo to No. 1 with "You Can't Hurry Love"?

6 Which Ms Franklin commanded Respect in 1967 and had A Deeper Love in 1994?

7 Which Icelandic singer's first Top 20 hit was "Play Dead" in 1993?

8 Who starred opposite Kevin Costner in *The Bodyguard*?

9 Which Chris was Driving Home for Christmas in 1988?

10 Which Elvis was supported by the Attractions?

11 Which Barbra sang "As If We Never Said Goodbye" in 1994?

12 What did Gabrielle say to give her a Little More of in 1996?

13 What did Gina G sing immediately after "Ooh aah"?

14 In 1986 George Michael sang about a Different what?

15 Which regal-sounding soloist had his first No. 1 with "The Most Beautiful Girl in the World"?

16 Which Lisa joined George Michael and Queen on the *Five Live* EP?

17 Who left Ike and carved out a successful solo career for herself?

18 Which Belinda said "Heaven is a Place on Earth" in 1988?

19 Which Mr Astley was Never Gonna Give You Up in 1987?

20 Which Ocean produced "When the Going Gets Tough, the Tough Get Going"?

Instrumentals (see Quiz 22)
1 Kennedy. 2 Germany. 3 *Chariots of Fire*. 4 Violin.
5 Brother. 6 Alpert. 7 Prado. 8 Buddy Holly. 9 "Don't Cry For Me Argentina". 10 Ireland. 11 Bagpipes. 12 Mike Oldfield.
13 Virgin. 14 Tony Meehan. 15 French. 16 Williams.
17 The Bad and the Ugly. 18 "Miami Vice". 19 Cockney Rebel.
20 "God Save the Queen".

Answers

32

Quiz 25 Pot Luck 13

Answers – see page 35

1   How many members were there in Dave Clark's group altogether?

2   Which David celebrated his 50th birthday on January 8, 1997?

3   What are the surnames of Robson and Jerome?

4   Which Life was a 1994 album for Blur?

5   What did Seal call his first two albums?

6   Which Prince were Adam and the Ants in 1981?

7   Which Alison's nickname is Alf?

8   In which part of the day did Starland Vocal Band experience Delight in 1976?

9   Which musical instrument does Richard Clayderman play?

10 Which Elvis Presley home gave Paul Simon an album title?

11 Who had albums in 1988 called *Mistletoe and Wine* and *Private Collection*?

12 What was the first name of the record producer called Most?

13 What was the surname of the Bros twins, Matt and Luke?

14 Which 90s group was made up of Howard, Gary, Jason, Robbie and Mark?

15 What is the home country of Julio Iglesias?

16 Marti Pellow is lead vocalist with which group?

17 Which musical instrument does the veteran musician Bert Weedon play?

18 Which surname is shared by Rolf and Emmylou?

19 Which Barbara was a 60s hit for the Beach Boys?

20 Who was lead singer with T. Rex?

Quiz 26 Oasis

Answers – see page 36

LEVEL 1

1 Which city do Oasis come from?

2 Which Gallagher brother is lead vocalist?

3 With which band was there a media feud to decide on the top BritPop act?

4 What is Paul McGuigan's nickname?

5 How many people are in Oasis?

6 What was the band's debut album?

7 What goes in brackets before *Morning Glory* on the album title?

8 Who is the elder of the two Gallagher brothers?

9 Which actress Patsy was Liam's name linked with in 1996?

10 Which drug was Liam charged with possession of in 1996?

11 Which football team do the Gallaghers support?

12 What is the nationality of Noel and Liam's parents?

13 What is their mother called?

14 Which musical instrument does Noel play?

15 In which country was a tour cancelled in 1996 when Liam returned home?

16 After which TV pop show did Oasis sack their drummer in 1995?

17 Which Wonder record was a 1995 hit for the band?

18 In 1996, how did Oasis say Don't Look Back?

19 At which Somerset Festival did Oasis perform in front of 30,000 fans in 1994?

20 What goes With It on the record title in 1995?

Answers

Kids' Stuff (see Quiz 28)
1 Osmond. 2 Paper. 3 Zavaroni. 4 In the Air. 5 Lee.
6 Shapiro. 7 Lulu. 8 Wonder. 9 New Kids on the Block.
10 Jackson. 11 Hopkin. 12 Kylie Minogue. 13 17.
14 Langford. 15 Osmond. 16 Shaw. 17 Sedaka. 18 Collins.
19 "Fame". 20 Diana.

1 Which surname is shared by sisters Janet and LaToya?

2 Which Annie had a 1992 album called Diva?

3 Which word goes before "In the Black Forest" and "On the Wild Side" in song titles?

4 Which Michael Caine film gave Cilla Black a hit record?

5 What is the first name of the songwriter called Bacharach?

6 How is Frederick Bulsara better known?

7 What is the home country of New Kids on the Block?

8 Which Joe and Jennifer were Up Where We Belong in 1983?

9 What is the singing daughter of Nat King Cole called?

10 Who makes up the trio with Peter and Paul?

11 Who was Adam's backing group?

12 Which Judy Collins record entered the charts an Amazing eight times in the 70s?

13 Which Elvis was backed by the Attractions?

14 Which Chameleon hit the top for Culture Club in 1983?

15 Which Nik was a Wide Boy in 1985?

16 What was the home country of Kraftwerk, who had a 1981 No. 1 with "Computer Love"?

17 Which surname is shared by the jazz singer Cleo and the 50s vocalist Frankie?

18 Which son of John Lennon has had 80s and 90s chart success?

19 Who were the Sutherland Brothers in the Arms of in 1976?

20 Who was lead singer with the Doors?

Quiz 28 Kid's Stuff

Answers – see page 34

LEVEL 1

1 Which Little Jimmy wanted to be A Long Haired Lover from Liverpool at the age of nine?

2 Which Roses did his 14-year-old sister Marie sing about in 1973?

3 Which 10-year-old Lena took "Ma, He's Making Eyes at Me" to No. 10?

4 Where was the choirboy Aled Jones Walking in 1985?

5 Which Brenda was known as "Little Miss Dynamite"?

6 Which Helen said "Don't Treat Me Like a Child" aged 14 in 1961?

7 Which 15-year-old girl from Glasgow was heard to "Shout" in 1964?

8 Which Stevie was called Little in his early showbiz years?

9 Which late-80s teen group were revamped as NKOTB in 1993?

10 Which Michael first sang with his four brothers at the age of six?

11 Which Mary hit the No. 1 spot with "Those Were the Days" after winning "Opportunity Knocks"?

12 Which Australian teenager had a No. 1 with "I Should Be So Lucky"?

13 To two years either way, how old was Cliff Richard when he had his first hit "Move It" in 1958?

14 Which dancer/singer called Bonnie won "Opportunity Knocks" aged six?

15 Which Donny sang professionally with his brothers from the age of six and had chart success with "Puppy Love" and "Too Young"?

16 Which 17-year-old Sandie had a 60s hit with "Always Something There to Remind Me"?

17 Which Neil wrote "Oh Carol" for Carole Klein, later Carole King, whom he met at high school?

18 Which Genesis drummer called Phil was a former child actor?

19 The kids from which TV dance show had chart success in the 80s?

20 Which girl, later the name of a famous Princess, gave 16-year-old Paul Anka chart success in 1957?

Answers

Oasis (see Quiz 26)
1 Manchester. 2 Liam. 3 Blur. 4 Guigsy. 5 Five.
6 *Definitely Maybe.* 7 *What's The Story.* 8 Noel. 9 Kensit. 10 Cocaine. 11 Manchester City. 12 Irish. 13 Margaret (Peggy). 14 Guitar. 15 USA. 16 "Top of the Pops". 17 "Wonderwall". 18 In Anger. 19 Glastonbury. 20 Roll.

36

Quiz 29 Pot Luck 15

Answers – see page 39

1 How many members of Bros were there?

2 Which Family group sang with Limmie in the 70s?

3 What is the home country of Daniel O'Donnell?

4 Which word describes the vocalists Eva and Richard?

5 What type of Love did Love Affair have in 1968?

6 Which People were "Moving On Up" in 1993?

7 Which country does Craig McLachlan come from?

8 Which blonde US singer appeared in the film *Who's That Girl*?

9 Which Street Preachers had a hit with the "Theme from M*A*S*H" in 1992?

10 Which song was a No. 1 for Elvis Presley and UB40?

11 Which Donna and Barbra had chart success in 1979 with "No More Tears (Enough is Enough)"?

12 How many people made up the 80s group Tears For Fears?

13 Which East London group had a No. 1 album called *Walthamstow*?

14 Which Sid recorded the 1979 album *Sid Sings*?

15 How many Seasons were in the group that sang "Rag Doll"?

16 Which group takes its name from an Unemployment Benefit card?

17 How is the Irishman Raymond Edward O'Sullivan better known?

18 Which surname is shared by Tom and Howard?

19 Who was Clyde's co-gangster on Georgie Fame's 60s Ballad?

20 Which Johnson was lead singer with Frankie Goes to Hollywood?

Quiz 30 Soul and Motown

Answers – see page 40

LEVEL 1

1 Which musical instrument does Ray Charles play?

2 Which Motown star's real name is Steveland Judkins?

3 Which Dionne had a hit with "Walk on By" in 1964 and "Heartbreaker" 18 years later?

4 Who completed the Holland, Dozier trio who wrote many of the Motown hits of the 60s and 70s?

5 Which major all-male Tamla Motown group recorded "I'm Gonna Make You Love Me" with Diana Ross and the Supremes?

6 Which Baby gave the Supremes their first No. 1?

7 Who sang "Endless Love" with Diana Ross in 1981?

8 Which letters took the Jackson Five into the Top Ten in 1970?

9 What did Michael Jackson say to his Summer Love in 1984?

10 Which Marvin was Too Busy Thinking 'Bout his Baby in 1969?

11 Which Queen is Aretha Franklin known as?

12 Which Four were Standing in the Shadows of Love in 1967?

13 Which Brothers charted with "This Old Heart Of Mine" in 1966 and 1968?

14 Which James was "Living in America" in 1986?

15 How were Martha Reeves and the Vandellas billed on their first Motown hits?

16 Who was Smokey Robinson's backing group?

17 How were Gladys Knight's brother Merald and cousins Edward and William known as collectively?

18 At the start of which decade did Berry Gordy set up the Tamla label?

19 Which Jackie recorded "Reet Petite" in 1957?

20 In which US city did Motown begin?

Answers

Novelty Songs (see Quiz 32)
1 "Mr Blobby". 2 Pat. 3 John Kettley. 4 Abbot. 5 Keith Harris. 6 Terry Wogan. 7 Harry Enfield. 8 Gazza. 9 Clary. 10 Ernie. 11 Kangaroo. 12 Woolpackers. 13 Billy Connolly. 14 Dudley Moore. 15 Elephant. 16 Snooker players. 17 Combine Harvester. 18 Roland Rat. 19 The Smurfs. 20 Dave Lee Travis.

Quiz 31 Pot Luck 16

LEVEL 1

1 Which surname is shared by Carole, Ben E. and B.B.?

2 Who has albums called *Bad* and *Dangerous*?

3 Which Caribbean island was Bob Marley from?

4 Which Neil added his name to Crosby, Stills and Nash in 1970?

5 Which Rita was married for six years to Kris Kristofferson?

6 Where were there Tears on Eric Clapton's 1990s single?

7 How are the duo Charles Hodges and Dave Peacock better known?

8 Which 70s group's name was abbreviated to AWB?

9 Which Marc once described himself as "The Acid House Aznavour"?

10 Which clothes were Swinging on the Hippy Hippy Shake in 1963?

11 Who sang with Ant on "When I Fall in Love"?

12 Which Luther duetted with Mariah Carey on "Endless Love"?

13 Which band took its name from the acronym for Rapid Eye Movement?

14 How did the soul singer Otis Redding meet his early death?

15 Who had a hit with "Strangers In the Night" in 1966?

16 How many Pet Shop Boys were there?

17 How did Madonna describe Jessie on her 1989 hit?

18 Who was lead singer with the Commodores?

19 What is the home country of Gilbert O'Sullivan?

20 How is Elaine Bikerstaff better known?

Quiz 32 Novelty Songs

Answers – see page 38

LEVEL 1

1   What was Mr Blobby's first No. 1 hit called?

2   Which Postman gave Ken Barrie an early 80s hit?

3   Which Weatherman was immortalized in song by Tribe of Toffs in '88?

4   Which Russ spread some Atmosphere in 1984?

5   Who helped Orville to sing "Orville's Song"?

6   Which Irish DJ performed a Floral Dance on disc?

7   Who had Loadsamoney in 1988?

8   Which soccer star joined Lindisfarne in a 1990 recording of "Fog on the Tyne"?

9   Which Julian made a 1988 record as the Joan Collins Fan Club?

10 What was the name of Benny Hill's "Fastest Milkman in the West"?

11 Which animal was the subject of Rolf Harris's first hit?

12 Which Packers danced a Hillbilly Rock in 1996?

13 Which Scots comedian filed for D.I.V.O.R.C.E. in 1975?

14 Who said "Goodbye-ee" with Peter Cook in 1965?

15 What type of animal was Nellie, who took the Toy Dolls to No. 4 in the charts in 1984?

16 Which type of sportsmen made up the Matchroom Mob with Chas and Dave in 1986?

17 Which piece of farm equipment gave the Wurzels a No. 1 to "Brand New Key" in 1976?

18 Which Superstar was Rat Rapping in 1983?

19 Which cartoon characters lost Father Abraham from the 70s and refound chart success in 1996?

20 Which bearded DJ joined Paul Burnett to become Laurie Lingo and the Dipsticks?

Soul and Motown (see Quiz 30)
1 Piano. 2 Stevie Wonder. 3 Warwick. 4 Holland.
5 The Temptations. 6 Baby Love. 7 Lionel Richie. 8 ABC.
9 Farewell. 10 Gaye. 11 Queen of Soul. 12 Tops. 13 Isley Brothers. 14 Brown. 15 Martha and the Vandellas. 16 The Miracles. 17 The Pips. 18 60s. 19 Wilson. 20 Detroit.

Answers

1   How many members were there in Dave Dee's group altogether?

2   Who had a 70s album called *Liza With a "Z"*?

3   What is the home country of Prince?

4   Who did Ben E. King say to Stand By in 1961 and again in 1987?

5   How did Charles Aznavour refer to the lady who gave him his '74 hit?

6   What was Blondie's Heart made of on their 70s single?

7   Which Irish group includes the vocalist Ronan Keating?

8   Which musical instrument is jazzman the Buddy Rich famous for?

9   Which Australian Helen is best remembered for "I Am Woman"?

10   Which former Radio 1 DJ is nicknamed Ginger?

11   How did Neil Sedaka describe Breaking Up in 1962 and 1976?

12   Which first name did the 70s singer/songwriter Gerald Hugh Sayer take?

13   Which Four had Frankie Valli as their lead singer?

14   Which Images sang "Happy Birthday" and "I Could Be Happy"?

15   Which 60s musical creatures included Eric Burdon and Alan Price?

16   Which Midlands city does Jasper Carrott come from?

17   How did the 6' 7" tall singer John Baldry describe himself?

18   Which group did Bob Geldof and Midge Ure found to raise money to combat famine in Africa?

19   Which Tori was a "Cornflake Girl" in 1994?

20   Which surname is shared by the rocker Jerry Lee and Huey?

Pot Luck 18   (see Quiz 35)
Answers
1 David Soul. 2 Reeves. 3 Meat Loaf. 4 Birmingham. 5 Beach Boys. 6 Guitar. 7 Showaddywaddy. 8 The Miami Sound Machine. 9 Scotland. 10 Jon Bon Jovi. 11 Mallett. 12 Boy George. 13 *Wuthering Heights*. 14 Red. 15 Lipstick. 16 The Who. 17 Wham!. 18 Scotland. 19 The Gibbs. 20 Chuck.

Quiz 34 Elvis Pesley

Answers – see page 44

1   Which Hotel gave Elvis his first UK hit?

2   Which 'rank' was Elvis's manager Tom Parker known by?

3   What was the first name of Elvis's wife?

4   What were Elvis's shoes made out of in his 1956 hit?

5   Elvis's gyrations on stage gave him which nickname?

6   In which European country was G.I. Elvis stationed?

7   What is the name of Elvis's mansion in Memphis?

8   What was the instruction with the letter Elvis sang about in 1962?

9   Although known as The King which King was he in the 1958 film?

10 Which Elvis film title contained the same word three times?

11 Which relatives are Kissin' in the 1964 Top Ten hit?

12 What is the name of Elvis's daughter?

13 Which country of the UK is the only one Elvis visited?

14 Which Rock was a film and a No. 1 hit in 1958?

15 Where was Elvis Crying in 1965?

16 What was special about the camera work on Elvis's up-tempo songs on the USA's "Ed Sullivan Show"?

17 Which "canine" hit did Elvis have in 1956?

18 Which commemoration to Elvis was issued by the US Post Office in 1993?

19 The name of which toy was the title of an Elvis hit in 1957?

20 Who did Elvis's daughter marry in 1994?

Answers

Late Greats (see Quiz 36)
1 T. Rex. 2 Joplin. 3 Roy Orbison. 4 Freddie Mercury.
5 Plane crash. 6 Big Bopper. 7 My Way. 8 Nirvana. 9 John Lennon. 10 Guitar. 11 Cline. 12 Otis Redding. 13 Nilsson.
14 Mamas and Papas. 15 Brian Jones. 16 Bill Haley. 17 Gaye.
18 The Supremes. 19 Sex Pistols. 20 Jim Morrison.

Quiz 35 Pot Luck 18

Answers – see page 41

LEVEL 1

1 How is David Solberg better known?

2 Which surname is shared by Martha of the Vandellas and the late country star Jim?

3 Whose 1993 album was called *Bat Out Of Hell II*?

4 Which Midlands city does Joan Armatrading come from?

5 Which Boys included three members of the Wilson family?

6 Which musical instrument does Jeff Beck play?

7 Who had a No. 1 with "Under The Moon Of Love"?

8 Who was Gloria Estefan's backing group?

9 What is the home country of Sheena Easton?

10 Who is Bon Jovi's lead vocalist?

11 Which zany TV Timmy joined Bombalurina on "Seven Little Girls Sitting in the Backseat" in 1990?

12 Which Boy's autobiography was called *Take It Like A Man*?

13 Which Emily Brontë novel inspired Kate Bush's 1978 No. 1?

14 What colour did Stevie Wonder's Woman wear in 1984?

15 What went with Powder and Paint on Shakin' Stevens's 1985 hit?

16 Pete Townshend and Keith Moon were members of which group?

17 Which 80s duo was Andrew Ridgeley part of?

18 Which part of the UK do Wet Wet Wet come from?

19 Which brothers wrote Dionne Warwick's 1982 hit "Heartbreaker"?

20 Which first name did the singer/guitarist Charles Edward Anderson Berry take?

Answers

Pot Luck 17 (see Quiz 33)
1 Five. 2 Liza Minnelli. 3 USA. 4 Me. 5 She. 6 Glass.
7 Boyzone. 8 Drums. 9 Reddy. 10 Chris Evans. 11 Hard to Do. 12 Leo. 13 Seasons. 14 Altered. 15 The Animals.
16 Birmingham. 17 Long. 18 Band Aid. 19 Amos.
20 Lewis.

Quiz 36 Late Greats

Answers – see page 42

1 Which group was Marc Bolan associated with?

2 Which Janis died in Hollywood in 1970?

3 Who won an award for his classic hit "Pretty Woman" after his death?

4 Whose death triggered "Bohemian Rhapsody/These Are the Days of Our Lives" entering the charts at No. 1?

5 How did Buddy Holly meet his death?

6 Which Big star died at the same time as Buddy Holly?

7 Which live recording of a Frank Sinatra classic went into the Top Ten for Elvis Presley in January 1978?

8 Kurt Cobain was a member of which band?

9 Which famous Liverpudlian was murdered outside his New York flat?

10 Which musical instrument did Jimi Hendrix play?

11 Which Patsy became the first female solo performer to be inducted into the Country Music Hall of Fame?

12 Whose first Top Ten hit, "(Sittin' On) The Dock of the Bay" charted after his death?

13 Who was without his first name Harry when he sang "Without You"?

14 Which was the most famous group Mama Cass was a member of?

15 Which Rolling Stone died in 1969?

16 Whose pioneering rock 'n' roll career came to an end in 1981 after selling more than 60 million discs Round the Clock?

17 Which soul singer Marvin was shot by his own father?

18 Which highly successful female Motown group was the late Florence Ballard a member of?

19 Which band did Sid Vicious belong to?

20 Which rock legend did Val Kilmer play in the film *The Doors*?

Answers

Elvis Presley (see Quiz 34)

1 Heartbreak. 2 Colonel. 3 Priscilla. 4 Blue Suede. 5 The Pelvis. 6 West Germany. 7 Graceland. 8 Return to Sender. 9 Creole. 10 *Girls, Girls, Girls*. 11 Cousins. 12 Lisa Marie. 13 Scotland. 14 Jailhouse. 15 In the Chapel. 16 Shown from the waist up. 17 "Hound Dog". 18 Stamp. 19 Teddy Bear. 20 Michael Jackson.

44

Quiz 37 Pot Luck 19

Answers – see page 47

LEVEL 1

1 What is the home country of Rolf Harris?

2 How many members of the Eurythmics were there?

3 Who was lead singer with the Boomtown Rats?

4 Which Toni was heard to Breathe Again in 1994?

5 What goes before "A-Lula" on the Gene Vincent classic?

6 In which branch of the armed services were the Village People in 1979?

7 How did Bobby Velline reduce his surname when he had chart success in the 50s?

8 Which American band was inspired by the all-UK Band Aid?

9 What sort of Dancer is Tina Turner on her first solo album?

10 How many members made up Tyrannosaurus Rex?

11 Which 70s star recorded the classic album *Sweet Baby James*?

12 Which Glen was a Rhinestone Cowboy?

13 Which Tracy made a memorable appearance at the Nelson Mandela 70th Birthday Tribute Concert at Wembley in 1988?

14 How is Salvatore Bono better known?

15 Which country are the Chieftains from?

16 For which war children did Luciano Pavarotti perform benefit concerts in the mid 1990s ?

17 Which musical instrument does James Galway play?

18 What did Connie Francis see on your Collar in 1959?

19 Which surname is shared by sisters Kylie and Dannii?

20 Which Eric has been part of Cream and Derek and the Dominoes?

Answers

Pot Luck 20 (see Quiz 39)
1 Nelson. 2 Ireland. 3 Clapton. 4 Drums. 5 Marty and Kim Wilde. 6 The Supremes. 7 Manchester. 8 Three. 9 The Cranberries. 10 Max Bygraves. 11 Tony Bennett. 12 Bad. 13 Spector. 14 Virgin and V2. 15 Cat Stevens. 16 Diamond. 17 Seal. 18 Piano. 19 The Shadows. 20 Captain.

Quiz 38 Film Links

Answers – see page 48

LEVEL 1

1   Who sang "The Shoop Shoop Song" in 1990?

2   Which group wrote the music for *Saturday Night Fever*?

3   Which hero was the subject of the film for which Bryan Adams sang "(Everything I Do) I Do It For You"?

4   Who sang "Ben" from the film about a rat?

5   Which Meg Ryan/Billy Crystal film's songs were sung by Harry Connick Jr?

6   Who appeared in and had hits with songs from *Grease* and *Xanadu*?

7   Which Dire Straits guitarist played "Going Home" from *Local Hero*?

8   What was Falling on my Head in the theme music from *Butch Cassidy and the Sundance Kid*?

9   In which Lloyd Webber film did Madonna play the title role?

10   Which 1981 film starring Dudley Moore, Liza Minnelli and John Gielgud had a Theme sung by Christopher Cross?

11   Who sang "Love Is All Around" from *Four Weddings and a Funeral*?

12   Whose first film was *A Hard Day's Night*?

13   Which Welsh-born female vocalist had a hit with "Goldfinger"?

14   Which film about the 1924 Paris Olympics won an Oscar for the composer Vangelis?

15   Which classic film with Humphrey Bogart and Ingrid Bergman includes the song "As Time Goes By"?

16   Which duo sang "Mrs Robinson" from *The Graduate* in 1968?

17   Who Does It Better according to Carly Simon from *The Spy Who Loved Me*?

18   Which creatures were the subject of the film *Born Free*?

19   Which Disney film does "Circle of Life" come from?

20   Who was Forever in the film to which Seal sang the theme song?

Answers

Cliff Richard (see Quiz 40)
1 Harry Webb. 2 India. 3 The Shadows. 4 *Summer Holiday*.
5 Wimbledon. 6 "Congratulations". 7 Knighthood.
8 *Heathcliff*. 9 "Livin' Doll". 10 "Bachelor Boy". 11 Mistletoe.
12 Sue Barker. 13 Twelfth. 14 Hello. 15 Sarah Brightman.
16 Newton-John. 17 Saviour's. 18 "Move It". 19 Lips.
20 Phil.

46

Quiz 39 Pot Luck 20

LEVEL 1

1 Which surname is shared by Rick, Sandy and Willie?

2 What is the home country of Sinead O'Connor?

3 Which Eric was Unplugged in 1993?

4 Which instrument did Dave Clark play?

5 How are Reginald Smith and his daughter Kim better known?

6 Who was Diana Ross's backing group?

7 Which city are the Hollies from?

8 How many Degrees were in the group which sang "When Will I See You Again?"?

9 Which fruity band's first album was *Everybody Else is Doing It, So Why Can't We?*?

10 Which showbiz veteran recorded the Singalonga series of albums?

11 Who has won Grammy awards for "I Left My Heart in San Francisco" 32 years apart?

12 What sort of Moon was Rising for Creedence Clearwater Revival in 1969?

13 Which Phil was record producer for the Crystals?

14 Which record labels were founded by Richard Branson?

15 Which Cat's debut single was "I Love My Dog"?

16 What sort of Life was a debut album for Sade?

17 Whose real name is Sealhenry Samuel?

18 Which musical instrument does Neil Sedaka play?

19 Which group's members have included Hank Marvin and Brian Bennett?

20 Which nautical chief joined Tennille on disc?

Quiz 40　Cliff Richard

Answers – see page 46

1 What is Cliff Richard's real name?

2 In which country was he born?

3 What was the name of his backing group, which included Bruce Welch?

4 In which film did Cliff head for the continent on a London Transport bus?

5 In 1996 where did Cliff give a concert with Martina Navratilova and Virginia Wade in his backing group?

6 Cliff came 2nd with which song in the 1968 Eurovision Song Contest?

7 Which award did Cliff receive from the Queen in 1995?

8 In which musical based on a novel by Emily Brontë did Cliff play the title role?

9 What was Cliff's first No. 1, later re-released with "The Young Ones"?

10 Which 60s hit began with "When I was young my father said ..."?

11 What features in the title with Wine on Cliff's Christmas No. 1 in 1988?

12 Which blonde tennis star had her name linked with Cliff in the 80s?

13 What date of Never was a hit for Cliff in 1964?

14 What did Cliff say to Samantha when he said Goodbye to Sam?

15 Which wife of Andrew Lloyd Webber did Cliff duet with in "All I Ask of You" from *Phantom of the Opera*?

16 Which Olivia sang with Cliff on "Suddenly" and "Had To Be"?

17 Whose Day was the Christmas No. 1 in 1990?

18 What was Cliff's first hit single?

19 Which part of Cliff was Lucky in the title of his 1964 hit?

20 Which Everly did Cliff duet with in "She Means Nothing to Me"?

Answers

Film Links (see Quiz 38)
1 Cher. 2 The Bee Gees. 3 Robin Hood. 4 Michael Jackson.
5 *When Harry Met Sally.* 6 Olivia Newton-John. 7 Mark Knopfler. 8 Raindrops. 9 *Evita.* 10 *Arthur.* 11 Wet Wet Wet.
12 The Beatles. 13 Shirley Bassey. 14 *Chariots of Fire.*
15 *Casablanca.* 16 Simon and Garfunkel. 17 Nobody.
18 Lions. 19 *The Lion King.* 20 Batman.

Quiz 41 Pot Luck 21

Answers – see page 51

LEVEL 1

1 Which surname is shared by Elvis and Reg?

2 How many Seasons were there?

3 Which Helen held the record for making more than 12 radio and TV appearances before the age of 15 in 1961?

4 Which barefoot pop star's autobiography was called *The World At My Feet*?

5 What was Tina Turner's first husband called?

6 Which song was a No. 1 for the Righteous Brothers and Robson and Jerome?

7 Whose second solo album was called *There Goes Rhymin' Simon*?

8 Which music paper is often abbreviated to *NME*?

9 Which football team does Simply Red's Mick Hucknall support?

10 Which Midlands town do Slade originate from?

11 Which Family group backed Sly?

12 Who makes up the trio with Stock and Aitken?

13 What is the home country of Shirley Bassey?

14 Which East End gangsters did Spandau Ballet's Kemp twins portray on film?

15 Which band were Rockin' All Over the World in 1977?

16 What was Sting's profession before he entered show business?

17 What do the letters CD stand for?

18 Who started out as the Guildford Stranglers?

19 Which Paul links the Style Council and the Jam?

20 What is Art short for in Art Garfunkel's name?

Pot Luck 22 (see Quiz 43)
1 Madness. 2 Denver. 3 French. 4 Lonnie. 5 Ian Dury.
6 "Ready Steady Go". 7 Tina Turner. 8 Harmonica. 9 Dawn.
10 Ireland. 11 "Dizzy". 12 9 to 5. 13 Royce.
14 The Shadows. 15 Enya. 16 David Essex. 17 Cuba.
18 Two. 19 Diamond. 20 Robinson.

Answers

49

Quiz 42 Pop on the Box

Answers – see page 52

1   The TV series "Heartbeat" features music from which decade?

2   In which TV series did Robson and Jerome find fame?

3   Which TV soap do the Woolpackers come from?

4   Which long-running pop show began on January 1, 1964?

5   For which TV programme did Dennis Waterman sing "I Could Be So Good For You"?

6   Which environmentalists sang their songs on Wimbledon Common?

7   Which company used Marvin Gaye's "I Heard It Through The Grapevine" to advertise their jeans?

8   Which Irish band provided the "Theme from Harry's Game" and "Robin (The Hooded Man)"?

9   Which TV series starring Don Johnson as Crockett gave Jan Hammer his first UK chart success with its theme tune?

10 Whose Crocodile Shoes entered the charts in 1994?

11 Which "EastEnders" landlady was played by Anita Dobson, who charted with "Anyone Can Fall In Love" in 1986?

12 Which TV show was introduced by Jools Holland and Paula Yates?

13 How was Charlene Mitchell better known in the pop charts?

14 Which singer Maguire played Aidan in "EastEnders"?

15 Which medical series theme was bracket titled "Suicide is Painless"?

16 Which two TV series have taken Nick Berry into the charts?

17 Which show asked a panel of four to judge a record a hit or a miss?

18 Which theme music from a series about a boatyard did Marti Webb record as "Always There"?

19 On which TV channel is the Eurovision Song Contest broadcast?

20 Which puppets hit the top of the charts with "The Chicken Song"?

Answers

All-Girl Groups (see Quiz 44)
1 Spice. 2 Nolans. 3 Eternal. 4 The Bangles. 5 Three.
6 Shakespear's. 7 Three. 8 Ronettes. 9 The Supremes.
10 2 Wilsons, 1 Phillips. 11 "Da Doo". 12 Love. 13 Reeves.
14 Yes. 15 Salt. 16 Of the Pack. 17 Sledge. 18 The Judds.
19 Spice Girls. 20 The Ronettes.

1 Who has had albums called *Complete Madness* and *Divine Madness*?

2 Which John's album chart debut was *Rocky Mountain High*?

3 In which language other than English did Celine Dion record in the 80s?

4 Which showbiz first name did Anthony James Donegan adopt?

5 Who was backed by the Blockheads?

6 Which TV pop show sounded like the start of a race?

7 How is Annie-Mae Bullock better known?

8 Which instrument does Bob Dylan play other than guitar?

9 Which group did Tony Orlando lead?

10 What is the home country of Van Morrison?

11 Which song has been a No. 1 for Tommy Roe and Vic Reeves?

12 What were Dolly Parton's working hours in 1981?

13 Which Rose shares her surname with part of the name of a car?

14 Which British group had to change its name from the Drifters because of the existence of the US group?

15 Who left Clannad and had her first solo single in 1988?

16 Which actor/singer was born David Cook in Plaistow?

17 Which Caribbean island is Gloria Estefan originally from?

18 How many performers were in the Eurythmics?

19 Which Neil made a Beautiful Noise in the 70s?

20 Which surname is shared by Smokey and Tom?

Quiz 44 All-Girl Groups

Answers – see page 50

1 Which Girls' debut single was "Wannabe"?

2 Which Irish sisters were In the Mood for Dancin' in the 70s?

3 Which groups's debut album was "Always and Forever" – like their name?

4 Which group were once called the Bangs?

5 How many people made up Bananarama?

6 Which Sister did Bananarama's Siobhan Fahey co-found after she left the group?

7 How many Degrees said Take Good Care of Yourself in 1975?

8 Which Phil Spector group had Ronnie Bennett on lead vocals?

9 Which Motown group consisted of Diana Ross, Mary Wilson and Florence Ballard?

10 In Wilson Phillips, do the Wilsons outnumber the Phillipses or vice versa?

11 What goes before "Ron Ron" on the title of the Crystals' first major hit?

12 The Chapel of what became a million seller for the Dixie Cups?

13 What was the surname of Martha who was often backed by the Vandellas?

14 Were the Pointer Sisters really sisters?

15 Who was Pepa's partner in the 80s rap group?

16 Which Leader provided a once-banned hit for the Shangri-Las?

17 Which Sister group had a No. 1 with "Frankie"?

18 Which mother-and-daughter country group consisted of Wynonna and Naomi?

19 Who switched on the London Christmas lights in December 1996?

20 Whose first hit was "Be My Baby" in 1963?

Answers

Pop on the Box (see Quiz 42)

1 The 60s. 2 "Soldier Soldier". 3 "Emmerdale". 4 "Top of the Pops". 5 "Minder". 6 The Wombles. 7 Levi's. 8 Clannad. 9 "Miami Vice". 10 Jimmy Nail. 11 Angie Watts. 12 "The Tube". 13 Kylie Minogue. 14 Sean. 15 M*A*S*H. 16 "EastEnders", "Heartbeat". 17 "Juke Box Jury". 18 "Howard's Way". 19 BBC1. 20 "Spitting Image".

Quiz 45 Pot Luck 23

Answers – see page 55

1   Which Brothers were known as Little Donnie and Baby Boy Phil?

2   Which Linda, Dolly and Emmylou recorded the album *Trio*?

3   What did Suzi Quatrocchio change her surname to?

4   Which Robert was Addicted to Love in 1986?

5   Which Boys had a hit with "Always On My Mind" in 1988?

6   On which soul record label was Jimmy Ruffin's version of "What Becomes of the Broken Hearted?"?

7   Who sang about a Smooth Operator in 1984?

8   Which Del was a Runaway in 1961?

9   Which Great Train Robber featured on the Sex Pistols' "No One Is Innocent/My Way"?

10 Which Percy released "When A Man Loves a Woman" in '66 and '87?

11 Who had a minor hit with "Doggy Dogg World"?

12 Which Billie Jo put her Blanket on the Ground in 1975?

13 Which "The Tube" presenter was a member of Squeeze?

14 How did Status Quo alter the title of "Rockin' All Over The World" to promote the Race Against Time in 1988?

15 How were Shakin' Stevens and Bonnie Tyler billed on "A Rockin' Good Way"?

16 In 1975 10 c.c., said Life was like which kind of soup?

17 What is the home country of k.d. lang?

18 Which group backed Brian Poole?

19 How many Pennies sang "Juliet"?

20 Which surname is shared by Hank and former Take That star Robbie?

Pot Luck 24 (see Quiz 47)

Answers

1 Turner. 2 Vienna. 3 Wales. 4 Vega. 5 My Everything.
6 Jive. 7 The Wonder Stuff. 8 Blue Jeans. 9 Norway.
10 Adam Faith. 11 The Sunshine Band. 12 USA. 13 Betty
Boo. 14 Piano. 15 The Cat. 16 The Pretenders. 17 Procul
Harum. 18 Cocker. 19 Dr. 20 Wilson.

Quiz 46 Queen

Answers – see page 56

LEVEL 1

1 Who was Queen's lead vocalist?

2 How many people made up Queen?

3 Which 1974 hit had the band's name in the title?

4 Which Rhapsody was at No. 1 for two months when first released?

5 Which Queen song has become a football anthem?

6 Which group of US comedy brothers made films whose titles gave Queen the names of two albums?

7 Which 1977 Queen album shares its name with a Sunday tabloid newspaper?

8 Which musical instrument is Brian May most famous for?

9 In 1980 Queen became the first rock band to appear in which annual publication as some of Britain's highest-paid executives?

10 Where did Bob Geldof say Queen's lead singer could "ponce about in front of the whole world"?

11 In which London Park did Queen give a free concert in 1976?

12 Which soap star's name was linked with Brian May's from the mid-80s?

13 Which Heart Attack gave Queen a No. 2 album in 1974?

14 Which Queen EP shares its name with a BBC radio network?

15 Which George joined Queen on a version of "These Are the Days of our Lives"?

16 What is the surname of the Queen drummer Roger?

17 According to its title, where was their 1995 No. 1 Made?

18 Which Olympic Games gave their lead singer a hit in 1992?

19 Which Radio gave Queen a hit in 1984?

20 Which David had a No. 1 with Queen in 1981?

Quiz 47 Pot Luck 24

Answers – see page 53

LEVEL 1

1 Which Tina's album was Simply the Best in 1991?

2 Which Austrian city was a No. 1 for Ultravox in 1981?

3 Which country is Mary Hopkin from?

4 Which Suzanne was in Tom's Diner in 1990?

5 How did Barry White complete the song title "You're the First the Last"?

6 Which dance did Wizzard See My Baby do in 1973?

7 Who is Vic Reeves's backing group?

8 What was Venus wearing according to Mark Wynter in 1962?

9 Abba are credited with being from Sweden and which other Scandinavian country?

10 How is Terry Nelhams better known?

11 Who was K.C.'s backing band?

12 What is the home country of Whitney Houston?

13 Whose debut album was called *Boomania*?

14 Which musical instrument does Harry Connick Jr play?

15 Curiosity Killed what according to the name of the 80s band?

16 Chrissie Hynde was lead singer with which group?

17 Who had the classic "Whiter Shade of Pale" in the 60s?

18 Which Jarvis sings with Pulp?

19 What qualification do Hook and Feelgood have?

20 Which surname is shared by the late Jackie and the beehive hair-do queen Mari?

Pot Luck 23 (see Quiz 45)

1 Everly Brothers. 2 Ronstadt, Parton, Harris. 3 Quatro.
4 Palmer. 5 Pet Shop Boys. 6 Tamla Motown. 7 Sade.
8 Shannon. 9 Ronald Biggs. 10 Sledge. 11 Snoop Doggy
Dogg. 12 Spears. 13 Jools Holland. 14 "Running All Over the
World". 15 Shaky and Bonnie. 16 Minestrone. 17 Canada.
18 The Tremeloes. 19 Four. 20 Williams.

Quiz 48 Two's Company

Answers – see page 54

1   What was the surname of Richard and Karen?

2   Who are Barbra and Neil who had a hit with "You Don't Send Me Flowers" in 1978?

3   Which Sarah duetted with Steve Harley on "Phantom of the Opera" 1986?

4   Which cockney duo had an album *Street Party* in 1995?

5   How were the comedy recording duo Pete and Dud better known?

6   Who was Dave Stewart's 'other half' in the Eurythmics?

7   Which Spanish star duetted with Willie Nelson on "All the Girls I Loved Before"?

8   Who sang "Ebony and Ivory" in 1982?

9   Which Neighbours hit No. 1 with "Especially For You" in 1988?

10 Which blonde did Cliff duet with on disc in 1980 and again in 1995?

11 What is the surname of the brother and sister Donny and Marie?

12 Who duetted with Elaine Paige on the No. 1 "I Know Him So Well"?

13 Who was Up Town Top Ranking with Althia?

14 Who duetted on "Barcelona" with Montserrat Caballe?

15 Whose Greatest Hits album was called *Tears Roll Down*?

16 Whose only album was *River Deep – Mountain High*?

17 Whose film soundtrack album *The Graduate* charted in 1968?

18 Which father and daughter sang "Somethin' Stupid" in 1967?

19 Who are Linda and James on the 1987 hit "Somewhere Out There"?

20 Who duetted with Womack on the hit "Teardrops"?

Answers

Queen (see Quiz 46)
1 Freddie Mercury. 2 Four. 3 "Killer Queen". 4 Bohemian.
5 "We Are the Champions". 6 Marx Brothers. 7 *News of the World*. 8 Guitar. 9 *Guinness Book of Records*. 10 Live Aid
Concert. 11 Hyde Park. 12 Anita Dobson. 13 Sheer. 14 *Five Live*. 15 Michael. 16 Taylor. 17 In Heaven. 18 Barcelona. 19
Ga Ga. 20 Bowie.

Quiz 49   Pot Luck 25

Answers – see page 59

1   Who was lead singer with the Faces?

2   Which pop star wrote a financial advice column "Faith in the City" for the *Mail on Sunday*?

3   What other word describes the Young Cannibals?

4   Which group took "Mamma Mia" to No. 1?

5   Which Convention had Sandy Denny on vocals?

6   Which group's only No. 1 in 25 years was "Down Down"?

7   Which Jose had a hit with "Light My Fire"?

8   Which flowers did Tiny Tim Tiptoe Through in the 60s?

9   Which model Jerry appeared on the cover of Roxy Music's *Siren* album?

10   Which country star's songs have taken him to Galveston, Phoenix and Wichita?

11   Which soap did Peter Noone of Herman's Hermits appear in the 60s?

12   In which city were Frankie Goes to Hollywood first based?

13   In which group did Axl Rose take lead vocals?

14   Who was the youngest of the Gibb brothers, who died in 1988?

15   How many Steps to Heaven did Eddie Cochran sing about?

16   Which Georgie's backing group were called the Blue Flames?

17   Which Billy, who died in 1983, was a former schoolmate of Ringo Starr?

18   Which group included brothers Ray and Dave Davies?

19   Who was Billy J. Kramer's backing group?

20   How many Tops sang "Reach Out"?

Answers

Pot Luck 26 (see Quiz 51)
1 Piano. 2 Julio Iglesias. 3 Van Morrison. 4 Destruction.
5 "Killing Me Softly". 6 The Beautiful South. 7 Cobain. 8 M.C.
Hammer. 9 Linda McCartney. 10 Gibson. 11 The News.
12 Birmingham. 13 The Monkees. 14 Madonna. 15 Madness.
16 Lulu. 17 Boy George. 18 Three. 19 UK. 20 Grant.

Quiz 50 Keep It in the Family

Answers – see page 60

LEVEL 1

1 What is the name of Dannii Minogue's older sister?

2 What is Paul McCartney's wife called?

3 What relation was Richard Carpenter to Karen?

4 Which group is made up of the Gibb brothers?

5 Which Brothers included Alan, Merrill, Jay and Donny?

6 What is their singing sister called?

7 How many Jacksons are credited on "I Want You Back"?

8 What is the name of John Lennon's elder son?

9 Which surf sound group included Brian, Dennis and Carl Wilson?

10 What relation are Whitney Houston and Dionne Warwick?

11 What is the first name of Marty Wilde's singing daughter?

12 What is the surname of Brothers Don and Phil whose hits included "Wake Up Little Susie"?

13 Which Brothers had hits with "You've Lost That Lovin' Feelin" and "Unchained Melody"?

14 Who has daughters called Fifi Trixibelle, Peaches and Little Pixie?

15 In the Sinatra duos what relation is Nancy to Frank?

16 What is Nat King Cole's vocalist daughter called?

17 Who is Sam Brown's dad who used to sing with The Bruvvers?

18 Which relative did Clive Dunn sing about in 1970?

19 Which trio included the twins Matt and Luke Goss?

20 Who had her first No. 1 hit when she was Mrs Sonny Bono?

Answers

The Beatles (see Quiz 52)
1 Liverpool. 2 Ringo Starr. 3 Paul McCartney. 4 Your Hand.
5 Epstein. 6 Paperback. 7 The Cavern. 8 Lonely Hearts Club.
9 "Yesterday". 10 Revolver. 11 Apple. 12 *Help*. 13 Yoko Ono. 14 New York. 15 Submarine. 16 "She Loves You".
17 Day. 18 Germany. 19 Love. 20 George Harrison.

Quiz 51 Pot Luck 26

Answers – see page 57

LEVEL 1

1   Which musical instrument does Bobby Crush play?

2   Which singer once played football for Real Madrid?

3   How is George Ivan Morrison better known?

4   What were we on the Eve of according to Barry McGuire in the 60s?

5   What did the Fugees call Roberta Flack's "Killing Me Softly With His Song"?

6   Who were Pretenders to the Throne in 1995?

7   Which Great was a hit for The Platters and Freddie Mercury?

8   Who had a US No. 1 album with "Please Hammer Don't Hurt 'Em"?

9   How is Linda Eastman better known?

10 Which Debbie played Sandy in the London revival of *Grease*?

11 Who was Huey Lewis's backing group?

12 Which Midlands city were the Move from?

13 Which 60s TV group included Mickey Dolenz and Mike Nesmith?

14 Which singer gave birth to baby Lourdes in 1996?

15 Suggs was lead singer with which crazy-sounding group?

16 Which Scots pop star married the hairdresser John Frieda?

17 How is George O'Dowd better known?

18 How many Lions feature on the Lightning Seeds' Euro '96 football anthem?

19 Which country are Japan from?

20 Which Eddy was lead singer with the Equals?

Quiz 52 The Beatles

Answers – see page 58

LEVEL 1

1 Which city did the Beatles come from?

2 Which Beatle's real name was Richard Starkey?

3 Which guitarist was left-handed?

4 What did the Beatles Want to Hold in their third No. 1 of 1963?

5 Which Brian was the Beatles' manager until his death in 1967?

6 What type of Writer was the subject of a song in 1966?

7 Which club in the Beatles' home town is linked with their success?

8 What kind of Band did Sgt Pepper have?

9 Which is the most recorded Beatles song of all time?

10 Which Beatles LP title was the name of a gun?

11 Which fruit was the Beatles' own record label?

12 What was the Beatles' second film?

13 Which Japanese artist did John Lennon marry?

14 In which city was John Lennon murdered?

15 Which Yellow craft was the subject of a single and album?

16 Which song has "Yeah, yeah, yeah" at the end of each chorus line?

17 Which Tripper could be found on the other side of "We Can Work it Out"?

18 In which European country did the Beatles work before finding fame in the UK?

19 According to their 1964 No. 1 money can't buy me what?

20 Which Beatle played lead guitar?

Answers

Keep It in the Family (see Quiz 50)
1 Kylie. 2 Linda. 3 Brother. 4 Bee Gees. 5 Osmonds.
6 Marie. 7 Five. 8 Julian. 9 Beach Boys. 10 Cousins.
11 Kim. 12 Everly. 13 Righteous Brothers. 14 Bob Geldof.
15 Daughter. 16 Natalie. 17 Joe Brown. 18 Grandad.
19 Bros. 20 Cher.

Quiz 53 Pot Luck 27

Answers – see page 63

 LEVEL 1

1 Which Marianne's first hit was written by the Rolling Stones?

2 Which Eurovision winning group was the TV presenter Cheryl Baker formerly a member of?

3 Which Dog was a big hit for Elvis Presley?

4 Which Busters gave Ray Parker Jr chart success?

5 Which Lace had a hit with "Agadoo"?

6 What were the Carpenters Calling Occupants of in 1977?

7 Where were there Orchestral Manoeuvres in the 80s and 90s?

8 Who have had No. 1 hits with "Pray" and "Everything Changes"?

9 Whose second album was called *Gentleman Jim*?

10 Which Chubby star was dubbed The King of Twist?

11 Which girl did Buddy Holly love with a heart so rare and true?

12 Who had a hit with "Rat Trap"?

13 Which Ruby gave Melanie a 70s hit?

14 Which singer/songwriters were nicknamed Mr and Mrs Music?

15 Which Johnny joined Deniece Williams on "Too Much Too Little Too Late"?

16 Which male vocalist shared his name with late-actress Miss Monroe?

17 Who had an album called *Everything Comes Up Dusty*?

18 Which US state were the Mamas and Papas Dreamin' of in 1966?

19 Which punk band was Malcolm McLaren manager of in the 70s?

20 How many members of the Hollies were there?

Answers

Pot Luck 28 (see Quiz 55)
1 Bell. 2 The Blockheads. 3 Jive Bunny. 4 Kevin Keegan.
5 George Harrison. 6 The Shadows. 7 Gayle. 8 Five.
9 Erasure. 10 Beethoven. 11 Ireland. 12 Dollar. 13 Nash.
14 k.d. lang. 15 42. 16 The Bluenotes. 17 Closer. 18 Flea.
19 O'Connor. 20 O'Donnell.

Quiz 54 Cover Versions

Answers – see page 64

1 Which all-male band had a hit with the Bee Gees' "Words" in 1996?

2 Which song was a hit for Roberta Flack and the Fugees?

3 Which date marked a special night for the Four Seasons and Clock?

4 Who had the 1995 No. 1 with "Unchained Melody"?

5 Bryan Hyland and Jason Donovan had letters sealed with what?

6 Which football anthem took Gerry and the Pacemakers, and then the Crowd to the top of the charts?

7 Who joined Cliff Richard on the second version of "Livin' Doll"?

8 What was No. 1 for Joe Cocker and Wet Wet Wet?

9 Which Osmond covered Tab Hunter's No. 1 "Too Young"?

10 Who backed Doctor on "Spirit in the Sky" a No. 1 for Norman Greenbaum in 1970?

11 Who did the 80s version of Rosemary Clooney's "This Ole House"?

12 Which Boy followed Ken Boothe's No. 1 of "Everything I Own"?

13 Who had the original No. 1 with "Take A Chance on Me" which featured on Erasure's No. 1 EP?

14 Which Mariah recorded a cover version of Nilsson's "Without You"?

15 Whose Boy Child gave hits for Boney M and Harry Belafonte?

16 Which Jimmy Ruffin hit did Robson and Jerome take to the top of the charts in autumn 1996?

17 What did Cher call Betty Everett's and Linda Lewis's "It's In His Kiss"?

18 Which revealing outfit did Bombalurina sing about 30 years after Bryan Hyland's original?

19 Who had the original hit with "You're the One That I Want"?

20 Where did first the Equals, then Pato Banton, tell their Baby to come?

90s BritPop (see Quiz 56)

1 Oasis. 2 Michael Jackson's. 3 Blur. 4 *Trainspotting*.
5 Different Class. 6 Blur, Oasis. 7 *The Great Escape*.
8 Sheffield. 9 "Country House". 10 "Parklife". 11 Food.
12 1991. 13 Keyboards. 14 Livingstone. 15 He jumped out of a window. 16 *Blurbook*. 17 Four. 18 Drums. 19 It was to be shared with Blur. 20 "Wonderwall".

Quiz 55 Pot Luck 28

Answers – see page 61

LEVEL 1

1 Which record label shares its name with the inventor of the telephone?

2 Who was Ian Dury's backing group?

3 Which Bunny had a string of party hits in the 80s?

4 Which former manager of Newcastle United had a 70s hit with "Head Over Heels in Love"?

5 Which Beatle had a solo No. 1 with "My Sweet Lord"?

6 Brian Bennett replaced Tony Meehan as drummer in which group?

7 Which surname is shared by the US star Crystal and the UK's Michelle?

8 How many Star members enjoyed great success in the 80s?

9 Who took the *Abba-esque EP* to No. 1 in 1992?

10 Which composer is told to Roll Over on the classic rock song?

11 Which country does Val Doonican come from?

12 Which 70s/80s duo shared its name with American money?

13 Who makes up the trio with Crosby and Stills?

14 Which Canadian sang "Miss Chatelaine" in 1993?

15 Which Level had "Lessons in Love" in 1986?

16 What was Harold Melvin's backing group?

17 Where did Phyllis Nelson invite us to Move in the 80s and 90s?

18 Which Spanish insect was a hit for Herb Alpert?

19 Which Des had Careless Hands in 1967?

20 Which Daniel pondered Whatever Happened to Old Fashioned Love in 1993?

Pot Luck 27 (see Quiz 53)
1 Faithfull. 2 Bucks Fizz. 3 Hound Dog. 4 Ghostbusters.
5 Black. 6 Interplanetary Craft. 7 In the Dark. 8 Take That.
9 Jim Reeves. 10 Checker. 11 Peggy Sue. 12 The Boomtown
Rats. 13 Tuesday. 14 Jackie Trent and Tony Hatch. 15 Mathis.
16 Marilyn. 17 Dusty Springfield. 18 California. 19 The Sex
Pistols. 20 Five.

Quiz 56 90s BritPop

Answers – see page 62

LEVEL 1

1 Which group were voted Best Newcomer at the 1995 Brit Awards?

2 Whose performance of "Earth Song" did Jarvis Cocker interrupt at the 1996 Brit Awards?

3 In which band does Damon Albarn sing lead vocals?

4 Which film about drug addiction released in 1996 features a Pulp song on the soundtrack?

5 Which Class was Pulp's first album?

6 Which two BritPop bands were the subject of a media-led feud?

7 Which film about prisoners of war shares its name with a Blur album?

8 Which Yorkshire city do Pulp hail from?

9 Which House entered the charts at No. 1 for Blur in 1995?

10 Which Life was a top selling single and album for Blur in 1994?

11 Which edible sounding record label do Blur record on?

12 To two years either way, in which year did Blur have their first Top Ten single?

13 Which musical instrument does Damon Albarn play?

14 Which Labour MP Ken appeared on a Blur No. 1 in 1995?

15 Why did Jarvis Cocker have to spend time in a wheelchair in 1986?

16 What was Blur's 1995 book called?

17 How many members of Blur are there?

18 Which instrument does Dave Rowntree play?

19 In May 1996 why did Noel Gallagher turn down an Ivor Novello Songwriter of the Year award?

20 The singing of which song at Manchester City's football ground made Noel Gallagher cry?

Answers

Cover Versions (see Quiz 54)
1 Boyzone. 2 "Killing Me Softly". 3 December '63. 4 Robson and Jerome. 5 A Kiss. 6 "You'll Never Walk Alone". 7 The Young Ones. 8 "With A Little Help From My Friends". 9 Donny. 10 The Medics. 11 Shakin' Stevens. 12 George. 13 Abba. 14 Carey. 15 Mary's. 16 "What Becomes of the Broken-Hearted?". 17 "The Shoop Shoop Song". 18 Itsy Bitsy Teeny Weeny Yellow Polka-Dot Bikini. 19 John Travolta and Olivia Newton-John. 20 Back.

Quiz 57 Pot Luck 29

Answers – see page 67

LEVEL 1

1 Which Kenny and Sheena duetted on "We've Got Tonight"?

2 Which first name links the Muffins and the Vandellas?

3 Which US state did Ray Charles have on his mind in 1960?

4 Paul Shane and the Yellowcoats sang the "Holiday Rock" from which TV show?

5 Who rhymed with Telegram on the title of the T. Rex single?

6 Which zany DJ recorded a "Snot Rap" in 1983?

7 Which country is Craig McLachlan from?

8 Which TV presenter Shane played the lead role in *Grease* in the West End?

9 Which Doctor had "Sexy Eyes" in 1980?

10 Who was Blondie's female singer?

11 In 1982 It Started With what for Hot Chocolate?

12 Who was backing Katrina when she was "Walking on Sunshine"?

13 What colour Box did Simply Red Open Up in 1986?

14 Matt Monro is famous for singing "Born Free", a film about which animals?

15 What is the surname of the country stars Johnny and Roseanne?

16 Which singer is nicknamed the Boss?

17 Which record label was founded in Detroit?

18 Whose first hit was "Space Oddity" in 1969?

19 Whose first solo hit was "Orinoco Flow" in 1988?

20 How is the jazz singer Clementine Campbell better known?

Answers

Pot Luck 30 (see Quiz 59)
1 Bruce Springsteen. 2 Kate Bush. 3 "That's My Home".
4 Neneh. 5 Piano. 6 Ireland. 7 UK. 8 Oasis. 9 Elvis
Costello. 10 The Police. 11 Tamla Motown. 12 Carly Simon.
13 John Lennon. 14 Jackie (he's one of the brothers).
15 Liverpool. 16 Gloria. 17 40. 18 The Coconuts.
19 Scotland. 20 Twice.

Quiz 58 Place the Place

Answers – see page 68

LEVEL 1

1 In which US west-coast city had you to be sure to "wear some flowers in your hair" in 1967?

2 Which Dutch city gave a hit to the Beautiful South?

3 Which group shares its name with Germany's capital city?

4 What did the Ferry cross in the hit by Gerry and the Pacemakers?

5 Which Scottish location gave Paul McCartney No. 1 in 1977?

6 Which US gangster town gave its name to the group who had a No. 1 with "If You leave Me Now"?

7 Where was the 1972 Long-Haired Lover from?

8 Where did Madonna implore them not to cry for her in 1996?

9 Which Triangle provided Barry Manilow with a Top Twenty hit?

10 Which Northern Irish city is in the title of Simple Minds' 1989 No. 1?

11 Which home of Sherlock Holmes was a hit for Gerry Rafferty?

12 Which 1992 Olympic venue was a hit for Montserrat Caballe and Freddie Mercury?

13 Where were Typically Tropical heading for on Coconut Airways in 1975?

14 Which west-coast state gave its name to the Eagles' Hotel in 1977?

15 What did Tony Bennett Leave in San Francisco?

16 The Streets of which city featured on a Ralph McTell classic song?

17 Where did Bruce Springsteen say he was born, in 1985?

18 Where did Supertramp have Breakfast in 1979?

19 Which features of Babylon did Boney M sing about in 1978?

20 Which city's name appears twice in the title of Frank Sinatra's 80s hit?

Quiz 59 Pot Luck 30

Answers – see page 65

LEVEL 1

1 Whose 80s best-selling album was Born in the USA?

2 Whose first hit was "Wuthering Heights"?

3 What completes the Paul Young song title "Wherever I Lay My Hat ..."?

4 What is the vocalist Ms Cherry's first name?

5 Which musical instrument does Barry Manilow play?

6 Which country do the Nolans come from?

7 Which country did Gina G represent in the Eurovision Song Contest in 1996?

8 Which band did No Way Sis try to imitate?

9 How is Declan McManus better known?

10 Who had a 1979 No. 1 album called *Reggatta De Blanc*?

11 Which record label did the Commodores first record on?

12 Which US vocalist is the daughter of the founder of the publishers Simon & Schuster?

13 Which Beatle's younger son is called Sean?

14 Who is not one of the Jackson sisters – Janet, LaToya, Jackie?

15 Which northern city is Sonia from?

16 Which first name is shared by Estefan and Gaynor?

17 What follows UB in the name of the band?

18 Who was Kid Creole's backing group?

19 Which part of the UK is Barbara Dickson from?

20 How many times did Celine Think on her best-selling 1995 single?

Answers

Pot Luck 29 (see Quiz 57)
1 Rogers, Easton. 2 Martha. 3 Georgia. 4 "Hi De Hi". 5 Sam. 6 Kenny Everett. 7 Australia. 8 Richie. 9 Hook. 10 Debbie Harry. 11 A Kiss. 12 The Waves. 13 Red. 14 Lions. 15 Cash. 16 Bruce Springsteen. 17 Tamla Motown. 18 David Bowie. 19 Enya. 20 Cleo Laine.

67

Quiz 60 Rod Stewart

Answers – see page 66

1 Which Maggie gave Rod Stewart his first No. 1 in 1971?

2 Which group, no longer Small, did Rod join in 1969?

3 What Tells a Story on Rod's first No. 1 album?

4 Which No. 1 was used for a BBC series about HMS *Ark Royal*?

5 Which Swedish actress did Rod begin an affair with in 1975?

6 What do blondes have more of according to the 70s single and album?

7 Which album cover showed a boot in the USA and one in the UK?

8 Which country's World Cup Squad did Rod record with in 1978?

9 Which Motown hit did Rod record in 1975 and again in 1989, the latter with Ronald Isley?

10 Which glamorous granny did Rod duet with in "It Takes Two"?

11 Rod asked Do You Think I'm what in 1978?

12 To which disaster fund did Rod donate the proceeds of a concert on his American tour in 1994?

13 Which New Zealand model did Rod marry in 1990?

14 What had Rod Reason to do with his first hit in 1971?

15 Which two solo singers joined Rod on the 1994 hit "All For Love"?

16 The second line of which Rod song is "You're in my soul"?

17 Which Alley was the title of Rod's first album?

18 Which traditional Australian song is "Tom Traubert's Blues" based on?

19 Which line followed "Have I Told You Lately" in 1993?

20 Rod was Foot Loose and what in 1977?

Place the Place (see Quiz 58)
1 San Francisco. 2 Rotterdam. 3 Berlin. 4 The Mersey.
5 Mull of Kintyre. 6 Chicago. 7 Liverpool. 8 Argentina.
9 Bermuda. 10 Belfast. 11 Baker Street. 12 Barcelona.
13 Barbados. 14 California. 15 His Heart. 16 London.
17 The USA. 18 America. 19 Rivers. 20 New York.

Quiz 61 Pot Luck 31

Answers – see page 71

1 Which 70s band's first No. 1 was "Coz I Love You"?

2 What sort of Bullets did 10 c.c. take up the charts in 1973?

3 Was it Sonny or Cher who wrote their single "I Got You Babe"?

4 Which singer was nicknamed Ol' Blues Eyes?

5 What sort of Fever did the Bee Gees have in the singles charts in 1978?

6 Which Army asked Are 'Friends' Electric in 1979?

7 What is the first name of Sharkey, who had a No. 1 with "A Good Heart" in 1985?

8 Which Spinners sang "Working My Way Back to You" in 1980?

9 Whose first hit was "Peggy Sue"?

10 Which comedians sang with the Lightning Seeds on "Three Lions"?

11 Who had the 1988 No. 1 "Theme From S Express"?

12 Which Alice sang "School's Out"?

13 Which country singer's autobiography is called *Stand By Your Man*?

14 Who was once backed by the Revolution?

15 Whose Ding-A-Ling took him to No. 1 in 1972?

16 What do the letters r.p.m. stand for?

17 Which family had a hit with "Love Me For A Reason" in 1974?

18 Which Simon and Garfunkel classic has the lines "When tears are in your eyes, I will dry them all"?

19 Which painter is Don McLean's hit "Vincent" about?

20 How many members of the Mamas and The Papas were there?

Pot Luck 32 (see Quiz 63)
1 Abba. 2 Paul McCartney. 3 Elton John. 4 Pickets.
5 Bangkok. 6 "My Way". 7 Echo. 8 Spain. 9 The Hermits.
10 First name. 11 Vertigo. 12 The Dominoes. 13 Carpenter.
14 Georgie Fame, Alan Price. 15 Alexis. 16 Cleo Laine.
17 k.d. lang. 18 They did not perform on any of their hit records.
19 Greece. 20 She died.

Quiz 62 Christmas Records

Answers – see page 72

 LEVEL 1

1 What gave Band Aid a Christmas No. 1 in 1984 and 1989?

2 Which Brenda was Rockin' Around the Christmas Tree in 1962?

3 What went with Mistletoe on Cliff Richard's 1988 Christmas No. 1?

4 Who recorded the evergreen "Merry Xmas Everybody"?

5 Who went from Crinkley Bottom to the Christmas top spot in 1993?

6 At Christmas 1980 St Winifred's School choir said There's No One Quite Like who?

7 Whose Day gave Cliff Richard a Christmas No. 1 in 1990?

8 Who had two little toys in Rolf Harris's 1969 hit?

9 Which 80s duo sang about Last Christmas in 1984, 1985 and 1986?

10 What colour Christmas did Elvis Presley have in 1964?

11 How was Chris Rea getting Home for Christmas in 1988?

12 Who did Greg Lake say he believed in in 1975?

13 Which Christmas cartoon film had "Walking in the Air" as its theme?

14 Which line follows "I'm dreaming of a White Christmas"?

15 In 1975 where is Santa Claus Coming, according to the Jackson Five?

16 Which Christmas song begins "Long time ago in Bethlehem, so the Holy Bible say"?

17 Which Little animal first entered the charts in 1959?

18 Which singer/piano player invited us to Step into Christmas in 1973?

19 Which Tale did David Essex take to No. 2 in 1982?

20 What are "roasting on an open fire" with "Jack Frost nipping at your nose"?

Country Style (see Quiz 64)
1 Cash. 2 Dolly Parton. 3 Julio Iglesias. 4 Her Man. 5 The County. 6 Jim Reeves. 7 Newton-John. 8 "Annie's Song". 9 Emmerdale. 10 Cline. 11 Kidnapped. 12 Billie Joe. 13 Lynn. 14 Ambridge. 15 Crystal Gayle. 16 Placido Domingo. 17 Guitar. 18 Hank Williams. 19 Mother and daughter. 20 Mary-Chapin.

Quiz 63 Pot Luck 32

Answers – see page 69

LEVEL 1

1   Which Scandinavians were a Super Trouper in 1980?

2   Who was Scaffold's Mike McGear's famous brother?

3   Whose first of many hits was "Your Song" in 1971?

4   Which Flying group had a No. 1 with "Only You" in 1983?

5   In which SE Asian capital did Murray Head spend One Night in 1984?

6   Which song has been recorded by Elvis Presley, the Sex Pistols and Frank Sinatra?

7   Which Beach were Martha and the Muffins on in 1980?

8   Where was Sylvia going on holiday in "Y Viva España"?

9   Who was Herman's backing group?

10 Was Donovan the singer's first name or surname?

11 Which record label shares its name with a feeling of dizziness?

12 Who sang with Derek on "Layla"?

13 Which surname is shared by Karen and Mary-Chapin?

14 Who were Fame and Price Together?

15 What was the first name of the Blues guitarist Korner?

16 Which UK jazz singer is married to John Dankworth ?

17 Whose first names are Kathryn Dawn although she does not use them in full as a stage name?

18 What was odd about the two members of Milli Vanilli's performances on their hit records?

19 Which country is Vangelis from?

20 What happened to Bobby Goldsboro's Honey in 1968?

Pot Luck 31 (see Quiz 61)

1 Slade. 2 Rubber. 3 Sonny. 4 Frank Sinatra. 5 Night.
6 Tubeway. 7 Feargal. 8 Detroit. 9 Buddy Holly. 10 Frank Skinner, David Baddiel. 11 S Express. 12 Cooper. 13 Tammy Wynette. 14 Prince. 15 Chuck Berry. 16 Revolutions per minute. 17 Osmonds. 18 "Bridge Over Troubled Water". 19 Vincent Van Gogh. 20 Four.

71

Quiz 64 Country Style

Answers – see page 70

LEVEL 1

1 Which Johnny had a hit with "A Boy Named Sue"?

2 Which country singer owns a theme park called Dollywood?

3 Which Spanish singer duetted with Willie Nelson on "To All the Girls I've Loved Before"?

4 Who did Tammy Wynette Stand By in her 70s No. 1?

5 Kenny Rogers was the Coward of where in 1980?

6 Which late country star had an album called Country Gentleman?

7 Which Olivia had a hit with "Take Me Home, Country Roads"?

8 Whose Song was a No. 1 for John Denver in 1974?

9 From which dale do the Woolpackers originate?

10 Which Patsy was the subject of a biopic called *Sweet Dreams*?

11 What real crime was committed against Tammy Wynette in 1979?

12 Who was Bobbie Gentry's Ode to?

13 Which Loretta was the subject of a film called *Coal Miner's Daughter*?

14 Which fictional village does the country "star" Eddie Grundy hail from?

15 Who had a hit with "Don't It Make My Brown Eyes Blue"?

16 Which opera tenor recorded "Perhaps Love" with John Denver?

17 Carl Perkins' early recordings were in country style on which musical instrument?

18 How is the country star Hiram Williams better known?

19 What was the relationship between the Judds, who enjoyed considerable success in the 80s?

20 Which Ms Carpenter had a debut chart album *Stones in the Road*?

Christmas Records (see Quiz 62)
1 "Do They Know It's Christmas?". 2 Lee. 3 Wine. 4 Slade.
5 Mr Blobby. 6 Grandma. 7 Saviour's. 8 Two Little Boys.
9 Wham! 10 Blue. 11 Driving. 12 Father Christmas. 13 *The Snowman*. 14 Just like the ones I used to know. 15 To Town.
16 "Mary's Boy Child". 17 Donkey. 18 Elton John.
19 "Winter's Tale". 20 Chestnuts.

1 Which Mac had a top-selling album with *Rumours*?

2 What do the initials R & B stand for?

3 Which song was a No. 1 for Nilsson and Mariah Carey?

4 Who had the original hit with "Cracklin' Rosie"?

5 Which football team recorded the "Anfield Rap"?

6 Which country is Sacha Distel from?

7 What is the TV actor Terence Donovan's son called?

8 Which famous US record label did Berry Gordy found?

9 Which royal couple attended the Live Aid Concert?

10 How was the jazzman Edward Kennedy Ellington better known ?

11 In which decade did Frankie Goes to Hollywood find success?

12 Which Gary's first hit was "Rock and Roll (Parts 1 & 2)" in 1972?

13 Which part of the UK is Aled Jones from?

14 Who was Zag's puppet partner on "Them Girls Them Girls" in 1994?

15 Which word goes before Affair and Unlimited in the names of groups?

16 Which band was originally called Curiosity Killed the Cat?

17 Which singer was nicknamed The King?

18 Which glam group went on a "Teenage Rampage"?

19 How is David Robert Jones better known?

20 How many members of Meat Loaf are there?

Quiz 66 Stage Shows

Answers – see page 76

LEVEL 1

1 Which Swedish group had members who co-wrote "Chess"?

2 Who joined Elaine Paige on the hit single "I Know Him So Well"?

3 Which 60s musical was controversial for its nudity and language?

4 Which musical gave Elaine Paige her first Top Ten hit "Memory"?

5 Which Michael got to No. 2 with "Love Changes Everything" from *Aspects of Love*?

6 Which show is Michael Crawford's "The Music of the Night" from?

7 Which musical about US high school kids in the 50s gave Craig McLachlan chart success?

8 Which rock opera by the Who is about a "deaf, dumb and blind kid"?

9 Which children's TV presenter had a hit with "Close Every Door" from *Joseph and the Amazing Technicolor Dreamcoat*?

10 Who had a No. 1 with "Any Dream Will Do" from the same show?

11 Which Boulevard provided Barbra Streisand with 90s hit singles?

12 Which Cliff Richard film did Darren Day take to the stage in 1996?

13 In which city did Cliff Richard's musical *Heathcliff* have its 1996 premiere?

14 On which day did Marti Webb say to Tell Me in 1980?

15 Which Superstar opened in the West End in 1971 and again in 1996?

16 Which musical includes the No. 1 "Don't Cry For Me Argentina"?

17 Which show based on a Dickens novel includes "As Long As He Needs Me"?

18 What do the performers in *Starlight Express* wear on their feet?

19 Which pop veteran did Sarah Brightman duet with in "All I Ask of You"?

20 The stage show that includes the hit song "On My Own" is based on which Victor Hugo novel?

Answers

Stock, Aitken and Waterman (see Quiz 68)
1 1980s. 2 Stock. 3 Kylie Minogue. 4 Samantha Fox. 5 Rick Astley. 6 Band Aid II. 7 Kim. 8 "Ferry 'Cross the Mersey".
9 Broken Hearts. 10 Britain. 11 Summer. 12 Cliff Richard.
13 Bananarama. 14 Ferry Aid. 15 Waterman. 16 Sonia.
17 On My Pillow. 18 Roadblock. 19 Ten. 20 Three.

74

Quiz 67 Pot Luck 34

Answers – see page 73

LEVEL 1

1 How many members of the Monkees were there?

2 Who was Joe Brown's backing group?

3 Whose first solo hit was "Careless Whisper" in 1984?

4 Which famous Manchester prison features on the title of an album by the Smiths?

5 Which country does Bob Geldof come from?

6 How did Michael Bolotin slightly change his name for show business?

7 Which group sold in excess of 8 million records with "I'm A Believer"?

8 What sort of Band were the Brighouse and Rastrick?

9 Which country is Belinda Carlisle from?

10 Which singer/drummer appeared in the UK and US performances of Live Aid?

11 Which blonde 60s and 70s star sang with the Pet Shop Boys in 1987?

12 Which word goes before Believe and Feel Fine in a song title?

13 Which film star's eyes were a hit for Kim Carnes?

14 What was Bruce Springsteen Born to do in 1987?

15 Which wine was Elkie Brooks singing about in 1978?

16 What went with Gypsys and Tramps on Cher's 1971 single?

17 Which Crisis had an 80s hit with "Arizona Sky"?

18 The Bangles were heard to Walk Like who in 1986?

19 Which Lynn had an international hit with "Rose Garden"?

20 Whose remix of "Downtown" re-entered the charts in 1988?

Pot Luck 33 (see Quiz 65)

1 Fleetwood. 2 Rhythm and Blues. 3 "Without You". 4 Neil Diamond. 5 Liverpool. 6 France. 7 Jason. 8 Tamla Motown. 9 The Prince and Princess of Wales. 10 Duke Ellington. 11 80s. 12 Glitter. 13 Wales. 14 Zig. 15 Love. 16 Curiosity. 17 Elvis Presley. 18 Sweet. 19 David Bowie. 20 One.

Quiz 68 S A W

Answers – see page 74

1 In which decade was the Stock, Aitken and Waterman "hit factory" established?

2 Which member of the trio's first name is Mike?

3 Which female "Neighbours" star was an early SAW signing?

4 Which Page 3 model's record "Nothing Gonna Stop Me Now" was an SAW production?

5 Which Rick from the SAW stable had Europe's best selling single of 1987, "Never Gonna Give You Up"?

6 Which Band's 1989 Christmas charity remake did SAW produce?

7 Who was Mel's singing partner on SAW's production of "F.L.M."?

8 On which charity No. 1 did they feature with the Christians, Holly Johnson, Paul McCartney and Gerry Marsden?

9 What were there Too Many of in the song sung by Jason Donovan?

10 What completes the SAW slogan "the sound of a bright young…"?

11 With which Donna did SAW produce "This Time I Know It's For Real"?

12 Which pop veteran had a hit with "I Just Don't have the Heart"?

13 Which female trio had a hit with "I Heard a Rumour" in 1987?

14 Which charity band had a SAW-produced No. 1 with "Let It Be" after the *Herald of Free Enterprise* tragedy?

15 Which of the trio introduced "The Hitman and Her" on TV?

16 Which single-named performer had a No. 1 with the SAW-written-and-produced "You'll Never Stop Me Loving You"?

17 Where were the Tears on Kylie Minogue's 1990 No. 1?

18 Which traffic hazard was a hit for SAW as performers in 1987?

19 How many Good Reasons were on the title of Jason Donovan's first No. 1 album?

20 How many charity No. 1's did SAW have?

Answers

Stage Shows (see Quiz 66)
1 Abba. 2 Barbara Dickson. 3 *Hair*. 4 *Cats*. 5 Ball.
6 *Phantom of the Opera*. 7 *Grease*. 8 *Tommy*. 9 Phillip Schofield.
10 Jason Donovan. 11 Sunset. 12 *Summer Holiday*. 13
Birmingham. 14 On a Sunday. 15 Jesus Christ. 16 *Evita*. 17
Oliver!. 18 Roller skates. 19 Cliff Richard. 20 Les Miserables.

Quiz 69 Pot Luck 35

Answers – see page 79

LEVEL 1

1 Whose first hit was "Heaven is a Place on Earth" in 1987?

2 Which word goes before Way and Pretty One in the song titles?

3 Where is the Fog on the best selling album by Lindisfarne?

4 Which Leppard were the most successful heavy-metal band of the 80s?

5 Which Club sang "Do You Really Want to Hurt Me?" in 1982?

6 Which heavy-rock band shares its name with a village in the Bible?

7 Which 50s vocal Girls were the name of a football pools company?

8 Which number follows Haircut in the name of the 80s band?

9 Which 60s band's first album was called *Are You Experienced?*?

10 Which country do Inxs come from?

11 Which record label shares its name with a substance in a thermometer?

12 Which number follows U in the name of the band?

13 Which singer was nicknamed the Big "O"?

14 Which Motown Brothers sang "Behind A Painted Smile" in 1969?

15 Which girl is the youngest of the singing Jackson family?

16 Which part of the UK is Annie Lennox from?

17 Which actress Julia was Lyle Lovett married to?

18 Which area of New York was transferred to the name of a vocal quartet?

19 Which actor/singer had an album called *Just Good Friends* after the sitcom in which he starred?

20 Which Monkee had the same name as David Bowie's real name?

Pot Luck 36 (see Quiz 71)
1 Iron Maiden. 2 Mud. 3 The Dreamers. 4 Ricky Nelson.
5 I'm. 6 Randy. 7 Sally. 8 Blue. 9 Partridge Family. 10 Italy.
11 Shirley. 12 Play. 13 Smoke. 14 Powell. 15 Simon Smith.
16 Quatro. 17 Right Said Fred. 18 *Great Expectations*.
19 Kylie Minogue. 20 Five.

Quiz 70 Big Ballads

Answers – see page 80

 LEVEL 1

1 What goes before "(Who Have Nothing)" in the title of the Shirley Bassey hit?

2 Who joined Elton John to take his composition "Don't let the Sun Go Down on Me" to the top of the charts?

3 Who went to the top of the charts with "One Moment in Time" in 1988?

4 Whose dream of The Green, Green Grass of Home went to No. 1?

5 Which Last dance gave Englebert Humperdinck a No. 1 in 1967?

6 Which Frank Sinatra classic entered the charts 10 times in 15 years?

7 Which Elaine Paige hit begins "Midnight, not a sound from the pavement"?

8 Which Canadian-born lady was All By herself at the start of 1997?

9 According to the Hollies, He Ain't Heavy He's what?

10 Which Boys had someone Always On their Mind in 1988?

11 What colour did Chris De Burgh's Lady wear in 1986 ?

12 The Power of what gave Jennifer Rush a No. 1 hit in 1985?

13 Which hit has the lines "Walk on, walk on, with hope in your heart"?

14 Which show did the hit "I Know Him So Well" come from?

15 How many times was someone a lady on the Commodores hit?

16 Which Barbra had a No. 1 hit with "Woman in Love"?

17 Love Changes what according to the Michael Ball ballad?

18 Which Beatles' ballad has been recorded more than any other?

19 What were Simply Red Holding Back in in 1986?

20 Which ballad had a record-breaking run at No. 1 with Bryan Adams?

Answers

Food For Thought (see Quiz 72)
1 Spice. 2 Carrott. 3 Bucks Fizz. 4 Wine. 5 Sweet. 6 Meat Loaf. 7 Breakfast. 8 Vanilla. 9 Almond. 10 Chicken. 11 Jam. 12 Cream. 13 Bread. 14 Marmalade. 15 Lollipop. 16 Hot Chocolate. 17 Orange. 18 Apple. 19 Brown. 20 Pie.

78

Quiz 71 Pot Luck 36

Answers – see page 77

 **LEVEL 1**

1 Which Maiden took "Bring Your Daughter to the Slaughter" to No. 1?

2 Which dirty-sounding group had a hit with "Tiger Feet"?

3 Who was Freddie's backing group?

4 How was Rick Nelson known in his early career?

5 Which word goes before Still Waiting and Alive in the song titles?

6 Which first name is shared by Messrs Newman and Travis?

7 What is Mike Oldfield's musical sister called?

8 Which colour goes before Angel and Bayou on Roy Orbison's singles?

9 Which TV/pop family included Shirley Jones and David Cassidy?

10 Which country does Luciano Pavarotti originate from?

11 Who was Pepsi's singing partner?

12 What did Pink Floyd See Emily do on their 1967 single?

13 What Gets In Your Eyes according to the Platters?

14 Which former DJ Peter is Anthea Turner married to?

15 Who had an Amazing Dancing Bear according to Alan Price?

16 Which Suzi's first No. 1 was "Can The Can"?

17 Which Fred said "I'm Too Sexy" in 1991?

18 Which Great book by Charles Dickens is the title of the debut album by Tasmin Archer?

19 Whose first hit was "I Should Be So Lucky" in 1988?

20 How many members of New Kids on the Block were there?

Pot Luck 35 (see Quiz 69)
1 Belinda Carlisle. 2 My. 3 The Tyne. 4 Def. 5 Culture Club.
6 Nazareth. 7 Vernons Girls. 8 100. 9 Jimi Hendrix Experience.
10 Australia. 11 Mercury. 12 2. 13 Roy Orbison. 14 Isley.
15 Janet. 16 Scotland. 17 Roberts. 18 Manhattan Transfer.
19 Paul Nicholas. 20 David Jones.

Quiz 72 Food for Thought

Answers – see page 78

1 Which Girls had the Christmas No. 1 single and album in 1996?

2 Which Jasper is known for comedy but has enjoyed chart success?

3 Which bubbly drink gave the UK Eurovision success in 1981?

4 Which drink went with Mistletoe on Cliff Richard's 1988 Christmas hit?

5 Which 70s glam-rock band were obviously not sour?

6 Who recorded "Bat Out Of Hell"?

7 Which meal did Deep Blue Something have at Tiffany's in 1996?

8 Which flavour Ice had a No. 1 with "Ice Ice Baby" in 1990?

9 Which Marc had a 1989 hit with Gene Pitney?

10 Which Song was an 80s No. 1 for Spitting Image?

11 Which group's name would go with scones or even tarts?

12 Which 60s band would make a good topping for strawberries?

13 Which David Gates group would be good if you wanted a sandwich?

14 Which 60s group would go well with toast?

15 According to Millie what was My Boy called?

16 Which Hot drink sang "You Sexy Thing"?

17 Which Jason was a member of Take That?

18 Which fruit was at the core of Beatles' singles on their own label?

19 Which type of Sugar was a hit for the Rolling Stones?

20 What American food was a hit for Don McLean?

Quiz 73 Pot Luck 37

Answers – see page 83

LEVEL 1

1   Whose *Bridge Over Troubled Water* album is one of the best sellers of all time?

2   Which singer was nicknamed Little Miss Dynamite?

3   Which record label shares its name with a London Circus?

4   Which American female has had more than 40 Top 40 hits?

5   Which Jimmy had the original hit with "What Becomes of the Broken Hearted?"?

6   Which Alexei asked "'Ullo John, Got a New Motor?" in 1984?

7   Which group's name sounds like a structure for execution?

8   What went after Scritti in the name of the 80s band?

9   Which haven't entered the UK charts – Singing Dogs, Singing Pigs or Singing Sheep?

10   Which Soft band had Tainted Love in 1981?

11   Which Bobby had a 50s No. 1 with "Mack the Knife"?

12   Which one-time Elton John duettist had a hit with "Amoureuse"?

13   What did the Drifters say to Save on their best-selling hit?

14   Which Boris sang "I Want To Wake Up With You" in 1986?

15   Which number was important for Paul Hardcastle in 1985?

16   Which country did 60s vocalist Françoise Hardy come from?

17   Which Frankie said "Welcome to the Pleasure Dome" in 1985?

18   Which two words followed Chirpy Chirpy on Middle of the Road's 70s No. 1?

19   Who recorded the album with his own name and "Schmilsson" in the title?

20   Whose first hit was "Move It" in 1958?

Pot Luck 38 (see Quiz 75)

Answers

1 Five. 2 When. 3 Blue. 4 The Luvvers. 5 Norway. 6 Eric Clapton. 7 Chubby Checker. 8 The Carpenters. 9 Buddy Holly. 10 "Living in a Box". 11 Long and Tall. 12 Bianco. 13 Trumpet. 14 Lizzy. 15 Ken Dodd. 16 Whittaker. 17 Dave Clark. 18 The Shadows. 19 "Wish You Were Here". 20 Spice Girls.

Quiz 74 Rock Rebels

Answers – see page 84

1 Whose video for "Like A Prayer" was banned by the Vatican?

2 Which 60s group was famous for breaking up guitars on stage?

3 Which Nirvana vocalist shot himself in 1994?

4 Which group's records were suspended on some radio networks in January 1997 after its former singer said Ecstasy was completely safe?

5 Which Doors member was buried in Paris after his family disowned him?

6 Which Alice appeared on stage with a guillotine and live snakes?

7 Which band was Noel Gallagher referring to when he said he hoped two of its members would die of AIDS?

8 Which member of the Sex Pistols was charged with the murder of his girlfriend Nancy Spungen?

9 Which singer Marianne was arrested with Mick Jagger in 1969?

10 Who was performing in New York when semi-nude female cyclists appeared as the band sang "Fat Bottomed Girls"?

11 Who was arrested at the 1996 Brit Awards for his behaviour when Michael Jackson was on stage?

12 Which Rolling Stone drowned "while under the influence of alcohol and drugs"?

13 Which Jane Birkin/Serge Gainsbourg song was banned by the BBC?

14 Which Jimi ended his act by playing guitar with his teeth then burning it?

15 Which Motown star Marvin was shot dead by his own father?

16 Which Jerry married his 13-year-old third wife when he was 22?

17 Who was shown on TV from the waist up only in 1957 as his gyrations were said to be too provocative?

18 Who caused a storm by saying the Beatles were more popular than Jesus?

19 In '86 16-year-old Mandy Smith revealed a two-year affair with whom?

20 Which Eric played with Cream before going solo?

Answers

Madonna (see Quiz 76)

1 Madonna. 2 *Evita*. 3 Susan. 4 Virgin. 5 The Groove. 6 Papa. 7 Sean Penn. 8 Blonde. 9 *Dick Tracy*. 10 Immaculate. 11 Sex. 12 Material. 13 Pyjamas. 14 "Top of the Pops". 15 Blue. 16 Vogue. 17 Stalking. 18 Daughter. 19 Bad. 20 Pepsi-Cola.

Quiz 75 Pot Luck 38

Answers – see page 81

LEVEL 1

1 How many members of Take That were there in the early 90s?

2 Which word goes before I Fall in Love and A Child is Born in two song titles?

3 Which colour Roses feature in Jimmy Nail's 1997 single?

4 Who was Lulu's backing group?

5 Which country were A-ha from?

6 Whose real name is Eric Clapp?

7 Which Twist artist was named after Fats Domino?

8 Whose first UK hit was "(They Long to Be) Close To You"?

9 Whose first No. 1 was "It Doesn't Matter Any More" in 1959?

10 What was Living in a Box's first single in 1987?

11 What was Little Richard's Sally like?

12 Which Matt sang "Get Out of Your Lazy Bed"?

13 Which musical instrument does Herb Alpert play?

14 Which Thin group sang "Whiskey in the Jar" in 1973?

15 Which Diddyman's first hit was "Love is Like a Violin"?

16 Which Roger was Leavin' Durham Town in 1969?

17 Which Five were Glad All Over in 1963?

18 Whose first hit was "Apache" in 1960?

19 Which TV holiday programme is also the title of an album by Pink Floyd?

20 Which group was a Wannabe in 1996?

Answers

Pot Luck 37 (see Quiz 73)
1 Simon and Garfunkel. 2 Brenda Lee. 3 Piccadilly. 4 Diana Ross. 5 Ruffin. 6 Sayle. 7 Scaffold. 8 Politti. 9 Singing Pigs. 10 Soft Cell. 11 Darin. 12 Kiki Dee. 13 The Last Dance for Me. 14 Gardiner. 15 19. 16 France. 17 Frankie Goes to Hollywood. 18 Cheep Cheep. 19 Nilsson. 20 Cliff Richard.

Quiz 76 Madonna

Answers – see page 82

 **LEVEL 1**

1   What is Madonna's real first name?

2   Which Madonna film was premiered in December 1996?

3   Who was Madonna Desperately Seeking in her first major film role?

4   Madonna was Like a what on her second album?

5   What was Madonna Into on her first UK No. 1?

6   Who did Madonna tell not to Preach on her 1986 single?

7   Which actor did Madonna marry in 1985?

8   What type of Ambition describes her world tour in 1990?

9   In which film based on a cartoon character did she co-star with Warren Beatty?

10   Which Collection album was made up of greatest hits?

11   What name was given to her 1992 album and accompanying book?

12   What type of Girl is Madonna on her 1985 hit?

13   What were Madonna fans wearing on her video "Bedtime Story"?

14   Which pop show did Madonna appear on in November 1995 after an 11-year gap?

15   Which True colour was Madonna in 1986?

16   Which magazine shares its name with a 1990 No. 1?

17   Robert Hoskins was convicted of which crime against Madonna in January 1996?

18   Did Madonna give birth to a son or a daughter in autumn 1996?

19   What type of Girl is Madonna on her 1993 hit?

20   "Like A Prayer" was used to advertise which drink?

Answers

Rock Rebels (see Quiz 74)
1 Madonna. 2 The Who. 3 Kurt Cobain. 4 East 17. 5 Jim Morrison. 6 Cooper. 7 Blur. 8 Sid Vicious. 9 Faithfull. 10 Queen. 11 Jarvis Cocker. 12 Brian Jones. 13 "Je t'aime (Moi Non Plus)".. 14 Hendrix. 15 Gaye. 16 Lee Lewis. 17 Elvis Presley. 18 John Lennon. 19 Bill Wyman. 20 Clapton.

Quiz 77 Pot Luck 39

Answers – see page 87

 LEVEL 1

1 Which daughter of a famous singer had hits with Lee Hazelwood?

2 Which Tony and Jackie wrote the theme music for "Neighbours"?

3 Which musical instrument is Buddy Greco famous for?

4 What type of guitar did Jimi Hendrix play– electric or acoustic?

5 Which Caribbean island does reggae originate from?

6 Which Sabbath are a heavy-metal band?

7 Which singer is nicknamed the Spanish Sinatra?

8 Which song was a No. 1 for Rosemary Clooney and Shakin' Stevens?

9 Which half of a 70s duo recorded his *Graceland* album?

10 What was Messrs Green and Flynn's No. 1 debut album?

11 What extra accessory does Gabrielle wear on her face?

12 Which 90s reptiles gave Partners in Kryme a No. 1 hit?

13 Whose first hit was "If Not For You" in 1971?

14 Which Fern sang "Together We Are Beautiful"?

15 How were the Motown Spinners later known?

16 For which country did Johnny Logan win the Eurovision Song Contest?

17 Who sang about Major Tom stranded in space?

18 Who had a triple platinum album with *Zenyatta Mondatta* in the 80s?

19 Which family of brothers wrote and co-produced Barbra Streisand's No. 1 "Woman in Love"?

20 Whose first album was called *Blue Gene* in 1964?

Pot Luck 40 (see Quiz 79)
1 Three. 2 1940s. 3 Kid Creole. 4 Abba. 5 England. 6 Whitney. 7 Lee. 8 Goss. 9 "Orinoco Flow". 10 South Korea. 11 Madonna. 12 Julio Iglesias. 13 Cash. 14 Her husband. 15 Long playing (record). 16 The Comets. 17 First name. 18 Roy Orbison. 19 17. 20 Snakes and Ladders.

85

Quiz 78 Stateside

1 Who was the 50s top-selling male artist?

2 Who had one of the best-selling US hits ever with "The Chipmunk Song"?

3 Which British singer was a top-selling artist in the USA in the 80s particularly when she got Physical?

4 What is the surname of Pat and Debby, US chart toppers in the 50s and 70s respectively?

5 Who were Stayin' Alive at the top of the US charts in 1978?

6 Which (originally Tamla) duo had Endless Love in the 80s?

7 Which Star film theme was a best-seller for Meco in 1977?

8 Which new dance made Chubby Checker and his song a 60s hit?

9 Which Garth is a US top-selling artist?

10 Which band, whose name is shared with a city famous for its tea party, had a best-selling album of the same name?

11 Which Boyz are among the top-selling bands of the 90s in the US?

12 Which Mariah joined them on a single in 1995?

13 Whose Boy Child provided a hit for Harry Belafonte?

14 What was the title of USA For Africa's charity record?

15 Who sang "White Christmas", the best-seller of all time in the US?

16 Which veteran US singer has had around 70 chart albums in his career?

17 Which film provided a No. 1 album for Whitney Houston?

18 Which King gave two British writers a top-selling US album?

19 Who backed Prince on the 80s album *Purple Rain*?

20 What sort of Dancing was a top film soundtrack?

Answers

Oldest Swingers in Town (see Quiz 80)
1 Louis Armstrong. 2 Righteous Brothers. 3 Frank Sinatra. 4 Tina Turner. 5 Gary Glitter. 6 Tom Jones. 7 Bing Crosby. 8 Jimmy Young. 9 Charles Aznavour. 10 If. 11 Cliff Richard. 12 Sedaka. 13 Pavarotti. 14 Grandad. 15 Rolf Harris. 16 Bassey. 17 O'Connor. 18 Stewart. 19 Como. 20 Mick Jagger.

Quiz 79 Pot Luck 40

Answers – see page 85

LEVEL 1

1   How many members of the Police were there?

2   Which decade was Cliff Richard born in?

3   Which Kid is also known as August Darnell?

4   Who had a No. 1 with "Super Trouper"?

5   Which country does Jimmy Nail come from?

6   Which daughter of Cissy Houston duetted with her on "I Know Him So Well" on the daughter's album?

7   Which Brenda had a hit with "Speak To Me Pretty"?

8   Which Matt and Luke were in a trio with Craig Logan?

9   Which Enya hit is subtitled "Sail Away"?

10 "1988 Summer Olympics/One Moment in Time" was made for the Games hosted by which country?

11 Which singer's surname is Ciccone?

12 Which Continental artist had a No. 1 with "Begin the Beguine" in 1981?

13 Which Johnny is nicknamed the Man in Black?

14 Which member of Cilla Black's family is her manager?

15 What do the letters LP stand for?

16 Who were Bill Haley's backing group?

17 Is Vangelis the artist's first name or surname?

18 Whose first hit was "Only The Lonely" in 1960?

19 Which number follows East in the name of the band?

20 Which game of reptiles and climbing apparatus is the title of an album by Gerry Rafferty?

Pot Luck 39 (see Quiz 77)
Answers
1 Nancy Sinatra. 2 Hatch, Trent. 3 Drums. 4 Electric.
5 Jamaica. 6 Black. 7 Julio Iglesias. 8 This Ole House. 9 Paul
Simon. 10 *Robson and Jerome.* 11 Eye patch. 12 Turtles (Turtle
Power). 13 Olivia Newton-John. 14 Kinney. 15 Detroit
Spinners. 16 Ireland. 17 David Bowie. 18 Police. 19 Gibb.
20 Gene Pitney.

87

Quiz 80 Oldest Swingers in Town

Answers – see page 86

LEVEL 1

1 Which gravel-voiced jazz trumpeter was nearly 68 when he had a No. 1 with "What a Wonderful World"?

2 Which duo's combined ages were over 100 when they hit the top spot with the reissued "Unchained Melody" in 1990?

3 Who was 78 when he re-entered the charts with "My Way" in 1994?

4 Which grandmother had a No. 1 album *What's Love Got to Do With It*??

5 Who was the Leader of the Gang in the 70s but kept rockin' into the 90s?

6 Which Welsh grandad, once described as "sweat personified" topped the bill at the 1996 Royal Variety Show and sang his 80s hit "Kiss"?

7 Which singer teamed up with David Bowie for the 1982 hit "Peace on Earth–Little Drummer Boy"?

8 Which 90s Radio 2 man had two consecutive No. 1s in the 50s?

9 Which French singer, most famous for "She", released a CD of songs in English in 1996?

10 Which two-letter song title did Telly (Kojak) Savalas take to No. 1?

11 Who had a No. 1 with "Saviour's Day" shortly after his 50th birthday?

12 Which Neil, famous for "Oh Carol", started in the 50s and was still touring in the 90s?

13 Which Italian over-60 joined Elton John on a 1996 single?

14 Which elderly relative did Clive Dunn portray when he was only 49?

15 Which TV presenter took "A Stairway to Heaven" to No 7 in 1993?

16 Which Shirley had her first hit in 1957 and enjoyed a 90s revival?

17 Which TV presenter Des was in the Top Ten in the 80s at the age of 54?

18 Which Rod is enjoying chart success in his 50s as he did in his 20s?

19 Which US singer Perry was enjoying chart success when he was over 60?

20 Which Dartford-born grandfather has been lead singer in one of the country's most controversial pop groups for more than 30 years?

Answers *Stateside* (see Quiz 78)

1 Elvis Presley. 2 The Chipmunks. 3 Olivia Newton-John. 4 Boone. 5 Bee Gees. 6 Diana Ross, Lionel Richie. 7 "Star Wars". 8 The Twist. 9 Brooks. 10 Boston. 11 Boyz II Men. 12 Carey. 13 Mary's. 14 "We Are the World". 15 Bing Crosby. 16 Frank Sinatra. 17 *The Bodyguard*. 18 The Lion King. 19 The Revolution. 20 Dirty.

Quiz 81 Pot Luck 41

Answers – see page 91

1 Which part did Elvis Presley play in the film Frankie and Johnny?

2 Which Brothers in Arms had Money For Nothing in album terms?

3 Which Brothers were Scott, John and Gary?

4 In which decade was Celine Dion born?

5 Is Toyah the artist's first name or surname?

6 Which Scots singer's first husband was the Bee Gee Maurice Gibb?

7 In which country was Elton John born?

8 Which singer is nicknamed the Queen of Soul?

9 Which DJ/pop pundit called Jonathan had a hit record with "Everyone's Gone to the Moon"?

10 Which Tommy was considered to be Britain's first rock 'n' roll star?

11 How many guitarists made up the Shadows?

12 Which 80s rock band possessed England's most common surname?

13 Which Park gave hit records for Donna Summer and Richard Harris?

14 Who has hosted the Eurovision Song Contest on BBC1 in the 90s?

15 Which country does Gina G come from?

16 Which Gilbert appeared on stage in short trousers, cropped hair and cloth cap?

17 Which Australian appeared in "The Sullivans" and "The Hendersons" before enjoying chart success?

18 Whose first hit was "Love Me For a Reason" in 1994?

19 What is George's surname and Mr Bolton's first?

20 Whose first album was called _Otis Blue_ in 1966?

Answers

Pot Luck 42 (see Quiz 83)
1 1960s. 2 Mama Cass. 3 The Partridge Family. 4 Paula Yates.
5 Simon. 6 England. 7 Marvin. 8 Leather. 9 Puckett.
10 His trousers. 11 The Rubettes. 12 Keyboards. 13 Hynde.
14 The 50s. 15 Pink Floyd. 16 Pickett. 17 Bing Crosby.
18 Telly Savalas. 19 10 c.c. 20 Four.

Quiz 82 Michael Jackson

Answers – see page 92

LEVEL 1

1 With which group did Michael Jackson have chart success?

2 Whose superstar's daughter did he marry in 1994?

3 Which Jackson album broke all records in 1982?

4 What type of dance "walking" did Jackson introduce in 1983?

5 On which soul label did Jackson record his early hits?

6 Which animal was the single "Ben" about?

7 *The Wiz*, in which he starred, was a remake of which film?

8 Which Beatle did Jackson duet with in "The Girl is Mine"?

9 Jackson was the narrator on the soundtrack of which "extra-terrestrial" film?

10 Jackson co-wrote "We Are the World" to raise money for the USA's campaign against what?

11 Which US TV talk-show hostess conducted a famous interview with the star in 1993?

12 Which much-married famous film star was married at Michael Jackson's ranch in 1991?

13 What type of animal is Jackson's pet Bubbles?

14 Which Billie took Jackson to No. 1 in 1983?

15 Which album was the follow-up to his 1982 massive success, which had a video showing Jackson in belts, buckles and straps?

16 Who was Rockin' on Jackson's 1972 hit?

17 Which anthem-like song went straight to No. 1 at Christmas 1995?

18 Which member of Pulp interrupted Jackson's receiving a BRIT Award in 1996?

19 Who did Jackson say Farewell to on his 1984 summer album?

20 Which ex-Supreme was credited with discovering the Jacksons?

Answers

Colour Coded (see Quiz 84)
1 Yellow. 2 Red. 3 Purple. 4 Whiter. 5 Suede. 6 Blue.
7 Black. 8 White. 9 Orange. 10 Green. 11 Brown.
12 Pink. 13 Gold. 14 Green. 15 Blue. 16 Green.
17 Brown. 18 Yellow. 19 Lilac. 20 Red, Red.

1 In which decade was Whitney Houston born?

2 How is Cass Elliott better known?

3 Who was David Cassidy's backing group?

4 Who was Mrs Bob Geldof at the start of the 1990s?

5 What is Paul's surname and Mr Le Bon's first?

6 Which part of the UK does Lisa Stansfield come from?

7 Which first name is shared by Messrs Gaye and Rainwater?

8 What were Suzi Quatro's stage outfits usually made from?

9 Which Gary sang with the Union Gap?

10 What was P.J. Proby's most famous split on stage?

11 Whose first hit was "Sugar Baby Love" in 1974?

12 Which instrument does Alan Price play?

13 Which Chrissie sang with the Pretenders?

14 In which decade did the Platters enjoy their greatest success?

15 Which 70s supergroup included Roger Waters and David Gilmour?

16 Which Wilson was "In the Midnight Hour" in the 60s and in the 80s?

17 Which late US crooner is nicknamed the Old Groaner?

18 Which TV detective star's only album was called *Telly*?

19 Who had a hit with "I'm Not In Love" in 1975?

20 How many members of Queen were there?

Quiz 84 Colour Coded

Answers – see page 90

LEVEL 1

1 What colour of Brick Road did Elton John say Goodbye to in 1973?

2 What colour is Simply Mick Hucknall?

3 What colour Rain did Prince sing about in 1984?

4 Which Shade of Pale featured on the Procul Harum classic?

5 What were Elvis Presley's Blue Shoes made from?

6 What is the Colour on the Beautiful South's 1996 album?

7 Which colour surname did Priscilla White change her name to?

8 What Christmas was a hit for Bing Crosby?

9 Which Jason had a colourful surname in Take That?

10 Which Robson duetted with Jerome Flynn?

11 Which Joe played with the Bruvvers?

12 What colour was Lily in the Scaffold song?

13 Which Finger provided Shirley Bassey with a hit record?

14 Which Door was Shakin' Stevens behind in 1981?

15 What colour Jeans were Swinging in the 60s group?

16 What colour was Tom Jones's Grass of Home?

17 According to Crystal Gayle, Don't It Make which Eyes Blue?

18 What colour was the Beatles' Submarine?

19 Which colour Wine gave Elkie Brooks chart success?

20 Which colour Wine gave UB40 chart success?

Answers

Michael Jackson (see Quiz 82)
1 Jackson 5. 2 Elvis Presley's. 3 *Thriller*. 4 Moonwalking.
5 Tamla Motown. 6 Rat. 7 *The Wizard of* Oz. 8 Paul
McCartney. 9 *E.T.* 10 Famine in Africa. 11 Oprah Winfrey.
12 Elizabeth Taylor. 13 Chimpanzee. 14 Jean. 15 *Bad*.
16 Robin. 17 "Earth". 18 Jarvis Cocker. 19 Summer Love.
20 Diana Ross.

Quiz 85 Pot Luck 43

Answers – see page 95

LEVEL 1

1   Which decade was Phil Collins born in?

2   What is Jackie's surname and Mr Pickett's first?

3   What name was given to the group made up of four Osmond sons?

4   Which Roy's vocal sound was once described as "the slow fall of teardrops"?

5   What was the nationality of John Lennon's second wife?

6   Which singer was nicknamed the First Lady of Jazz?

7   Who is the country singer Margo O'Donnell's famous brother?

8   Which Irish band has the Edge?

9   How did Sinead O'Connor's hair add to her striking appearance?

10 Which record label shares its name with a long book or film?

11 In 1983 Gary Numan gave public support to whose re-election campaign?

12 Which surname is shared by the country star Willie and Prince?

13 Which Alison sang with Yazoo?

14 Is Morrissey the performer's first name or surname?

15 Which corporation did George Michael begin his lawsuit against in the 1990s?

16 Which Jamaican singer was given a state funeral in 1980?

17 Whose first hit was "My Coo-Ca-Choo" in 1973?

18 Which four herbs were the title of an album by Simon and Garfunkel?

19 On which comedy duo's show did Shirley Bassey sing wearing a hobnail boot?

20 Who had a 70s No. 1 album with *Slayed*?

Answers

Pot Luck 44 (see Quiz 87)
1 1940s. 2 Paul. 3 McTell. 4 McGuire. 5 "Shout". 6 Little Richard. 7 North East England. 8 Piano. 9 Joplin. 10 Jones. 11 Uptown Girl. 12 Jarre. 13 Japan. 14 England. 15 Tamla Motown. 16 Prince Charming. 17 John Lennon. 18 Two. 19 The Wailers. 20 Medium wave.

Quiz 86 Abba

Answers – see page 96

1 Which Song Contest shot Abba to fame?

2 Which song won it for them?

3 Why is the group called Abba?

4 Which Abba song includes the line "It's a rich man's world"?

5 The name of which Abba hit is also a distress signal?

6 Which musical did two group members write with Tim Rice?

7 Abba's income was said to exceed which Swedish motor company's?

8 Which Abba hit had an Italian title?

9 In which Abba song is the line "Since many years I haven't seen a rifle in your hand"?

10 Which album did the single "Super Trouper" come from?

11 Which Abba song title repeats the same two words five times?

12 What are the first names of the two Abba members who wrote most of their songs?

13 What did Abba Thank You For in 1983?

14 Which two female singers had a No. 1 in 1985 with "I Know Him So Well" written by two of the group?

15 What did The Winner take in the title of the 1980 No. 1?

16 Which Abba hit has a French title?

17 What did Abba ask you to Take A Chance on in 1978?

18 Which monarch was Dancing in 1976?

19 What follows Gimme, Gimme, Gimme in the 1979 hit title?

20 Which song title is the same as a famous quote by Martin Luther King?

Quiz 87 Pot Luck 44

LEVEL 1

1 In which decade was Elton John born?

2 Which name is Billy's first and Mr Anka's second?

3 What did folk singer Ralph May change his surname to?

4 Which Barry had a hit with the 60s protest song "Eve of Destruction"?

5 Which Lulu song has been a hit for her twice?

6 How is the rock 'n' roller Richard Penniman better known?

7 Which part of the UK do Lindisfarne come from?

8 Which musical instrument did Liberace play?

9 Which Janis was the subject of the Bette Midler film *The Rose*?

10 Which singer Grace is famous for hitting Russell Harty during his chat show?

11 Which Girl was an 80s hit for Billy Joel?

12 What is the surname of father and son composers Maurice and Jean-Michel?

13 David Sylvian was lead singer of which oriental-sounding group?

14 In which country was Engelbert Humperdinck brought up?

15 Which record label did Holland-Dozier-Holland leave in 1968?

16 Which hero of *Cinderella* gave his name to an album by Adam Ant?

17 Whose first solo hit was "Give Peace A Chance" in 1969?

18 How many members of the Righteous Brothers are there?

19 Who was Bob Marley's backing group?

20 What do the letters MW stand for on your radio?

Quiz 88 Classic Hits

Answers – see page 94

1   Which animals were in the title of an Elton John/Pavarotti hit?

2   What was the 1990 Pavarotti hit used for the 1990 World Cup Finals?

3   How are Pavarotti, Domingo and Carreras known collectively?

4   What is Domingo's first name?

5   What is the nationality of Carreras?

6   Which musical instrument does Nigel Kennedy play?

7   Which BBC radio network broadcasts 24-hour classical music?

8   Which Sarah sang "Amigos Para Siempre (Friends For Life)" with Carreras?

9   Which '96 sports event sent Beethoven's "Ode to Joy" into the charts?

10 Which TV theme is made up of classical-sounding music with dots and dashes?

11 Which opera singer Lesley recorded "Ave Maria" with the young Amanda Thompson?

12 Which flute-player had a 70s hit with "Annie's Song"?

13 Which Jennifer had chart success with Domingo in 1989?

14 Which former Motown star joined Carreras and Domingo on the album *Christmas in Vienna*?

15 What is the home country of the "World In Union" singer Kiri Te Kanawa?

16 "World in Union" was recorded for a championship in which sport?

17 What is the nationality of Montserrat Caballe, who joined Freddie Mercury on "Barcelona"?

18 Which fellow Welshman did the opera baritone Bryn Terfel join on a 1996 TV Christmas special?

19 In which rainy London Park did Pavarotti give a concert in 1992?

20 Which opera star did John Denver make an album with in 1981?

Quiz 89 Pot Luck 45

LEVEL 1

1   Whose first hit was "Mandy" in 1975?

2   Who had a No. 1 album with *Bolan Boogie*?

3   Which singer/comedian is nicknamed the Big Yin?

4   In which decade was Michael Jackson born?

5   What did Charles Hardin Holley change his name to?

6   Which 60s group had Allan Clarke on lead vocals?

7   Which jazz vocalist called Billie was portrayed by Diana Ross on film?

8   Which Happy gospel hit was sung by the Edwin Hawkins Singers?

9   Which North London suburb was the birthplace of Elton John and Tony Hatch?

10   Emmylou Harris was born in Birmingham. True or false?

11   Which song begins "One Two Three o'clock"?

12   Which drink did "I'd Like to Teach the World to Sing" advertise?

13   Which song's second line is "And I'll cry if I want to"?

14   Which comic actor had a hit album *Songs for Swinging Sellers*?

15   What did Seal sing about a Kiss From in 1994?

16   Which Gary was famous for his platform soles and silver outfits?

17   Which Bob formed the company that first produced Channel 4's "The Big Breakfast"?

18   Which Gloria sang "Never Can Say Goodbye" in 1974?

19   Which battle provided Abba with the title of their first album?

20   Who played bass guitar in Suzi Quatro's group?

Quiz 90 On Tour

Answers – see page 100

LEVEL 1

1   What did soccer fan Rod Stewart throw to the audience on tour?

2   Who had a tour called "Blonde Ambition"?

3   In which city is the NEC?

4   In which country might an artist play at Sun City?

5   At which London venue did Cliff Richard end his 1990 "From A Distance" tour?

6   How many times did Elvis Presley tour Britain?

7   Which Fab Four were a support act for Helen Shapiro on her 1963 tour?

8   In which country is the famous Shea Stadium?

9   In which country did Tina Turner play at the "Rock in Rio" festival?

10 Who used to return from tour between gigs to watch Watford play?

11 In which city is the Hammersmith Odeon?

12 What do the initials NEC stand for?

13 On a tour of which continent was Michael Jackson crowned King of the Sanwis in 1992?

14 In which country are the Maple Leaf Gardens a tour venue?

15 In which US city is Carnegie Hall?

16 Who introduced his character Ziggy Stardust on a 70s UK tour?

17 In which country did the Beatles play their last live show?

18 Which area of Los Angeles has a famous venue called the Bowl?

19 Which London Park is a popular open-air tour venue?

20 Buddy Holly perished in a plane crash during a tour of which country?

Answers

Elton John (see Quiz 92)
1 Glasses. 2 Marilyn Monroe. 3 *The Lion King*. 4 Fantastic.
5 Piano. 6 *Tommy*. 7 Kiki Dee. 8 Sorry. 9 AIDS.
10 Fighting. 11 Watford. 12 Live Aid Concert. 13 Crocodile.
14 Bennie. 15 Elvis Presley. 16 Bernie Taupin. 17 "Your Song". 18 Rocket. 19 Daniel. 20 Christmas.

Quiz 91 Pot Luck 46

Answers – see page 97

LEVEL 1

1 In which decade was Olivia Newton-John born?

2 What is Lee's surname and Mr Gaye's first?

3 How is Elaine Bookbinder better known?

4 Which country is Joe Cocker from?

5 Which band included Phil Collins and Peter Gabriel?

6 Which band's name was sometimes abbreviated to FGTH?

7 Which top Motown group did not change their line up for 30 years?

8 Which band was led by Mick Fleetwood?

9 Which Jose recorded the Doors' "Light My Fire"?

10 Which singer's maiden name was Gloria Maria Fajardo?

11 Which Moons were a best selling album for Enya?

12 What was Duane Eddy's musical instrument?

13 Which west-coast US state were the Eagles from?

14 Which east-coast state provided a hit for the Bee Gees?

15 Who wrote the music for *Evita*?

16 How many members of the Shadows were there?

17 Which David and Adam co-starred in the film *Stardust*?

18 Which musical instrument does Georgie Fame play?

19 Which word for an exciting book or film is the name of an album by Michael Jackson?

20 Whose first hit was "American Pie" in 1972?

Answers

Pot Luck 45 (see Quiz 89)
1 Barry Manilow. 2 T. Rex. 3 Billy Connolly. 4 1950s.
5 Buddy Holly. 6 The Hollies. 7 Holiday. 8 "Oh Happy Day".
9 Pinner. 10 True – Birmingham, Alabama. 11 "Rock Around the Clock". 12 Coca-Cola. 13 "It's My Party". 14 Peter Sellers.
15 A Rose. 16 Glitter. 17 Geldof. 18 Gaynor. 19 Waterloo.
20 Suzi Quatro.

Quiz 92 Elton John

Answers – see page 98

Answers – see page 98

LEVEL 1

1 Which outrageous optical accessories was Elton John famous for?

2 Who is Elton singing about with the song which begins "Goodbye Norma Jean"?

3 Which Disney movie provided Elton with an Oscar in 1995?

4 What Captain is named on a 1975 album title?

5 Which instrument did Elton John study at the Royal Academy?

6 In which rock opera film by the Who did Elton John sing "Pinball Wizard"?

7 Who did Elton duet with on "Don't Go Breaking My Heart" in 1976?

8 What seemed to be the Hardest Word in 1975?

9 To combat which illness is the Elton John Foundation providing funds?

10 According to the 1973 hit, what is Saturday Night Alright for?

11 Which Football Club did Elton become chairman of in 1977?

12 Where did Elton John sing "Don't Let the Sun Go Down on Me" with George Michael in July 1985?

13 Which reptile Rock was a hit in 1972?

14 Who is linked with the Jets on the 1976 single?

15 In 1992 Elton John matched which American singer's run of 22 consecutive years of Top 40 hits in the Top 100 in the USA?

16 Which lyricist collaborated with Elton John on his early hits?

17 Which hit began "It's a little bit funny, This feeling inside"?

18 Which Man gave Elton his second hit in 1972?

19 Who was "travellin' tonight on a plane" in 1973?

20 Which festival did Elton Step Into in 1973?

On Tour (see Quiz 90)
1 Footballs. 2 Madonna. 3 Birmingham. 4 South Africa.
5 Wembley. 6 Never. 7 The Beatles. 8 USA. 9 Brazil.
10 Elton John. 11 London. 12 National Exhibition Centre.
13 Africa. 14 Canada. 15 New York. 16 David Bowie.
17 USA. 18 Hollywood. 19 Hyde Park. 20 USA.

Answers

Quiz 93 Pot Luck 47

Answers – see page 103

1   Which Scottish city is Sheena Easton from?

2   In which decade was Roy Orbison born?

3   Which type of Singer was Neil Diamond in his 1980 film?

4   Which time of day is associated with Dexy's Runners?

5   Which singer is nicknamed the Rhinestone Cowboy?

6   Desmond Dekker was one of the first artists in which brand of Jamaican music?

7   Which Chris had a hit on both sides of the Atlantic with "Who Pays the Ferryman?"?

8   Which illness did Ian Dury suffer from in childhood?

9   Which jazz singer called Cleo duetted with the guitarist John Williams?

10 Which record producer called Phil was famous for his "wall of sound"?

11 Which national football side recorded "Back Home" in 1970?

12 Which Harry is famous for his songs on the soundtrack of *When Harry Met Sally*?

13 Which part of house gave its name to an album by Pink Floyd?

14 Which veteran Perry enjoyed chart success in the 70s with "And I Love You So"?

15 Who had a top-selling album with *The Rise and Fall of Ziggy Stardust And The Spiders From Mars*?

16 Which Judy had a best-seller with "Amazing Grace"?

17 Which Eddie had a hit with "Summertime Blues" in 1958?

18 Which country star Patsy was an inspiration to k.d. lang?

19 What is the home country of Richard Clayderman?

20 Whose first hit was "Holiday" in 1984?

Answers

Pot Luck 48 (see Quiz 95)
1 England. 2 Wings. 3 1940s. 4 It was the surname of three of them. 5 Chicago. 6 London. 7 Piano. 8 Of the Board. 9 Cassidy. 10 The Medics. 11 Yesterday. 12 Take That. 13 Wizzard. 14 The Roof. 15 Bob Marley and the Wailers. 16 Two. 17 Stevens. 18 Dee. 19 Jamaica. 20 Caribou.

Quiz 94 60s Revisted

Answers – see page 104

LEVEL 1

1 Which Joan had a hit with "There But For Fortune"?

2 In which language was the banned Serge Gainsbourg/Jane Birkin song recorded in?

3 What were These Boots Made For according to Nancy Sinatra in 1966?

4 Which former member of the Springfields took "You Don't Have To Say You Love Me" to No. 1?

5 Which word described Manfred Mann's Flamingo?

6 Which Ray sang "I Can't Stop Loving You" in 1962?

7 In which country did Frank Ifield begin his singing career?

8 Which Miss Clark had a hit with "Sailor"?

9 Which precious jewels took Jet Harris and Tony Meehan to No. 1?

10 Who were Sweets for in the Searchers' No. 1 hit?

11 Which Brian had a backing group called the Tremeloes?

12 Which former cloakroom attendant from Liverpool's Cavern Club had a No. 1 with "Anyone Who Had a Heart"?

13 Whose real name was Clive and found Fame in the 60s?

14 Who had a No. 1 with "It's Not Unusual" in 1965?

15 What were the initials of the outrageous Mr Proby?

16 What was innovative about the Beatles jackets?

17 Which Adam sang "Poor Me" in 1960?

18 What was on a String on Sandie Shaw's third No. 1 hit?

19 What went with Pins on the Searchers' 1964 hit?

20 Which Lily was a hit for Scaffold?

Answers

70s Revisited (see Quiz 96)
1 George Harrison. 2 Ernie. 3 "Amazing Grace". 4 Metal.
5 Osmond. 6 Partridge. 7 Guitar. 8 Rubber. 9 Stardust.
10 French. 11 Pink Floyd. 12 Mother. 13 In a Bottle.
14 Mondays. 15 Of Babylon. 16 Bush. 17 "New Faces".
18 Dancing. 19 Scotland. 20 Barbados.

Quiz 95 Pot Luck 48

1 Which country is Petula Clark from?

2 Who was Paul McCartney's backing group?

3 In which decade was Eric Clapton born?

4 Why were the Christians so-called?

5 Which band was originally called Chicago Transit Authority?

6 Which city are Chas and Dave from?

7 Which musical instrument does Ray Charles play?

8 Which Chairmen asked: Give Me Just a Little More Time?

9 Which David played the role of Keith Partridge on TV?

10 Who was Doctor's backing group?

11 What follows "Yester-me, Yester-you" on Stevie Wonder's hit?

12 Who had No. 1 hits with "Babe" and "Sure" before disbanding in '96?

13 Which Roy Wood group sounds like a magician?

14 Where did the Supremes Go Up the Ladder to in 1970?

15 Whose first hit was "No Woman No Cry" in 1975?

16 How many members of the Style Council were there?

17 Which Cat had a 70s hit with "Morning Has Broken"?

18 Which surname is shared by the 60s group leader Dave and Kiki?

19 Which Caribbean island do Chaka Demus and Pliers come from?

20 Which type of deer gave its name to an album by Elton John?

Answers

Pot Luck 47 (see Quiz 93)
1 Glasgow. 2 1930s. 3 Jazz Singer. 4 Midnight. 5 Glen Campbell. 6 Reggae. 7 De Burgh. 8 Polio. 9 Laine. 10 Spector. 11 England. 12 Connick Jr. 13 The Wall. 14 Como. 15 David Bowie. 16 Collins. 17 Cochran. 18 Cline. 19 France. 20 Madonna.

Quiz 96   70s Revisted

Answers – see page 102

LEVEL 1

1 Which Beatle had a No. 1 with "My Sweet Lord"?

2 What was the name of the Fastest Milkman in the West?

3 Which Amazing record was by the Scots Dragoon Guards and played on the bagpipes?

4 Which type of Guru did T. Rex sing about?

5 Which Donny had a No. 1 with "Puppy Love"?

6 Which TV family was David Cassidy a member of?

7 Which electric instrument did Suzi Quatro play?

8 What type of bullets did 10 c.c. fire in 1973?

9 Which Alvin had a Jealous Mind?

10 What is the nationality of Charles Aznavour?

11 Which band were the final chart-toppers of the 70s with "Another Brick in the Wall"?

12 Which relative of Sylvia was Dr Hook a hit with?

13 Where did the Police put their Message?

14 Which day of the week did the Boomtown Rats not like?

15 Which Rivers were a hit for Boney M?

16 Which Kate scaled Wuthering Heights in 1978?

17 On which New TV talent show did Showaddywaddy get their big break?

18 Which Queen was a 1976 hit for Abba?

19 Which country were the Bay City Rollers from?

20 Where in the Caribbean were Typically Tropical heading in 1975?

Answers

60s Revisited (see Quiz 94)
1 Baez. 2 French. 3 Walkin'. 4 Dusty. 5 Pretty. 6 Charles.
7 Australia. 8 Petula. 9 Diamonds. 10 My Sweet. 11 Poole.
12 Cilla Black. 13 Georgie Fame. 14 Tom Jones. 15 P.J.
16 Collarless. 17 Faith. 18 Puppet. 19 Needles. 20 The Pink.

Quiz 97 Pot Luck 49

Answers – see page 107

LEVEL 1

1 Which Mode were regular chart members in the 80s?

2 In which decade was Tina Turner born?

3 Which two months were an 80s hit for Barbara Dickson?

4 What is Sacha Distel's only UK chart success?

5 Whose "Riders on the Storm" entered the chart at least four times?

6 Which Night did the Drifters enjoy at the Movies?

7 Which Attraction were Perfect in 1988?

8 How many made up the Fun Boy band of the 80s?

9 In which decade did Gabrielle have her first chart success?

10 Who joined Guys on the 1975 song "There's a Whole Lot of Loving"?

11 Which record label sounds like a sweet or savoury pastry dish?

12 Which comedy duo were backed by the Stonkers?

13 Which number follows in East and Heaven in band names?

14 What colour Haze was a hit for Jimi Hendrix?

15 Which flower was a hit for Vince Hill in 1967?

16 Whose first hit was "Hangin' Tough" in 1989?

17 How is the punk star John Lydon better known?

18 Which word to describe a workout is used by Olivia Newton-John on her 1981 album?

19 Which particular style of alpine singing was Frank Ifield famous for?

20 Which Irish band had a top-selling album with *The Joshua Tree*?

Answers

80s Revisited (see Quiz 98)
1 Jealous. 2 John Lennon. 3 Bucks. 4 Julio Iglesias. 5 Shakin' Stevens. 6 Ebony. 7 Dance. 8 Spandau. 9 That's My Home. 10 Police. 11 Flying. 12 Live Aid. 13 Sledge. 14 Lennox. 15 Hynde. 16 Chain. 17 Wilson. 18 Kim. 19 Star Trekkin'. 20 Up.

Quiz 98 80s Revisited

Answers – see page 105

LEVEL 1

1   What kind of Guy gave Roxy Music a No. 1 hit in 1980?

2   Which Beatle was murdered in December 1980?

3   Which Fizz were telling you to Make Your Mind Up in 1981?

4   Which Spanish singer took "Begin the Beguine" into the charts in 1981?

5   Which 80s singer was known as Shaky?

6   What went with Ivory on the Paul McCartney/Stevie Wonder hit?

7   What did Eddy Grant Not Wanna do in '82?

8   Which Ballet had a No. 1 with "True"?

9   What follows "Wherever I Lay My Hat" on the Paul Young single?

10 "Every Breath You Take" was a final No. 1 for which band, who were a great force in the 80s?

11 Which Pickets took "Only You" to the top?

12 Which pop concert was organized for famine in Africa in July 1985?

13 Which Sister had a hit with "Frankie"?

14 Which Annie was one half of the Eurythmics?

15 Which Chrissie sang guest vocals on UB40's "I Got You Babe"?

16 What Reaction did Diana Ross have in 1986?

17 Which Jackie hit the top with "Reet Petite" nearly 30 years after the record was released?

18 Who was Respectable with Mel?

19 Where were the Firm Trekkin' in 1987?

20 What was the Only Way, according to Yazz in 1988?

Answers

Pot Luck 50 (see Quiz 99)
1 Two. 2 Police. 3 1970s. 4 "Mary's Boy Child". 5 Terry Waite. 6 Louis Armstrong. 7 Lee. 8 John Lennon. 9 *Phil Everly*. 10 Lennox. 11 New Seekers. 12 OMD. 13 Pinky and Perky. 14 Sisters. 15 Ike. 16 Abba. 17 August. 18 Queen. 19 Miller. 20 Fire.

1 How many members of Wham! were there?

2 Whose albums include *Regatta de Blanc* and *Every Breath You Take – The Singles*?

3 In which decade was Mariah Carey born?

4 Which song was a No. 1 for Harry Belafonte and Boney M?

5 Which former Lebanese hostage made a 90s single with Carol Kidd?

6 Which singer/jazz trumpeter was nicknamed Satchmo?

7 Which surname is shared by Brenda and Peggy?

8 Who founded the Plastic Ono Band?

9 What was Phil Everly's first solo album called?

10 Which Annie had a No. 1 album with *Diva*?

11 Which New group had a 70s No. 1 with "You Won't Find Another Fool Like Me"?

12 How are Orchestral Manoeuvres in the Dark sometimes known?

13 Which porky pair recorded "Reet Petite" in 1993?

14 What relation are the individual members of the Nolans to each other?

15 What did Isaiah Turner change his first name to?

16 Which supergroup was Agnetha Faltskog a member of?

17 Which summer month gave its name to an album by Eric Clapton?

18 Whose first hit was "Seven Seas of Rhye" in 1974?

19 Which Roger was King of the Road in 1965?

20 What completes the trio with Earth and Wind?

Answers

Pot Luck 49 (see Quiz 97)
1 Depeche. 2 1930s. 3 January February. 4 "Raindrops Keep Falling on My Head". 5 The Doors. 6 Saturday. 7 Fairground. 8 Three. 9 1990s. 10 Dolls. 11 Pye. 12 Hale and Pace. 13 17. 14 Purple. 15 Edelweiss. 16 New Kids on the Block. 17 Johnny Rotten. 18 Physical. 19 Yodelling. 20 U2.

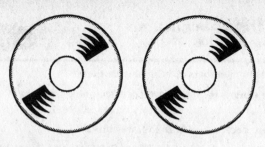

The Medium Questions

This next selection of questions is getting a little more like it. For an open entry quiz you should have a high percentage of medium level questions – don't try to break people's spirits with the hard ones, just make sure that people play to their ability.

Like all questions, this level of question can be classed as either easy or impossible depending on whether you know the answer or not and although common knowledge is used as the basis for these questions there is a sting in the tail of quite a few. Also, if you have a serious drinking squad playing then they can more or less say goodbye to the winners' medals, but that isn't to say they will feel any worse about it.

Specialists are the people to watch out for, as those with a good knowledge of a particular subject will doubtless do well in these rounds so a liberal sprinkling of pot-luck questions is needed to flummox them.

Quiz 1 Pot Luck 1

Answers – see page 111

1   In which decade was Bruce Springsteen born?

2   Which Baby girl did Helen Reddy sing about in 1975?

3   Who had a No. 1 with "Angel Fingers"?

4   Whose first hit was "Shout"?

5   Who had a 70s album called *Arrival*?

6   Which film star's Eyes did Kim Carnes sing about?

7   Which band was King of the Road in 1990?

8   How is Terence Nelhams better known?

9   Which surname is shared by Michael and Randy?

10   Which city did the Smiths hail from?

11   Who sang about Love and Affection in 1976?

12   Which Barry Manilow hit song became a stage show?

13   Which record label showed a dog listening to a gramophone?

14   Which university town do Supergrass come from?

15   Who had a 1953 hit with "She Wears Red Feathers"?

16   Whose backing group were the Rebel Rousers?

17   What is Whigfield's home country?

18   Who was the female member of the Eurythmics?

19   Who had a 1992 hit with "You're All That Matters to Me"?

20   In which decade did Roxy Music have their first hit?

1 Who sang with the Checkmates?

2 Which film did "The Harry Lime Theme" come from?

3 Which girl was on the other side of "All I Have to Do is Dream" for the Everly Brothers?

4 Which first No. 1 for Adam Faith was a question?

5 What was the 50's best-selling single?

6 Who took "Mary's Boy Child" in to the charts in the 50s?

7 Which 50s classic begins "I'm so young and you're so old"?

8 Which singer was married to Debbie Reynolds and Elizabeth Taylor?

9 Who had a Secret Love in 1954?

10 Who sang "Yes Tonight Josephine"?

11 Which singer with which group had a hit with "Livin' Doll"?

12 Whose girl was Only Sixteen at No. 1 in 1959?

13 Which instrumentalist hit the top with "Let's Have Another Party"?

14 Which Buddy Holly hit was the first after his death and went to No. 1?

15 Who told The Story of His Life in 1958?

16 Who went from the Green Door to the Garden of Eden?

17 Who had a 1955 No. 1 with "Unchained Melody"?

18 Who had a "Dreamboat" in 1955?

19 Which 50s musical provided Vic Damone with a 1958 No. 1?

20 What does Anne Shelton finally sing after "Lay Down Your Arms" in her 1956 No. 1?

Answers

The 60s (see Quiz 4)
1 "Release Me". 2 The Archies. 3 Manfred Mann. 4 The Kinks.
5 The Hollies. 6 The Beach Boys. 7 The Seekers. 8 The
Bachelors. 9 The Shondelles. 10 The Dave Clark Five.
11 Telstar. 12 The Move. 13 The Searchers. 14 The drummer.
15 The Moody Blues. 16 The Spencer Davis Group. 17 Six
(Unit Four Plus Two). 18 Wind. 19 Dusty Springfield.
20 Andy Fairweather-Low.

Quiz 3 Pot Luck 2

Answers – see page 109

1 Who had an 1989 hit with "Love Changes Everything"?

2 Which Baby girl did Rod Stewart sing about in 1983?

3 Which Park was Donna Summer in in 1978?

4 Whose backing group was the Mindbenders?

5 Which musical instrument does Johnny Marr play?

6 Whose first hit was "Denis"?

7 Who has recorded under the name of Eivets Rednow?

8 Who was the female member of Wings?

9 Which Goffin and King song by the Chiffons shares its name with an aria from Puccini's *Madame Butterfly*?

10 Who was Cilla Black's first manager?

11 How did T. Rex's Marc Bolan meet his death?

12 Which duo with combined ages of over 80 topped the charts in September 1985 for four weeks?

13 Who were the first husband-and-wife team to top the charts?

14 Who had a 90s album called *Waking Up the Neighbours*?

15 In which decade was Karen Carpenter born?

16 In which decade did the Beautiful South have their first hit?

17 Who had a No. 1 with "Caravan of Love"?

18 How is Michael Barratt better known?

19 Which Summer song did Lovin' Spoonful sing in 1966?

20 Who had a 1953 hit with "Don't Let the Stars Get in Your Eyes"?

Quiz 4 The 60s

Answers – see page 110

1   What was Engelbert Humperdinck's first single?

2   Who had a hit with "Sugar Sugar"?

3   Which 60s band started life as The Mann-Hug Blues Brothers?

4   Who took "You Really Got Me" to No. 1 in 1964?

5   Which group included Tony Hicks and Graham Nash?

6   Who recorded the album *Pet Sounds*?

7   Which group had Judith Durham as lead singer?

8   Which trio included the two Clusky brothers?

9   Who was Tommy James's backing group?

10 Who were famous for their Tottenham Sound?

11 Which satellite was a hit for the Tornados?

12 Which 60s group included Carl Wayne and Roy Wood?

13 Whose first No. 1 was "Sweets For My Sweet"?

14 Which instrumentalist in the Honeycombs was female?

15 Who had a 1965 No. 1 with "Go Now"?

16 Which Group included Steve and Muff Winwood?

17 How many people sang "Concrete and Clay"?

18 What was Wayward on Frank Ifield's 1963 No. 1?

19 Who spent the early part of her career with brother Tom plus Tim Field before going solo?

20 Who was lead singer with Amen Corner?

The 50s (see Quiz 2)
1 Emile Ford. 2 *The Third Man*. 3 Claudette. 4 "What Do You Want?". 5 "Rock Around the Clock". 6 Harry Belafonte. 7 Diana. 8 Eddie Fisher. 9 Doris Day. 10 Johnny Ray. 11 Cliff Richard and the Drifters. 12 Craig Douglas. 13 Winifred Atwell. 14 "It Doesn't Matter Anymore". 15 Michael Holliday. 16 Frankie Vaughan. 17 Jimmy Young. 18 Alma Cogan. 19 *My Fair Lady* ("On the Street Where You Live"). 20 "And surrender to mine".

Quiz 5 Pot Luck 3

Answers – see page 115

LEVEL 2

1 Who was the female member of the Pretenders?

2 In which decade did Jeff Beck have his first solo hit?

3 Whose backing group was the MG's?

4 Who had a No. 1 with "Clair"?

5 Whose first No. 1 under his name alone was "Pipes of Peace" in 1984?

6 What did Tina Charles say "I Love" to do in 1976 and 1986?

7 How is Steven Demetri Georgiou better known in the charts?

8 Which surname is shared by Cleo and Frankie?

9 Who sang "Heart and Soul" in 1987?

10 When was Barry Blue Dancing in 1973?

11 Which song title links Jennifer Rush and Frankie Goes to Hollywood?

12 Which group was once called the Anni-Frid Four?

13 Which David Bowie song hero was "floating in my tin can"?

14 In which film did Madonna play the part of Breathless Mahoney?

15 Whose first hit was "Make It With You"?

16 Which colour provided a hit for Los Bravos and La Belle Epoque?

17 What was Johnny Logan's original home country?

18 In which decade was Adam Faith born?

19 Which girl who "doesn't live here any more" did Cliff Richard sing about in 1980?

20 Who had a 90s album called *Said and Done*?

Answers

Pot Luck 4 (see Quiz 7)
1 1960s. 2 Georgie Fame. 3 Neil Young. 4 Blue. 5 Dusty Springfield. 6 Itchycoo. 7 Men At Work. 8 Happy Birthday. 9 Robbie Williams. 10 Debbie Harry. 11 1930s. 12 The Stylistics. 13 "Spread a Little Happiness". 14 Tommy Steele. 15 Sinitta. 16 "Summer Night City". 17 Your Smile. 18 Alice Cooper. 19 Chris Rea. 20 Cathy's.

Quiz 6 The 70s
Answers – see page 116

LEVEL 2

1 Who had a best-selling album called *Rumours*?

2 Whose first No. 1 was "Tiger Feet"?

3 Who had Tony Orlando as their lead singer?

4 Who had a "Year of Decision" in 1974?

5 Whose first hit was "Get Down and Get With It"?

6 Which instrument did Marc Bolan play on "Ride a White Swan"?

7 Which pop sensation included Derek and Alan Longmuir?

8 Which record label were Wings' early records on?

9 Which Sweet No. 1 began with police sirens wailing?

10 Who was the original drummer with the ELO?

11 Who sang about Pretty Little Angel Eyes in 1978?

12 How many founder members of the Eagles were there?

13 Which musical instrument did Karen Carpenter play?

14 Whose debut album was *New Boots and Panties!*?

15 Which 1978 Bee Gees album was the best seller of all time at that time?

16 Which Brotherhood of Man No. 1 shares its name with an opera?

17 Which group had Errol Brown as lead singer?

18 Which rock legend died in August 1977?

19 How was the chart-topper Detective Ken Hutchinson better known?

20 Which US state did Pussycat sing about?

Answers

The 80s (see Quiz 8)
1 The Jam. 2 John Lennon. 3 Scottish. 4 "Begin the Beguine".
5 Tight Fit. 6 Irene Cara. 7 Men At Work. 8 Duran Duran.
9 Christie Brinkley. 10 Mike Read. 11 99. 12 Lionel Richie.
13 Andrew Ridgeley. 14 Stock, Aitken and Waterman.
15 T'Pau. 16 Matt and Luke Goss (Bros). 17 A-ha.
18 Lennon and McCartney. 19 New Kids on the Block. 20 U2.

Quiz 7 Pot Luck 4

Answers – see page 113

Answers – see page 113

LEVEL 2

1   In which decade did the Bee Gees have their first hit?

2   Whose backing group was the Blue Flames?

3   Who sang "Heart of Gold" in 1972?

4   Which colour Monday was a hit for New Order in 1983 and 1988?

5   How is Mary O'Brien better known?

6   Which Park were the Small Faces in in 1967?

7   Who had a No. 1 with "Down Under"?

8   Which greeting linked Stevie Wonder and Altered Images in 1981?

9   Who was the first member to leave Take That in 1995?

10 Who was the female member of Blondie?

11 In which decade was Neil Sedaka born?

12 Who had a No. 1 with "I Can't Give You Anything (But My Love)"?

13 What was Sting's first solo single?

14 Who had a backing group called the Steelmen?

15 Whose man was So Macho in 1986?

16 Which Summer song did Abba sing in 1978?

17 What did Shanice say "I Love" in 1991 and 1992?

18 Whose first hit was "School's Out"?

19 Who had a 90s album called *Auberge*?

20 Whose Clown were the Everly Brothers in 1960?

Quiz 8 The 80s
Answers – see page 114

1   Who had Paul Weller as their lead singer at the beginning of the 80s?

2   Who was Roxy Music's "Jealous Guy" recorded in honour of?

3   What was the nationality of Aneka who performed "Japanese Boy" on *Top of the Pops* dressed in a kimono?

4   How was Julio Iglesias's single "Volver A Empezar" better known?

5   Who took "The Lion Sleeps Tonight" to the top of the charts?

6   Who played Coco Hernandez in *Fame* and charted with the single?

7   Who had an album called *Business as Usual*?

8   Which group took its name from the Jane Fonda film *Barbarella*?

9   Which girlfriend/supermodel did Billy Joel dedicate "Uptown Girl" to?

10 Which Radio 1 DJ refused to play Frankie Goes to Hollywood's "Relax" on his breakfast show?

11 How many Red Balloons did Nena release in 1984?

12 Who sang "All Night Long" at the closing ceremony of the Los Angeles Olympics?

13 Who was the elder of the two Wham! members?

14 Which trio produced Dead or Alive's "You Spin Me Round (Like a Record)"?

15 Which band was named after Mr Spock's Vulcan friend in *Star Trek*?

16 Which twins did Craig Logan leave when he left their band?

17 Which band was Morten Harket part of?

18 Who wrote the Ferry Aid No. 1 which charted in 1987?

19 Whose first No. 1 was "You Got It (The Right Stuff)" in 1989?

20 Who had an album called *Rattle and Hum*?

Answers

The 70s (see Quiz 6)
1 Fleetwood Mac. 2 Mud. 3 Dawn. 4 The Three Degrees.
5 Slade. 6 Electric Guitar. 7 The Bay City Rollers. 8 Apple.
9 Blockbuster. 10 Bev Bevan. 11 Showaddywaddy. 12 Four.
13 Drums. 14 Ian Dury and the Blockheads. 15 *Saturday Night Fever*. 16 "Figaro". 17 Hot Chocolate. 18 Elvis Presley.
19 David Soul – Hutch from "Starsky and Hutch". 20 Mississippi.

Quiz 9 Pot Luck 5

Answers – see page 119

Answers – see page 119

LEVEL 2

1 What did T. Rex say "I Love" to do in 1976?

2 Which surname is shared by Iris and Deniece?

3 What was Abba's Anni-Frid Lyngstad's home country?

4 In which decade did Blondie have their first hit?

5 Who sang "Heart on My Sleeve" in 1976?

6 How is Christopher John Davidson better known?

7 Who had a No. 1 with "Eternal Flame"?

8 Which colour Lady provided a hit for David Soul in 1977?

9 In which decade was Lisa Stansfield born?

10 What time did Smokie say to Meet You in 1976?

11 Which song title linked Demis Roussos and Slik in 1976?

12 Which planet was a hit for Shocking Blue?

13 Whose first No. 1 was "Runaway" in 1961?

14 Who took "Ebeneezer Goode" to the top in 1992?

15 Which girl did Tyrannosaurus Rex sing about in 1968?

16 Who was the female member of the Seekers?

17 Who had a 90s album called *Our Town – Greatest Hits*?

18 Whose first hit was "Sylvia's Mother"?

19 Who had a 70s album called *Voulez-vous*?

20 Whose backing group was the Crickets?

Answers

Pot Luck 6 (see Quiz 11)
1 2525. 2 Jane. 3 My Dog. 4 Pepsi and Shirlie. 5 Maddy Prior. 6 "Summer Nights". 7 Black. 8 Foreigner. 9 Johnny Logan. 10 "Tears on My Pillow". 11 The Searchers. 12 Phillip Schofield. 13 Scotland. 14 Leo Sayer. 15 1930s. 16 Diana Ross. 17 Sheena Easton. 18 Mamas and Papas. 19 1970s. 20 Johnny Kidd.

Quiz 10 The 90s

Answers – see page 120

LEVEL 2

1　Who sang about "Saturday Night" in 1994?

2　What was on the other side of Robson and Jerome's "I Believe"?

3　What goes after Meat Loaf's "I Would Do Anything For Love"?

4　Which soundtrack was a top-selling 1992 album in the UK and the US?

5　Which '91 chart toppers share a name with an instrument of torture?

6　Which band included Siobhan Fahey and Marcella Detroit?

7　Which 1994 chart topper was written by the Troggs' Reg Presley?

8　Who are Baby, Posh, Scary, Ginger and Sporty?

9　Who had the album *Automatic for the People*?

10　Who was Take That's usual lead vocalist?

11　Which No. 1 artist was the creation of the TV producer Mike Leggo?

12　Whose first No. 1 was "End of the Road"?

13　What was Boyzone's first chart hit?

14　Which superstar did Bobby Brown marry in 1992?

15　Who had the best-selling album *Blue is the Colour*?

16　What was the Dunblane single called?

17　Which veteran band released "Voodoo Lounge" in 1994?

18　Whose 1994 Greatest Hits album was called *End of Part One*?

19　Which band includes the bass player Paul McGuigan?

20　What was reported in the press as "Cliffstock"?

Stevie Wonder (see Quiz 12)

Answers

1　Piano, drums, harmonica. 2　Little Stevie Wonder. 3　Tamla Motown. 4　"Uptight". 5　Frank Sinatra's. 6　*Woman in Red*. 7　1950s. 8　Julio Iglesias. 9　Eiffel Tower. 10　Duke Ellington. 11　Syreeta. 12　"I Just Called to Say I Love You". 13　Nelson Mandela. 14　Elton John, Gladys Knight. 15　Of Life. 16　His daughters. 17　Michael Jackson. 18　"I Was Made to Love Her". 19　Detroit. 20　Paul McCartney.

Quiz 11 Pot Luck 6

Answers – see page 117

LEVEL 2

1   Zager and Evans sang about which year – among others – in 1969?

2   Which girl did Slade say Gudbuy T' in 1972?

3   What did Cat Stevens say "I Love" to in 1966?

4   Which duo sang "Heartache" in 1987?

5   Who was the female member of Steeleye Span?

6   Which Summer song did Hylda Baker and Arthur Mullard sing in the 80s?

7   Which colour Velvet provided a hit for Alannah Myles in 1990?

8   Who had a No. 1 with "I Want to Know What Love Is"?

9   How is Sean Sherrard better known?

10 Which song title links Johnny Nash in 1975 and Kylie Minogue in 1990?

11 Whose first No. 1 was "Sweets for My Sweet"?

12 Which TV presenter had a hit with "Close Every Door"?

13 Which national soccer side had a hit with "Ole Ola (Mulher Brasileira)"?

14 Which 70s chart-topper often performed dressed as a circus clown?

15 In which decade were the Everly Brothers born?

16 Who had a 90s album called *One Woman – The Ultimate Collection*?

17 Whose first hit was "Modern Girl"?

18 Who were in Creeque Alley in 1967?

19 In which decade did the Carpenters have their first hit?

20 Whose backing group were the Pirates?

Pot Luck 5 (see Quiz 9)
1 To Boogie. 2 Williams. 3 Norway. 4 1970s. 5 Gallagher and Lyle. 6 Chris De Burgh. 7 The Bangles. 8 Silver. 9 1960s. 10 Midnight. 11 "Forever and Ever". 12 Venus. 13 Del Shannon. 14 The Shamen. 15 Debora. 16 Judith Durham. 17 Deacon Blue. 18 Dr Hook. 19 Abba. 20 Buddy Holly.

Answers

Quiz 12 Stevie Wonder

Answers – see page 118

1 Which three instruments could Stevie play by the age of seven?

2 How was Stevie known in his early days on stage?

3 What was the first record label he recorded on?

4 Which single had the subtitle "Everything's Alright"?

5 On whose *Duets II* album did he sing in 1994?

6 Which 1984 album was from a film soundtrack?

7 In which decade was Stevie Wonder born?

8 Who did he duet with on "My Love" in 1988?

9 To which monument did he sing "Happy Birthday" in Paris in 1989?

10 Who was his song "Sir Duke" dedicated to?

11 Which Miss Wright did Stevie Wonder marry in 1970?

12 For which song did he win an Oscar in 1985?

13 To which black leader did he dedicate his Oscar to?

14 Who were the other named Friends on Dionne Warwick's "That's What Friends Are For"?

15 In which Key were the Songs on his 1976 album?

16 Who are Aisha Zakia and Kita Swan Di?

17 Who did he sing "Get It" with?

18 What was his first Top Five hit?

19 In 1984 Stevie was given the keys to which city where he enjoyed much success?

20 Who sang with Stevie on his first No. 1?

Quiz 13 Pot Luck 7

Answers – see page 123

LEVEL 2

1 Whose backing group was the Dakotas?

2 What did Nick Lowe Love the Sound of in 1978?

3 Which surname is shared by Dinah and Geno?

4 Where was Billy Ocean born?

5 Who sang "Black Betty" in 1977 and 1990?

6 How is Marvin Lee Aday better known?

7 Which month was a No. 1 for Pilot in 1975?

8 Who sang "Heartbreaker" in 1982?

9 Which song title links Frankie Laine in 1956 and Barbra Streisand in 1980?

10 Who was Happy to Be on an Island in the Sun in 1975?

11 Who accompanied First Edition on "Ruby Don't Take Your Love to Town"?

12 In which decade was Annie Lennox born?

13 Which association was a hit for Jeannie C. Riley in 1968?

14 Which girl took the Overlanders to No. 1 in January 1966?

15 Whose first hit was "Rock On"?

16 Which girl did the Damned sing about in 1986?

17 In which decade did the Jacksons have their first hit?

18 Who had a No. 1 with "I'm Into Something Good"?

19 Who had a 90s album called *In Utero*?

20 Who was the female member of Fairport Convention?

Pot Luck 8 (see Quiz 15)

Answers

1 Sunday. 2 Pet Shop Boys. 3 Marty Wilde. 4 Spencer Davis Group. 5 Love Me Love. 6 Whitney Houston. 7 Walker. 8 1940s. 9 Pet Shop Boys. 10 Gold. 11 "Long Live Love". 12 "48 Crash". 13 1999. 14 "Killer Queen". 15 Elkie Brooks. 16 "Summertime Blues". 17 The Kinks. 18 Juliet. 19 1970s. 20 Paul Revere.

Quiz 14 Karaoke

Answers – see page 124

LEVEL 2

---

1 Which song has the words "Scaramouche, will you do the fandango?"?

2 Which No. 1 had the line "Ya I'll tell you what I want, what I really want"?

3 Which title line follows "our thoughts to them are winging, when friends by shame are undefiled" in the Enya song?

4 Which Dire Straits hit starts "Here comes Johnny singing oldies goldies"?

5 Which song begins "When I was young, I never needed anyone"?

6 In which song would you find the lines "Daylight. I must wait for the sunrise, I must wait for a new life. And I mustn't give in"?

7 Which Christmas classic has the lines "Man will live for evermore, because of Christmas Day"?

8 Which film song begins "From the day we arrive on the planet and blinking step into the sun"?

9 In the 60s who sang "We skipped the light fandango…"?

10 What is the first line of Kiki Dee's "Amoureuse"?

11 Which song has the line "Do the fairies keep him sober for a day"?

12 Which excuse for a massacre gave the Boomtown Rats a hit song?

13 What follows "The truth is I never left you" in the song from *Evita*?

14 In which song did Phil Collins sing "Wouldn't you agree, baby you and me?

15 What follows "When I find myself in times of trouble, Mother Mary comes to me"?

16 What is the first line of the Supremes' "You Keep Me Hangin' On"?

17 Which Bee Gees hit has the line "Cause we're livin' in a world of fools"?

18 Who sang "Isn't she precious, less than one minute old?"?

19 Which song has the line "And just like the guy whose feet were too big for his bed"?

20 Which classic begins "She packed my bags last night, pre-flight"?

Answers

Groups (see Quiz 16)
1 Abba. **2** The Tremeloes. **3** "Brown Girl in the Ring". **4** "I'm a Believer". **5** Stewart Copeland. **6** Huey Lewis. **7** Clannad. **8** 1980s. **9** The Pet Shop Boys. **10** Simply Red. **11** Guns N' Roses. **12** Madness. **13** Mott the Hoople. **14** Cream. **15** Ray Davies. **16** Manfred Mann. **17** Beautiful South. **18** Barry. **19** Mungo Jerry. **20** Diana Ross and the Supremes and the Temptations.

122

Quiz 15 Pot Luck 8

Answers – see page 121

LEVEL 2

1 What was a Lazy day for the Small Faces in 1968?

2 Who had a 90s album called *Very*?

3 How is Reginald Smith better known?

4 Who had a No. 1 with "Keep On Running"?

5 What did Gary Glitter follow "I Love You" with in 1973?

6 Whose first hit was "Saving All My Love for You"?

7 Which surname is shared by Scott and Junior?

8 In which decade was Gilbert O'Sullivan born?

9 Who sang "Heart" in 1988?

10 Which colour provided a hit for Spandau Ballet in 1983?

11 Which song title links Sandie Shaw and Olivia Newton-John?

12 Which Crash was a hit for Suzi Quatro?

13 Which year was a hit for Prince in 1983?

14 What was Queen's second hit?

15 Who was the female member of Vinegar Joe?

16 Which Summertime song did Eddie Cochran sing in 1958 and 1968?

17 Who were in a Dead End Street in 1966?

18 Which girl did the Four Pennies sing about in 1964?

19 In which decade did Kool and the Gang have their first hit?

20 Whose backing group were the Raiders?

Answers

Pot Luck 7 (see Quiz 13)
1 Billy J. Kramer. 2 Breaking Glass. 3 Washington. 4 Trinidad.
5 Ram Jam. 6 Meat Loaf. 7 January. 8 Dionne Warwick.
9 "Woman in Love". 10 Demis Roussos. 11 Kenny Rogers.
12 1950s. 13 Harper Valley P.T.A. 14 Michelle. 15 David
Essex. 16 Eloise. 17 1970s. 18 Herman's Hermits.
19 Nirvana. 20 Sandy Denny.

Quiz 16 Groups
Answers – see page 122

1 Which group included Agnetha and Anni-Frid?

2 Who was Brian Poole's backing group?

3 What was on the other side of Boney M's "Rivers of Babylon"?

4 What was the Monkees' first and best-selling single?

5 Who was percussionist with the Police?

6 Who was vocalist with the News?

7 Which Irish group's name means "family"?

8 In which decade did Simple Minds have their first No. 1?

9 Who had a 1988 album called "Introspective"?

10 Which group's 1991 best-selling album was "Stars"?

11 Who had an Appetite for Destruction in 1987?

12 Which band's line-up included "Chrissie Boy" Foreman and Lee "Kix" Thompson?

13 Which band were All the Way From Memphis in 1973?

14 Who were Eric Clapton, Jack Bruce and Ginger Baker?

15 Which singer/guitarist published his autobiography *X-Ray* in 1995?

16 Paul Jones and Mike D'Abo were separately members of which group?

17 Paul Heaton formed which group after the Housemartins?

18 Which Gibb brother is the eldest Bee Gee?

19 Whose first No. 1 was "In the Summertime" in 1970?

20 Which two Tamla groups combined on "I'm Gonna Make You Love Me" in 1969?

Answers

Karaoke (see Quiz 14)
1 "Bohemian Rhapsody". 2 "Wannabe" (Spice Girls). 3 "How can I keep from singing?" 4 "Walk of Life". 5 "All By Myself". 6 "Memory". 7 "Mary's Boy Child". 8 "The Circle of Life". 9 Procul Harum. 10 "Strands of light across a bedroom floor". 11 "Merry Xmas Everybody". 12 I don't like Mondays. 13 "All through my wild days, my mad existence". 14 "A Groovy Kind of Love". 15 "Speaking words of wisdom, let it be". 16 "Set me free, why don't you babe?". 17 "How Deep is Your Love". 18 Stevie Wonder. 19 "Raindrops Keep Fallin' On My Head". 20 "Rocket Man".

Quiz 17 Pot Luck 9

LEVEL 2

1   Which song was a No. 2 for both Nat King Cole and Rick Astley?

2   How is Clive Powell better known?

3   What did Jim Reeves follow "I Love You" with in 1964 and 1971?

4   Who sang "Anyone Who Had a Heart" in 1964?

5   Who was the female member of the Captain and Tennille?

6   Who had a No. 1 with "Let's Party"?

7   In which decade was Little Jimmy Osmond born?

8   Which colour Corvette provided a hit for Prince in 1983 and 1985?

9   Which song title links Dolly Parton and Sheena Easton?

10   Whose backing group were the All Stars?

11   Who sang with the Beatles on their 1969 No. 1 "Get Back"?

12   Who sang "Band of Gold" in 1970?

13   Which singer/songwriter's wife was "Claudette" in the Everly Brothers' song?

14   Which port was a hit for Mike Oldfield?

15   Who sang with Robert Palmer on "I'll Be Your Baby Tonight" in 1990?

16   Whose first hit was "Pictures of Matchstick Men"?

17   What is the home country of Linda McCartney?

18   Who had a 90s album called *Black Tie White Noise*?

19   In which decade did Meat Loaf have his first hit?

20   Which girl did Derek and the Dominoes sing about in 1972?

Answers

Pot Luck 10 (see Quiz 19)
1 Geri. 2 Kenya. 3 Harrison. 4 "D.I.V.O.R.C.E". 5 Bonnie Tyler. 6 Willcox. 7 1950s. 8 The Medicine Show. 9 Parlophone. 10 Midge Ure. 11 Bob Dylan. 12 Silk. 13 Sisters With Voices. 14 Eric Clapton. 15 Starland Vocal Band. 16 Chairmen of the Board. 17 Pat Boone. 18 Robert de Niro. 19 Nashville Teens. 20 Petula Clark.

Quiz 18 George Michael

Answers – see page 128

1   In which city was George Michael brought up?

2   What was his debut solo album called?

3   Who did he duet with on "I Knew You Were Waiting (For Me)"?

4   On whose version of "Nikita" did George sing backing vocals?

5   Where did George first meet Wham!'s Andrew Ridgeley?

6   What is George Michael's real first name?

7   In which decade was he born?

8   With which band did he record the "Five Live EP"?

9   Which female vocalist was on the same record?

10 From which newspaper did he receive damages in 1989 after accusations about gatecrashing a party?

11 What is the name of his autobiography?

12 Which item of his clothing is burned on his "Freedom 90" video?

13 What was his second solo album called?

14 Which Elton John song did he sing at the Live Aid concert?

15 Which 1990/91 conflict helped the fortunes of "Praying For Time" because of its lyric?

16 What was his 1996 comeback ballad?

17 Which album was released the same year?

18 Which Corporation became parent company of Epic Records, which caused a legal battle with George?

19 What was his first solo No. 1?

20 Which film soundtrack contained the controversial, sometimes banned single "I Want Your Sex"?

Answers

No. 1s (see Quiz 20)
1 "Barbados". 2 George McCrae. 3 "The Streak". 4 Queen and David Bowie. 5 Angelo. 6 Baccara. 7 "I'm Working My Way Back to You". 8 David Bowie. 9 John Lennon. 10 Rosemary Clooney. 11 The Lion Sleeps Tonight. 12 Kraftwerk . 13 His record label Motown would not allow it. 14 "Happy Talk". 15 Jimmy Young. 16 The Crazy World of Arthur Brown. 17 Union Gap. 18 Louis Armstrong. 19 Mike D'Abo. 20 "Chanson d'Amour".

Quiz 19 Pot Luck 10

Answers – see page 125

LEVEL 2

1   Which Spice Girl is Ginger Spice?

2   In which country was Roger Whittaker born?

3   Which surname is shared by Noel and George?

4   Which song title links Tammy Wynette and Billy Connolly?

5   How is Gaynor Hopkins better known?

6   What is Toyah's surname?

7   In which decade was Michael Bolton born?

8   Who was Dr Hook's backing group on "Sylvia's Mother"?

9   What was the Beatles' first record label?

10 Who has topped the charts with Slik and Band Aid?

11 Who closed the American side of the Live Aid concert?

12 What is Steve Hurley's "middle" nickname?

13 What does SWV stand for?

14 Who had a solo album called *Journeyman*?

15 Who experienced "Afternoon Delight" in 1976?

16 Whose first hit was "Give Me Just a Little More Time"?

17 Who celebrated April Love in 1957?

18 Who's Waiting according to Bananarama?

19 Who had a 60s hit with "Tobacco Road"?

20 Who sang "Don't Sleep in the Subway"?

Pot Luck 9 (see Quiz 17)
1 "When I Fall in Love". 2 Georgie Fame. 3 "Because". 4 Cilla Black. 5 Toni Tennille. 6 Jive Bunny and the Mastermixers. 7 1960s. 8 Red. 9 "9 to 5". 10 Junior Walker. 11 Billy Preston. 12 Freda Payne. 13 Roy Orbison's. 14 Portsmouth. 15 UB40. 16 Status Quo. 17 USA. 18 David Bowie. 19 1970s. 20 Layla.

Quiz 20 No. 1s

Answers – see page 126

LEVEL 2

1 Which No. 1 includes vocals by Captain Tobias Wilcock?

2 Who had a 1974 No. 1 with "Rock Your Baby"?

3 Which 70s No. 1 was about a nudist?

4 Who teamed up Under Pressure in 1981?

5 What was Brotherhood of Man's Mexican shepherd boy called?

6 Who had a British No. 1 with "Yes Sir I Can Boogie"?

7 What was on the other side of the Detroit Spinners' "Forgive Me Girl"?

8 Who wore a Pierrot costume for his "Ashes to Ashes" video?

9 Who had three No. 1's in the first two months of 1981?

10 Who had their first No. 1 with "This Ole House"?

11 Which No. 1 was based on the Zulu folk tune "Wimoweh"?

12 Who was the first German band to have a UK No. 1 in 1982?

13 Why did Stevie Wonder not receive full billing on his No. 1 with Paul McCartney?

14 Which 80s No. 1 was a song from the musical *South Pacific*?

15 Who had the first No. 1 in the UK with "Unchained Melody"?

16 Who had a 60s hit with "Fire"?

17 Which 60s group were named after an American Civil War battle and wore period army uniforms?

18 Who was the oldest ever artist at the time to have a No. 1 record in 1968?

19 Who was lead singer on the 1968 No. 1 "Mighty Quinn"?

20 Which 70s No. 1 had a French title?

Answers

George Michael (see Quiz 18)
1 London. 2 *Faith*. 3 Aretha Franklin. 4 Elton John's. 5 At school. 6 Georgios. 7 1960s. 8 Queen. 9 Lisa Stansfield. 10 The *Sun*. 11 *Bare*. 12 Biker jacket. 13 *Listen Without Prejudice Vol 1*. 14 "Don't Let the Sun Go Down on Me". 15 The Gulf War. 16 "Jesus to a Child". 17 *Older*. 18 Sony. 19 "Careless Whisper". 20 *Beverley Hills Cop II*.

Quiz 21 Pot Luck 11

Answers – see page 131

1   Whose first hit was "Rock with the Caveman"?

2   Which surname is shared by Tony and Lou?

3   In which decade was Petula Clark born?

4   Who wanted to be Bobby's Girl in 1962?

5   Who was Vic Reeves's backing group?

6   What is the home country of Paul Anka?

7   What was on the other side of Louis Armstrong's "What a Wonderful World"?

8   Which Beach Boys album included goats on the album cover?

9   Whose 1996 album was called *K*?

10 Dolores O'Riordan is lead singer with which band?

11 How is Vincent Furnier better known?

12 Who had Joe Strummer as lead vocalist?

13 A 1991 TV concert by Clannad was a tribute to which Irishman?

14 How are David, Stephen, Graham and Neil better known?

15 Which Gibb was not a Bee Gee?

16 Whose real surname is Gudmundsdóttir?

17 Whose first chart entry was "Chantilly Lace"?

18 Who was keyboard player with the Dave Clark Five?

19 In which decade did the Faces have their first hit record?

20 Whose album *Diva* topped the charts in 1993?

Pot Luck 12 (see Quiz 23)

Answers

1 1970s. 2 Bobby Darin. 3 "Joanna". 4 Bill Haley and his Comets. 5 Colin Blunstone. 6 Enya. 7 None. 8 Paul Young. 9 Shane Fenton. 10 Bonzo Dog Doo-Dah Band. 11 Germany. 12 1940s. 13 Slade. 14 George Harrison. 15 Frogman. 16 Australia. 17 Cheryl Baker. 18 Hot Gossip. 19 A & M. 20 The Men in Hats.

Quiz 22 Instrumentals

Answers – see page 132

1 "Eye Level" was the theme music for which detective series?

2 Who had a 1962 No. 1 with "Nut Rocker"?

3 Which music by which composer was it based on?

4 What was the nickname of the Shadows' Brian Locking?

5 Which music was a No. 1 twice for Eddie Calvert and Perez Prado?

6 Who had a 50s hit with "Hoots Mon"?

7 What was Lieutenant Pigeon's only hit?

8 How is the instrumentalist Philippe Pages better known?

9 Which 60s instrumental is said to be a favourite of Lady Thatcher?

10 Which Shadows hit was a theme for a series of Edgar Wallace stories?

11 Who became the Shadows' drummer after Tony Meehan left?

12 Which 60s March became a minor hit for Joe Loss and his Orchestra?

13 Which No. 1 was accompanied by 1920s flappers?

14 Who had the longest name of any group to have a No. 1?

15 Which instrument did Fleetwood Mac's Mick Fleetwood play?

16 Who had a 1977 instrumental hit with "The Floral Dance"?

17 Who had a 1968 hit with "Classical Gas"?

18 Who was the soloist on the 1976 hit "Aria"?

19 Which pianist had a 50s hit with "Unchained Melody"?

20 To the nearest five, how many instrumental No. 1s were there between 1974 and 1994?

Quiz 23 Pot Luck 12

Answers – see page 129

LEVEL 2

1   In which decade did the Smurfs have their first hit record?

2   How was Walden Robert Cassotto better known?

3   Which song title links Scott Walker and Kool and the Gang?

4   Whose first hit was "Shake, Rattle and Roll" in 1954?

5   Who was lead vocalist with the Zombies?

6   Whose album *Shepherd Moons* topped the charts in 1992?

7   How many hit singles did Frank Zappa have in the 70s?

8   Whose debut album was *No Parlez*?

9   How was Alvin Stardust previously known in the charts?

10 Which group's members included Neil Innes and Vivian Stanshall?

11 In which country were Boney M based?

12 In which decade was Dolly Parton born?

13 Whose first hit was "Get Down and Get With It"?

14 Who had an 80s hit with "Got My Mind Set On You"?

15 What is Clarence Henry's nickname?

16 What is the home country of Bjorn Again?

17 Who took part in the Eurovision Song Contest in Co-Co and in Bucks Fizz?

18 Who did Sarah Brightman sing with on her first chart hit?

19 Which record label did Herb Alpert co-found?

20 What name was given to the new country stars of the 1990s?

Pot Luck 11   (see Quiz 21)

Pot Luck 11   (see Quiz 21)
1 Tommy Steele. 2 Christie. 3 1930s. 4 Susan Maughan.
5 The Wonder Stuff. 6 Canada. 7 "Cabaret". 8 *Pet Sounds*.
9 Kula Shaker. 10 The Cranberries. 11 Alice Cooper. 12 The
Clash. 13 Brian Keenan. 14 Crosby, Stills, Nash and Young.
15 Andy. 16 Björk. 17 The Big Bopper. 18 Mike Smith.
19 The 70s. 20 Annie Lennox.

Quiz 24 Solo Singers

Answers – see page 130

1 Which solo singer had a hit with "Spirit in the Sky"?

2 What was Des O'Connor's first No. 1 hit?

3 Who had a 90s No. 1 with "The Real Thing"?

4 Which singer was named after the Wind in "Paint Your Wagon"?

5 Who wrote Take That's "Babe" before pursuing a solo career?

6 Who was the first soloist to have a No. 1 hit with the same name as himself?

7 How is Londoner Ms Bobb better known?

8 Whose first single "The One and Only" went to No. 1 in 1991?

9 What is Wink Martindale's most famous hit?

10 Who took "Stairway to Heaven" into the charts in 1993?

11 Who had a 60s hit with "Where Do You Go To My Lovely?"?

12 Who has recorded with Richard Carpenter and the Pet Shop Boys?

13 Which singer's songs ranged from "Little Green Apples" to "You Can't Roller Skate in a Buffalo Herd"?

14 Who was famous for having a rabbit's foot swinging from his belt?

15 Who had a best-selling album called *Tapestry*?

16 Who went to No. 1 in her first-ever week in the charts in 1994?

17 Who had the first-ever No. 1 in the UK?

18 Which female soloist has recorded on at least nine different record labels in a 30-year career?

19 Who sang about "Me and Mrs Jones" in 1973?

20 Which American had a 1989 hit with "The Wind Beneath My Wings"?

Answers

Instrumentals (see Quiz 22)
1 "Van der Valk". 2 B. Bumble and the Stingers. 3 Tchaikovsky's *Nutcracker* Suite. 4 Licorice. 5 "Cherry Pink and Apple Blossom White". 6 Lord Rockingham's XI. 7 "Mouldy Old Dough". 8 Richard Clayderman. 9 "Telstar". 10 "Man of Mystery". 11 Brian Bennett. 12 "March of the Mods". 13 "Doop". 14 The Pipes and Drums and Military Band of the Royal Scots Dragoon Guards. 15 Drums. 16 Brighouse and Rastrick Brass Band. 17 Mason Williams. 18 Acker Bilk. 19 Liberace. 20 None.

Quiz 25 Pot Luck 13

LEVEL 2

1   In which country was Neneh Cherry born?

2   Who sang "Billy Don't Be A Hero" in 1974?

3   How is Ernest Evans better known?

4   Which record label shares its name with a nautical aid?

5   Who were All Out of Love in 1980?

6   Whose album *High on the Happy Side* topped the charts in 1992?

7   Who took "Charmaine", "Diane" and "Ramona" into the Top Ten?

8   Who did Kate Bush duet with on "Don't Give Up"?

9   Which song was a hit for Elvis Presley and Andy Williams?

10 Who had the Bell Bottom Blues in 1954?

11 In which decade was Frankie Valli born?

12 Which song title links the Three Degrees and Barbra Streisand?

13 Whose first hit was "Hong Kong Garden"?

14 What was Midge Ure's first solo No. 1?

15 What is the home country of Berlin?

16 What was Cilla Black's first single?

17 Which surname is shared by Ronnie and Dina?

18 Whose singles include "Call Up the Groups" and "Pop Go the Workers"?

19 Who had their second No. 1 with "Spirit in the Sky"?

20 In which decade did Genesis have their first hit record?

1   Which Bob Dylan composition was a US hit for Peter, Paul and Mary and Stevie Wonder?

2   What was his first UK hit single?

3   What was the first chart-topping composition by Dylan?

4   Which album includes the lengthy "Sad Eyed Lady of the Lowlands"?

5   Why was Dylan booed off stage in 1965 and 1966?

6   Which Dylan song was a hit for Manfred Mann in 1968?

7   Which album did he record with the help of Johnny Cash?

8   To the nearest £1,000 how much did Dylan receive for a one-hour session at the Isle of Wight festival in 1969?

9   What was the name of the novel he published in 1970?

10 Which album was said to have been due to the end of his marriage?

11 Which Dylan song was a hit for Eric Clapton and Guns N' Roses?

12 Which film did he act in and provide the music for in Mexico?

13 When asked what were the most overrated and underrated books of the last 75 years, what did he reply?

14 What was the name of his own record label?

15 Which UK guitarist co-produced "Infidels"?

16 Which religion did he embrace in the late 70s?

17 Which Dylan song was a hit for Jimi Hendrix in 1968?

18 For which film did he write "Lay Lady Lay" – though it was not chosen?

19 Which Dylan band also included George Harrison and Roy Orbison?

20 Which cricketer added Dylan to his first names?

Quiz 27 Pot Luck 14

Answers – see page 133

LEVEL 2

1　Which country did Baccara come from?

2　How is Stuart Goddard better known?

3　Which actor was Under The Boardwalk in 1987?

4　Who had a 60s No. 1 with "Where Are You Now (My Love)"?

5　Whose album *Innuendo* topped the charts in 1991?

6　Who had a 1969 hit with "Melting Pot"?

7　Who had a Total Eclipse of the Heart in 1983?

8　In which decade did Neil Sedaka have his first hit record?

9　What was the Byrds' debut No. 1?

10　Which car was Natalie Cole's first hit record?

11　How many members of D:Ream are there?

12　What are the home countries of the members of Los Bravos?

13　Who was a Sunshine Superman in 1966?

14　Whose first hit was "House of Love"?

15　Who recorded the original "This Wheel's On Fire"?

16　In which decade was Enya born?

17　Who had a Horse With No Name in 1971?

18　Which song title links Kylie Minogue and Sonia?

19　Which day of the week did the Easybeats have on their mind in 1966?

20　Which numbers were a 60s hit for Len Barry?

Answers

Pot Luck 13 (see Quiz 25)

1　Sweden. 2　Paper Lace. 3　Chubby Checker. 4　Anchor. 5　Air Supply. 6　Wet Wet Wet. 7　The Bachelors. 8　Peter Gabriel. 9　"Can't Help Falling In Love". 10　Alma Cogan. 11　1930s. 12　"Woman in Love". 13　Siouxsie and the Banshees. 14　"If I Was". 15　USA. 16　Love of the Loved. 17　Carroll. 18　The Barron Knights. 19　Doctor and the Medics. 20　The 70s.

Quiz 28 Soap Rock

Answers – see page 134

1   Who sang "Something Outa Nothing" with Paul Medford in 1986?

2   Who was Just This Side of Love in 1990?

3   How was Michelle Gayle known in "EastEnders"?

4   Which "Street" couple sang "Somethin' Stupid"?

5   How is Bill Tarmey better known?

6   What was the title of the song based on the "EastEnders" theme tune?

7   Who had a hit with it in 1986?

8   Who had an album called *Emmerdance*?

9   Who sang "Passing Strangers" with Joe Longthorne in 1994?

10   Wendy Richard, a.k.a. Pauline Fowler, was heard on which 1962 No. 1?

11   Who was the male vocalist on the record?

12   Who replaced Shane Richie in *Grease* in 1997?

13   How was Sean Maguire better known in Albert Square?

14   Which song did Mike Reid, alias Frank Butcher, take into the charts?

15   Which "Coronation Street" character was originally a singer in the soap's storyline?

16   Which 60s singer played Len Fairclough's son Stanley?

17   Whose grandson in "Coronation Street" was played by the future Monkee Davy Jones?

18   What was the title of Nick Berry's 1986 chart topper?

19   Cindy from "EastEnders" was formerly a backing singer for which artist?

20   Which musical star once played Kevin Webster's rival Malcolm Nuttall?

Bob Dylan (see Quiz 26)

Answers
1   "Blowin' in the Wind". 2   "Times They Are A-Changin'".
3   "Hey Mr Tambourine Man". 4   *Blonde on Blonde*. 5   Playing
electric guitar. 6   Mighty Quinn. 7   *Nashville Skyline*. 8   £35,000.
9   *Tarantula*. 10   *Blood on the Tracks*. 11   "Lay Lady Lay". 12   *Pat
Garrett and Billy the Kid*. 13   The Bible. 14   Accomplice Records. 15
Mark Knopfler. 16   Christianity. 17   "All Along the Watchtower".
18   *Midnight Cowboy*. 19   Traveling Wilburys. 20   Bob Willis.

1 In which decade did Shakin' Stevens have his first hit record?

2 Which villain was a 70s hit for Boney M?

3 Who took "Ma He's Making Eyes at Me" into the Top Ten in 1974?

4 Whose first chart hit was "Wild Thing"?

5 Whose album "Sleeping With the Past" topped the charts in 1990?

6 Who said "Please Mr Postman" in 1975?

7 Which comedian sang "Don't Laugh At Me" in 1954?

8 Who pleaded to Honey to Come Back in 1970?

9 Who was Terry Dactyl's backing group?

10 Who spent "Seven Drunken Nights" in 1967?

11 In which decade was Suzi Quatro born?

12 What was Simon Dupree's backing group?

13 Whose first hit was "Planet Earth"?

14 Who made a hit Easy in 1977?

15 Who had a 60s hit with "Rescue Me"?

16 What is the home country of the Cranberries?

17 Who sang "Come and Get It" in 1970?

18 What was Tori Amos's first Top Ten hit?

19 Which surname is shared by Glen and Junior?

20 Who was John Fred's backing group?

Quiz 30 Ready to Rap

Answers – see page 140

LEVEL 2

1 What was M.C. Hammer's debut single?

2 How was the 1990 "Geordie Boys" subtitled?

3 How is Alison Moira Clarkson better known?

4 In which city did Rap originate?

5 Who said "(You Gotta) Fight For Your Right (To Party)" in 1987?

6 Which singer's and band's bass-line music features on "Ice Ice Baby"?

7 What does KRYME stand for in Partners in Kryme?

8 What was their first No. 1?

9 Which duo had a hit with "Whatta Man" in 1994?

10 What is the home country of the Rapper Derek B?

11 Who backed Queen Latifah on "Mama Gave Birth to the Soul Children"?

12 What was En Vogue's first chart success?

13 Which Mattel product did M.C. Hammer help launch in 1991?

14 Which Rap was an 80s hit for MC Miker "G" and Deejay Sven?

15 Who backed Morris Minor on "Stutter Rap"?

16 Who had a 1993 No. 1 with "Boom! Shake the Room"?

17 Who had a Top Ten album called *Fear of a Black Planet*?

18 Which Blondie single features the name of Grandmaster Flash?

19 Which blond Rapper's real name was Robert Van Winkle?

20 What was Liverpool F.C.'s 1988 Rap single?

Answers

Charity Songs (see Quiz 32)
1 AIDS charities. 2 Victoria Wood. 3 Hillsborough. 4 The *Sun*.
5 *Sergeant Pepper Knew My Father*. 6 Wet Wet Wet. 7 Billy Bragg.
8 Bradford Football Club. 9 Michael Jackson, Lionel Richie.
10 Sailing. 11 Lesley Garrett. 12 Gerry Marsden.
13 "Do They Know It's Christmas?". 14 Marti Webb. 15 Stock,
Aitken and Waterman. 16 "That's What Friends Are For".
17 "Knockin' On Heaven's Door". 18 War Child. 19 Lennon
and McCartney. 20 "Livin' Doll".

Quiz 31 Pot Luck 16

Answers – see page 137

1   What was Joan Baez's first Top Ten hit?

2   Which song was a hit for Shirley Bassey and Harry Belafonte in 1957?

3   Whose album *But Seriously* topped the charts in 1990?

4   Who duetted with Frank Sinatra on the 1993 single "I've Got You Under My Skin"?

5   Who sang "The Sun Ain't Gonna Shine Any More" in 1966?

6   Which conservationists' "Minuetto Allegretto" charted in 1974?

7   Who was lead singer with the Troggs?

8   Which two 80s Wimbledon tennis champions had a Top 100 hit in 1991?

9   Who was Echo's backing group?

10 According to Edison Lighthouse what happens Where the Rosemary Goes?

11 In which decade was Donny Osmond born?

12 Which fellow Western actor was on the flip side of Lee Marvin's "Wandrin' Star"?

13 Who had Magic Moments in 1958?

14 Whose first hit was "One of These Nights"?

15 Who was a Yesterday Man back in 1965?

16 Which day of the week was Beautiful to Daniel Boone in 1972?

17 How is Arnold Dorsey better known?

18 Which song title links Don Partridge and Elton John?

19 In which decade did Jackie Wilson have his first hit record?

20 What is the home country of Jimmy Cliff?

Pot Luck 15 (see Quiz 29)
1 1980s. 2 Rasputin. 3 Lena Zavaroni. 4 The Troggs. 5 Elton John. 6 The Carpenters. 7 Norman Wisdom. 8 Glen Campbell. 9 The Dinosaurs 10 The Dubliners. 11 1950s. 12 The Big Sound. 13 Duran Duran. 14 The Commodores. 15 Fontella Bass. 16 Ireland. 17 Badfinger. 18 Cornflake Girl. 19 Campbell. 20 The Playboy Band.

139

Quiz 32 Charity Songs

Answers – see page 138

LEVEL 2

1 Which charities benefited from the "Five Live EP" in 1993?

2 Which comedienne featured on the B side of "The Stonk" for Comic Relief?

3 Which disaster prompted the release of "Ferry 'Cross the Mersey"?

4 Which newspaper created Ferry Aid?

5 Which album was a reinterpretation of songs from *Sgt Pepper*?

6 Who sang "With a Little Help From My Friends" for Childline?

7 Which male artist sang "She's Leaving Home" for the same charity?

8 Where was the fire which prompted the release by the Crowd?

9 Which two Motown stars wrote "We Are the World" for USA For Africa?

10 What did Rod Stewart release in aid of the Zeebrugge ferry disaster?

11 Who sang "Ave Maria" in aid of the Malcolm Sargent Cancer Fund for Children?

12 Who was lead vocalist with the Crowd?

13 Which charity record reached No. 1 twice?

14 Who released "Ben" as a charity single?

15 Who have produced three charity singles?

16 Which Dionne Warwick single raised money for AIDS research?

17 What was the Dunblane single called?

18 Which charity benefited from "Live Like Horses"?

19 Who wrote "With a Little Help From My Friends/She's Leaving Home"?

20 Which Cliff Richard single helped famine relief?

Ready to Rap (see Quiz 30)

Answers

1 "U Can't Touch This". 2 "Gazza Rap". 3 Betty Boo. 4 New York. 5 The Beastie Boys. 6 David Bowie and Queen. 7 Keep Rhythm Your Motivating Energy. 8 "Turtle Power". 9 Salt-N-Pepa. 10 UK. 11 De La Soul. 12 "Hold On". 13 Hammer doll. 14 "Holiday Rap". 15 The Majors. 16 Jazzy Jeff and the Fresh Prince. 17 Public Enemy. 18 "Rapture". 19 Vanilla Ice. 20 "Anfield Rap".

1 Which surname is shared by Debby and Pat?

2 What is the home country of Doop?

3 Whose album *Take Two* topped the charts in 1996?

4 In which decade did Sonia have her first hit record?

5 Whose first hit was "In the Midnight Hour"?

6 Who had a No. 1 in 1967 with "Let the Heartaches Begin"?

7 Who sang "The Letter" in 1967?

8 What was Clifford T. Ward's only Top Ten hit?

9 What did "Paloma Blanca" become – Wurzels style?

10 Who was in Nutbush City Limits in 1973?

11 Who were On the Road Again in 1968?

12 Which James Bond married the 1950s singer Dorothy Squires?

13 Who was the most long-haired of the Eurythmics?

14 Which Shakespeare play was the title of a David Essex hit?

15 Who took the "Legend of Xanadu" to No. 1 in 1968?

16 Who had A Little Love and Understanding in 1975?

17 Who was vocalist with Aphrodite's Child?

18 In which decade was Chuck Berry born?

19 Who were Reparata's backing group?

20 Who were singing about Lady Lynda in 1979?

Quiz 34 Elvis Presley
Answers – see page 144

LEVEL 2

1   What was Elvis's job before he shot to fame?

2   What was Elvis's middle name?

3   Which Elvis hit was based on the Italian song "O Sole Mio" also used to advertise Cornetto ice cream?

4   What follows "I'm Left, You're Right" in the song title?

5   Which No. 1 is Elvis singing at a live show when he dissolves into giggles in a section that is spoken?

6   In which movie does he sing "Wooden Heart"?

7   Which Nashville quartet backed Elvis on many records starting with "Don't Be Cruel" in 1956?

8   Which Beatle, critical of Elvis's post-*G.I.* music said that Elvis died the day he joined the army?

9   Which two US states are named on album titles in the Sixties?

10   Which part of Elvis was removed in an operation in 1960?

11   Which Tom Jones No. 1 was a Top Thirty hit for Elvis in 1975?

12   What follows "Don't Cry" in the 1970 hit?

13   What Official Elvis organization was launched in 1957?

14   In which film does Elvis play Vince Everett, a man accused of manslaughter, who becomes a rock star?

15   What were the first names of Elvis's parents?

16   Which up-tempo song went to No. 1 on Elvis's death?

17   Who was In Disguise in the 1963 No. 1?

18   Why did saying he went to L.C. Humes High School convince sceptical listeners that Elvis was white, not black?

19   What was Priscilla Presley's surname before her marriage?

20   Who did Elvis say Lawdy to in 1957?

Answers

Dead Famous (see Quiz 36)
1 "You Got It". 2 "C'mon Everybody". 3 John Lennon. 4 Sam Cooke. 5 Billie Holiday. 6 Billy Fury. 7 Paul Kossoff. 8 Phil Lynott. 9 Marvin Gaye. 10 Serge Gainsbourg. 11 Gene Vincent. 12 Ritchie Valens. 13 Conway Twitty. 14 Père Lachaise. 15 Bobby Darin. 16 Nilsson. 17 Chas Chandler. 18 Mini. 19 The Big Bopper. 20 Buddy Holly's.

Quiz 35 Pot Luck 18

Answers – see page 141

Answers – see page 141

LEVEL 2

1 Whose album *Live at the BBC* topped the charts in 1994?

2 Whose first hit was "Uptight"?

3 In which decade did Squeeze have their first hit record?

4 What is the link between Evita and Charlie Chaplin?

5 How is Pauline Matthews better known?

6 What was on the other side of Rick Astley's "My Arms Keep Missing You"?

7 Who was Belle's backing group?

8 Who took A Picture of You in 1962?

9 With which song did Cilla Black beat Dionne Warwick to the top spot?

10 Who said "Tell Laura I Love Her" in 1960?

11 In which decade was Robin Gibb born?

12 Which two Tina Turner singles are also the names of albums?

13 What was on the other side of David Cassidy's "Cherish"?

14 Who had the original No. 1 with "Don't Cry For Me, Argentina"?

15 Which city links Spinners and Emeralds?

16 What is the home country of Falco, who had a No. 1 with "Rock Me Amadeus"?

17 Which song title links Patsy Cline and Mud?

18 Which day of the week is included in a Rolling Stones song title in 1967 and again in 1991?

19 In 1961 where was Kenny Ball and at what time?

20 What year was the Bee Gees' "New York Mining Disaster"?

Pot Luck 17 (see Quiz 33)

1 Boone. 2 Holland. 3 Robson and Jerome. 4 1980s. 5 Wilson Pickett. 6 Long John Baldry. 7 The Box Tops. 8 "Gaye". 9 "I Am a Cider Drinker". 10 Ike and Tina Turner. 11 Canned Heat. 12 Roger Moore. 13 Dave Stewart. 14 *A Winter's Tale*. 15 Dave Dee, Dozy, Beaky, Mick and Tich. 16 Gilbert Becaud. 17 Demis Roussos. 18 1920s. 19 The Delrons. 20 Beach Boys.

Quiz 36 Dead Famous

Answers – see page 142

1 Which Roy Orbison single peaked at No. 3 after his death?

2 Which Eddie Cochran hit was rereleased in 1988?

3 Who had the quickest hat trick of No. 1's in 1981?

4 Which soul singer died in 1964 during a shooting incident at a motel?

5 Who was the subject of "Lady Sings the Blues"?

6 Which contemporary of Marty Wilde and Tommy Steele died aged 41 in 1983?

7 Which member of Free died in 1976?

8 Who was bass guitarist with Thin Lizzy?

9 Which late Motown great was married to Berry Gordy's sister?

10 Who was famous for a banned single in French at first intended for Brigitte Bardot?

11 Which late great's songs were the subject of Jeff Beck's *Crazy Legs* album?

12 Who was the subject of the 80s biopic *La Bamba*?

13 Whose first No. 1 was "It's Only Make Believe"?

14 In which Parisian cemetery is Jim Morrison buried?

15 Who had a UK hit with "Mack the Knife"?

16 Who wrote and sang "I Guess the Lord Must Be in New York City"?

17 Which former Animal and Jimi Hendrix manager died in 1996?

18 What type of car was Marc Bolan in when he met his death?

19 *Hellooo Baby* was a Greatest Hits album of which late great?

20 Whose "Winter Dance Party" tour ended in tragedy?

Answers

Elvis Presley (see Quiz 34)
1 Truck driver. 2 Aaron. 3 "It's Now or Never". 4 "She's Gone". 5 "Are You Lonesome Tonight?". 6 *G.I. Blues*. 7 The Jordanaires. 8 John Lennon. 9 (Blue) Hawaii, California (Holiday). 10 Tonsils. 11 "Green, Green Grass of Home". 12 "Daddy". 13 UK Fan Club. 14 *Jailhouse Rock*. 15 Vernon, Gladys. 16 "Way Down". 17 The Devil. 18 Whites-only school. 19 Beaulieu. 20 Miss Clawdy.

144

Quiz 37 Pot Luck 19

Answers – see page 147

LEVEL 2

1   Who had the 50s Top Ten hit with "Seven Little Girls Sitting in the Back Seat"?

2   Whose album *Daydream* topped the charts in 1995?

3   In which decade was Noel Gallagher born?

4   Who duetted with Celine Dion on "Beauty and the Beast"?

5   Who was leaving Durham Town in 1969?

6   Who joined John Travolta and Olivia Newton-John on "Grease – The Dream Mix" in 1991?

7   Whose first hit was "Kids in America"?

8   Which former model hit the charts with "Here I Go Again"?

9   In which decade did Lisa Stansfield have her first hit record?

10   Who charted with "Harvest for the World" in 1988?

11   Who has duetted with the future Princess Grace of Monaco and David Bowie?

12   Which song title links Marcella Detroit with Robson and Jerome?

13   Who had a 60s hit with "This Little Bird"?

14   Who was Wide Eyed and Legless in 1975?

15   What is the home country of Foster and Allen?

16   Which surname is shared by Howard and Paul?

17   Who sang about Victoria in 1970?

18   Who were Disco Tex's backing group?

19   Who joined Bananarama on their first two hits?

20   How is George Benson nicknamed on his first hit single?

Pot Luck 20   (see Quiz 39)

Answers
1 1960s. 2 Connie Francis. 3 In the Old Fashioned Way. 4 His Paramount Jazz Band. 5 Three Degrees. 6 Harmonica. 7 Take That. 8 "I Can't Explain". 9 Bobby Vee. 10 The Turtles. 11 Cockerel Chorus. 12 Chris Farlowe. 13 Jamaica. 14 "1-2-3". 15 Ken Dodd. 16 Crosby, Stills and Nash. 17 Three. 18 1950s. 19 Saturday. 20 Crocodile – Rock, Shoes.

Quiz 38 Film Links

Answers – see page 148

1 Which film title provided a hit for Ray Parker Jr?

2 Which film other than *The Bodyguard* featured "I Will Always Love You"?

3 "The Shoop Shoop Song" was heard at the end of which Cher film?

4 In which film did Kylie Minogue play Lola Lovell and sing on the soundtrack?

5 In which film did Phil Collins revive the 60s hit "Groovy Kind of Love"?

6 Which River Phoenix film sent Ben E. King to the top of the charts?

7 Which film does "The John Dunbar Theme" come from?

8 For which film did Van Morrison sing "Brown-Eyed Girl"?

9 Which Woody Allen film starring Peter Sellers had Tom Jones singing the theme song?

10 Who sang the title song from *Grease* in 1978?

11 Who sang "Raindrops Keep Falling on My Head" in the film?

12 Which film had the theme "Take My Breath Away"?

13 Who sang "Be Prepared" in *The Lion King*?

14 Who played Madonna's night-club-singer lover in *Evita*?

15 "You'll Never Walk Alone" appears in which film musical?

16 Which song is the most famous on the "Woman in Red" soundtrack?

17 Who won an Oscar for "Flashdance – What a Feeling"?

18 What is the link between Barbra Streisand and the film *M*A*S*H*?

19 In which movie did Madonna sing "Into the Groove"?

20 Who sang "Up Where We Belong" from *An Officer and a Gentleman*?

Answers

Cliff Richard (see Quiz 40)
1 "Power to All Our Friends". 2 *Time*. 3 *Wonderful Life*. 4 *Cliff*.
5 *Expresso Bongo*. 6 ...*Famous*. 7 VE Day celebrations. 8 Norrie
Paramor. 9 The Drifters. 10 Grey. 11 Devil. 12 Satisfaction.
13 Cliff himself. 14 Melvyn Hayes. 15 Sooty. 16 Light.
17 Billy Graham. 18 Bruce Welch. 19 "O Little Town of
Bethlehem". 20 Stevie Wonder.

1 In which decade did Stevie Wonder have his first hit record?

2 How is Concetta Rosemarie Franconero better known?

3 How did Charles Aznavour Dance in the 70s?

4 Who were Acker Bilk's backing band?

5 Whose first hit was "Year of Decision"?

6 Which musical instrument does Larry Adler play?

7 Whose album *Nobody Else* topped the charts in 1995?

8 What was the Who's first chart hit?

9 Who was like a Rubber Ball in 1961?

10 Who thought Elenore was swell in 1968?

11 Who sang "Nice One Cyril" in 1973?

12 Who was Out of Time in 1966?

13 What is the home country of Boris Gardiner?

14 Which song title links Len Barry and Gloria Estefan?

15 Whose first hit was "Love is Like a Violin"?

16 Who was on the Marrakesh Express in 1969?

17 How many times in the 80s did "Do They Know It's Christmas?" enter the charts?

18 In which decade was Sade born?

19 Which Night did Robson and Jerome spend at the movies?

20 Which creature links song titles by Elton John and Jimmy Nail?

1   What was Cliff's Eurovision Song Contest entry in 1973?

2   Which musical by Dave Clark did Cliff star in in the West End?

3   Which film did Cliff make after *Summer Holiday*?

4   What was Cliff's first hit album called?

5   In which film did Cliff play the role of Bongo Herbert in 1959?

6   In 1976 Cliff recorded an album called *I'm Nearly*... what?

7   Why did Cliff sing at Buckingham Palace in May 1995?

8   Which record producer signed Cliff to the Columbia label in 1958?

9   How are the Shadows known on the hit "Move It"?

10   What does Blue Turn to in the 1966 hit written by the Rolling Stones' Jagger and Richards?

11   Which Woman gave Cliff his first Top Ten US hit?

12   What was Guaranteed according to the title of Cliff's 1987 album?

13   Who co-wrote "Bachelor Boy" with Bruce Welch?

14   Which future "It Ain't Half Hot Mum" actor starred with Cliff in *The Young Ones* and *Summer Holiday*?

15   Which TV puppet did Cliff co-star with on TV in 1969?

16   How was Cliff Travellin' in his 1959 No. 1?

17   Which evangelist did Cliff join on stage at Earl's Court in 1966?

18   Which member of the Shadows produced "Miss You Nights" in 1976?

19   "Little Town" was an up-tempo version of which carol?

20   Which soul star played all the instruments on "She's So Beautiful"?

Answers

Film Links (see Quiz 38)

1 *Ghostbusters.* 2 *The Best Little Whorehouse in Texas.*
3 *Mermaids.* 4 *The Delinquents.* 5 *Buster.* 6 *Stand By Me.*
7 *Dances With Wolves.* 8 *Sleeping with the Enemy.* 9 *What's New Pussycat?.* 10 Frankie Valli. 11 B.J. Thomas. 12 *Top Gun.*
13 Jeremy Irons. 14 Jimmy Nail. 15 *Carousel.* 16 "I Just Called to Say I Love You". 17 Irene Cara. 18 She was married to its star Elliott Gould. 19 *Desperately Seeking Susan.* 20 Joe Cocker and Jennifer Warnes.

Quiz 41 Pot Luck 21

Answers – see page 151

Answers – see page 151

LEVEL 2

1 Where was Pat Boone's gold mine in 1957?

2 Who replaced Brian Jones when he left the Rolling Stones?

3 What was the Osmonds' only No. 1 UK hit?

4 Who released an album titled *No Parlez*?

5 What novelty song was the only UK No. 1 single for Chuck Berry?

6 How old was Elvis Presley when he died? 41, 42 or 43?

7 Where are Aria electric guitars produced?

8 Which US State did the Bee Gees sing about?

9 Which Buddy Holly hit asks: "Oh misery, misery, what's gonna become of me"?

10 Who released a million-selling album in 1983 titled *Let's Dance*?

11 Which film featured the song "Bright Eyes"?

12 How is Paul Hewson better known?

13 Who was Jimmy James's backing group?

14 In which decade was David Essex born?

15 Which band shares its name with an instrument of torture?

16 Which song title links Elvis Presley and Bobby Brown?

17 Which Spice Girl is Posh Spice?

18 Which UK female singer had two records in the Top Ten in the same week in 1980?

19 Who was lead singer with the Sugarcubes?

20 Who released the album *Goodbye Cruel World* in 1984?

Pot Luck 22 (see Quiz 43)
1 The Partridge Family. 2 "She Loves You". 3 Midge Ure and Bob Geldof. 4 1959. 5 Janis Joplin. 6 1950s. 7 Kissing. 8 Def Leppard. 9 Bob Marley. 10 Dakota. 11 Chuck Berry. 12 David Bowie. 13 Wet Wet Wet. 14 John Kettley (Is a Weatherman). 15 French Kissing. 16 Roger Whittaker. 17 "Summerlove Sensation". 18 Italian. 19 Mel B. 20 Charles.

Quiz 42 TV Ads

Answers – see page 152

1 Which Hollies hit was used in a 1997 campaign by Boots?

2 Who had the ad hit "Jeans On"?

3 Which song to advertise jeans showed two young women holding a guy's jeans as he takes a swim?

4 Who sang it?

5 Which Steve Miller Band single hit the top after being used by Levi's?

6 Which band went to No. 1 with "Should I Stay or Should I Go" after it was used in an ad?

7 In which decade did Levi's begin to use classic hits to advertise?

8 Which was the first such record used in the UK?

9 Which Eddie Cochran hit has been used?

10 Which superstar advertised Diet Coke in 1991?

11 Who sang "It Takes Two" as part of a Pepsi TV ad deal?

12 The melody of "O Sole Mio" has been used to advertise which treat?

13 Who used Elvis's "You Were Always on My Mind" to advertise their services?

14 Whose "Guaglione" advertised Guinness?

15 The tune from "I Can't Let Maggie Go" advertised what?

16 Which product did "Like A Prayer" advertise?

17 Which Ben E. King single was used in a jeans ad?

18 Who sang "Wonderful World" to advertise the same product?

19 Out of the first five songs used to advertise Levi's how many were from performers already dead?

20 Who was dropped from an advertising campaign by Coca-Cola after publicity about his private life?

Girls! (see Quiz 44)
1 Emma. **2** Tina Turner. **3** Bonnie Tyler. **4** The Shangri-Las.
5 Toni Braxton. **6** Raffaella Carra. **7** Two. **8** Elkie Brooks.
9 Kate Bush. **10** Piano. **11** Samantha Fox. **12** The Bangles.
13 Bananarama. **14** *Dick Tracy*. **15** Alison Moyet.
16 Switzerland. **17** Alanis Morissette. **18** "The Man Who Sold the World". **19** Cher. **20** Barbra Streisand.

Quiz 43 Pot Luck 22

Answers – see page 149

1 Whose first single "I Think I Love You" sold in excess of 4 million copies?

2 What Beatles song begins "You think you've lost your love ... "?

3 Who co-produced "Do They Know It's Christmas?"?

4 In which year was Cliff Richard's first album released?

5 Who had the nickname Pearl?

6 In which decade was the Grammy award introduced?

7 What are John Lennon and Yoko Ono doing on the cover of the *Milk and Honey* album?

8 Who recorded the heavy-metal album *Hysteria*?

9 Who was commemorated on Jamaican stamps in 1982?

10 Where were Doris Day's Black Hills?

11 Who was the subject of the film tribute *Hail! Hail! Rock 'N' Roll*?

12 Who formed the rock band Tin Machine in 1989?

13 Who was Wishing He Was Lucky in 1987?

14 Which TV personality did Tribe of Toffs celebrate in song in 1988?

15 What was Deborah Harry doing In the USA in 1986?

16 Who sang "The Last Farewell" in 1975?

17 Which Summer song was a 1974 hit for the Bay City Rollers?

18 What is the nationality of the "Do It Again" singer Raffaella Carra?

19 Which Spice Girl is Scary Spice?

20 What was Buddy Holly's real first name?

1 Which Spice Girl is Baby Spice?

2 Who was the "Acid Queen" in the film *Tommy*?

3 Whose first hit was "Lost in France"?

4 Who had a hit with "Remember (Walkin' In the Sand)"?

5 Whose "Breathe Again" won a US award for Song of the Year in 1995?

6 Who said "Do It Do It Again" in 1978?

7 How many girls were in Ace of Base?

8 Whose real name is Elaine Bookbinder?

9 Whose first album was *The Kick Inside*?

10 Which musical instrument did Lynsey De Paul play?

11 Which Page Three girl hit the charts in 1986?

12 Which group has Susanna Hoffs on guitar and vocals?

13 Which group scrapped a video made as part of the "In At the Deep End" TV show?

14 On which 90s movie soundtrack did Brenda Lee feature?

15 Whose debut album was called *Alf*?

16 Which country did Celine Dion represent in the Eurovision Song Contest?

17 Whose top-selling album featured the Red Hot Chili Peppers's bassist Flea on one track?

18 What was Lulu's only 70s hit?

19 Who participated in the opening of Euro Disney in Paris in 1992?

20 Who had a top-selling album called *Guilty* in 1980?

1 Who had a highly successful album titled *Never For Ever*?

2 Which Spice Girl is Sporty Spice?

3 Who pleaded "Hold Me Close" in 1975?

4 Which artist originated the rock classic "Tutti Frutti"?

5 Who has recorded under the name Kris Carson?

6 Which group included Mick Avory and Pete Quaife?

7 Which Eddie Cochran hit did the Sex Pistols do a cover version of in 1979?

8 Which Boney M single sold over 2 million copies on the UK?

9 In which decade was Bryan Adams born?

10 Which song title links Petula Clark and S.W.V.?

11 Who was going to Dress You Up in 1985?

12 Which TV show opened to Manfred Mann's "5-4-3-2-1"?

13 Which Wild West hero features on a Cher single?

14 Whose first single was "I Lost My Heart to a Starship Trooper"?

15 Who rightly sang "We Are Family" in 1979?

16 Who had a 1996 album called *Everything Must Go*?

17 Who in 1997 said drug taking was as normal as having a cup of tea?

18 What was on the other side of Boney M's "Oh My Lord"?

19 Which two Fleetwood Mac albums are two of the best sellers of all time?

20 Which band leader is the one with the most chart albums in the UK?

Quiz 46 Elton John

Answers – see page 156

1 What was Elton John's first chart album called?

2 What was the name of his first solo No. 1?

3 In which north London suburb was Elton born and brought up?

4 Which Beatles song did Elton have a hit with in 1974?

5 Which song from *High Society* did Elton record with Kiki Dee in 1993?

6 Which tabloid paid £1 million damages to Elton John in 1988?

7 Which UK singer did Elton duet with on "Slow Rivers"?

8 Which blues singer provided Elton with his surname?

9 What completes the album title, *Don't Shoot Me...*?

10 Which middle name did Elton choose when he changed his name legally in 1972?

11 Who were Ann Orson and Carte Blanche who are credited with writing "Don't Go Breaking My Heart"?

12 Which album was recorded at Château d'Herouville in 1972?

13 Which song won Elton his Best Original Song Oscar in 1995?

14 What follows in brackets after Breaking Hearts in the 1985 hit?

15 Who with her friends joined Elton on "That's What Friends Are For"?

16 Which instrumental record was dedicated to a motor-cycle messenger boy who died in an accident?

17 What follows "Sad Songs" in the title of the 1984 hit?

18 In 1991 he was the central figure in an ad campaign for which drink?

19 In 1976 where did Elton John become the first rock star to be immortalized since the Beatles?

20 Which very big star did Elton duet with in 1996?

Answers

Two's Company (see Quiz 48)

1 Sheena Easton. 2 Althia and Donna. 3 Peter Asher (Peter and Gordon). 4 David and Jonathan. 5 Simon and Garfunkel. 6 10 c.c. 7 The Righteous Brothers. 8 Dave Tucker, Paddy Garvey. 9 Peaches and Herb. 10 Kalin. 11 Nina and Frederick. 12 Sutherland. 13 Windsor Davies and Don Estelle. 14 Billy Eckstine and Sarah Vaughan. 15 Marvin Gaye. 16 Hall and Oates. 17 Hue and Cry. 18 Dave Stewart and Barbara Gaskin. 19 The Weather Girls. 20 Donny and Marie Osmond.

Quiz 47 Pot Luck 24

Answers – see page 153

LEVEL 2

1 Where does Susie fall asleep in the hit "Wake Up Little Susie"?

2 Which artist had a No. 3 hit in 1972 with "You're A Lady"?

3 What Killed The Radio Star according to the Buggles?

4 On which Neil Diamond album is the track "Play Me"?

5 What was Golden for the Tremeloes?

6 Which rock guitarist first set a guitar ablaze at the '67 Monterey Pop Festival?

7 In which West End musical did David Essex play the role of Jesus?

8 Who sang "Papa's Got A Brand New Bag"?

9 Where did Supertramp have Breakfast?

10 Which German phrase did Ian Dury rhyme with "Rhythm Stick"?

11 Which group included Al Jardine and Mike Love?

12 Which Sheryl Crow song was Grammy Record of the Year in 1994?

13 Who sang "How Am I Supposed to Live Without You?" in 1989?

14 Who had an instrumental version of "Don't Cry For Me Argentina"?

15 Which comedy actor appeared on Annie Lennox's *Walking on Broken Glass* video?

16 Which "group" was founded by Ian Broudie?

17 Who was Frankie Lymon's backing group?

18 Which song with Love in the title was a hit for the Beatles and Ella Fitzgerald?

19 What was the home city of Bob Marley's father?

20 How many Vandellas were there?

Pot Luck 23 (see Quiz 45)

Answers

1 Kate Bush. 2 Mel C. 3 David Essex. 4 Little Richard. 5 Kris Kristofferson. 6 The Kinks. 7 "C'mon Everybody". 8 "Rivers Of Babylon". 9 1950s. 10 "Downtown". 11 Madonna. 12 "Ready Steady Go". 13 (Just Like) Jesse James. 14 Sarah Brightman. 15 Sister Sledge. 16 Manic Street Preachers. 17 Noel Gallagher. 18 "Mary's Boy Child". 19 *Rumours, Tango in the Night*. 20 James Last.

155

Quiz 48 Two's Company

Answers – see page 154

LEVEL 2

1 Who sang "We've Got Tonight" with Kenny Rogers?

2 How were Ms Forest and Ms Reid better known?

3 Who was Gordon Waller's singing partner?

4 Which duo were Roger Cook and Roger Greenaway?

5 Who were originally known as Tom and Jerry?

6 Godley and Creme were members of which chart-topping group?

7 How are Bill Medley and Bobby Hatfield better known?

8 What were Robson and Jerome's characters called in "Soldier Soldier"?

9 How were Linda Greene and Herb Fame better known?

10 What was the surname of the twins Hal and Herbert?

11 How were the Danish duo Baron and Baroness van Pallandt known in the pop charts?

12 What is the surname of the Brothers Iain and Gavin?

13 Who had a 70s hit with "Whispering Grass"?

14 Who were Passing Strangers back in 1957?

15 Who recorded with Mary Wells, Kim Weston and Tammi Terrell?

16 Which Daryl and John took "Maneater" into the charts?

17 Whose first hit was "Labour of Love"?

18 Who had a 1981 No. 1 with "It's My Party"?

19 Who sang "It's Raining Men" in 1984?

20 Who recorded "I'm Leaving It (All Up to You)" in 1974 ?

Answers

Elton John (see Quiz 46)
1 *Elton John*. 2 "Sacrifice". 3 Pinner. 4 "Lucy in the Sky with Diamonds". 5 "True Love". 6 The *Sun*. 7 Cliff Richard. 8 Long John Baldry. 9 *I'm Only the Piano Player*. 10 Hercules. 11 Elton John and Bernie Taupin. 12 *Honky Chateau*. 13 "Can You Feel the Love Tonight". 14 "Ain't What It Used to Be". 15 Dionne Warwick. 16 "Song For Guy". 17 "Say So Much". 18 Diet Coke. 19 Madame Tussaud's. 20 Luciano Pavarotti.

1   What was Smokey Robinson and the Miracles 1970 No. 1 hit?

2   What company had a No. 2 hit in 1968 with "Simon Says"?

3   Who played the title role in *Tommy*?

4   Which rocker had a kiss curl over his forehead as his trademark?

5   Who is almost naked on a bed, on the cover of his *1999* album?

6   Which group were giving "Lessons in Love" in 1986?

7   Where was Gene Chandler the Duke of?

8   Who was lead singer with the Spencer Davis Group?

9   What was the name of the priest in "Eleanor Rigby"?

10 What four people are on the front cover of the *Saturday Night Fever* album?

11 Which film did the theme "A Whole New World" come from?

12 How are Chris Lowe and Neil Tennant better known?

13 Which Street is named on a 10 c.c. single?

14 Which song with Love in the title was a 1980 hit for Neil Diamond?

15 Who was lead singer with the Bluesbreakers?

16 Candida Doyle plays keyboards with which group?

17 In which decade was Chris Rea born?

18 Who left Velvet Underground in 1970?

19 Which musical instrument does Bryan Ferry play?

20 In which country were the Shamen founded?

Answers

Pot Luck 26 (see Quiz 51)
1 Simple Minds. 2 Sainsbury's. 3 1930s. 4 David Bowie.
5 West Virginia. 6 Chicory Tip. 7 Peter Gabriel. 8 Queen.
9 16. 10 Tears For Fears. 11 Roxy Music. 12 1970s. 13 The
Blackhearts. 14 Betty Boo. 15 Barbra Streisand. 16 Alanis
Morisette. 17 Chaka Khan. 18 PJ and Duncan. 19 England Dan
and John Ford Coley. 20 "Forever Love".

1   Who is the famous mum of Crispian in Kula Shaker?

2   Whose daughter did Jermaine Jackson marry?

3   Who were Marion Ryan's sons?

4   Who is the sister of Peter from Peter and Gordon?

5   Under what name had Peter Sarstedt's elder brother had a chart hit?

6   What is Julian Lennon's mother called?

7   Who has been married to George Harrison and Eric Clapton?

8   Which rock star's daughter has Heavenly and Tiger Lily among her first names?

9   Which member of the "Spitting Image" voice team is a cousin of Paul McCartney?

10 Which pop star was married to top hairdresser John Frieda?

11 Which clothes designer did Sandie Shaw marry?

12 Which fellow country singer was a sister of Crystal Gayle?

13 Which comic record-maker's daughter plays John Archer's girlfriend Hayley in "The Archers"?

14 What were the first names of the Bellamy Brothers?

15 Which 50s hit makers were Joy, Babs and Teddy?

16 How were Veronica and Estelle Bennett, plus cousin Nedra Talley, better known?

17 Which group was made up of sisters Debbie, Kathie, Kim and Joni?

18 Who is Mrs Bobby Brown?

19 Who was Liza Minelli's mother?

20 Who are Shane Richie's sisters-in-law?

Answers

The Beatles (see Quiz 52)
1 James. 2 The Silver Beetles. 3 Stuart Sutcliffe. 4 Pete Best.
5 Hamburg. 6 18. 7 *But Goldies*. 8 "Twist and Shout". 9 "I Want to Hold Your Hand". 10 "Please Please Me". 11 Ringo.
12 *How I Won the War*. 13 From Winston to Ono. 14 His wedding day. 15 George Harrison. 16 *With The Beatles*.
17 "Thomas the Tank Engine". 18 "Free As a Bird". 19 Barbara Bach. 20 *Sgt Pepper's Lonely Hearts Club Band*.

Quiz 51 Pot Luck 26

Answers – see page 157

LEVEL 2

1 What group had a No. 1 album titled *Once Upon A Time* in 1986?

2 Who do Chas and Dave say "You've got more rabbit than…"?

3 In which decade was Dusty Springfield born?

4 Which David released *David Live* in 1974?

5 Which state is "almost heaven" for John Denver?

6 Which group had a hit with "Son of My Father"?

7 Which member of the group Genesis left in 1975?

8 Whose second No. 1 album was *A Day At The Races*?

9 How many "vestal virgins" were leaving in "Whiter Shade Of Pale"?

10 Who sang the official "Sport Aid" song?

11 Brian Eno was a member of which group?

12 In which decade did Billy Joel have a hit with "Just the Way You Are"?

13 Who was Joan Jett's backing group?

14 Who was "Doin' The Do" in 1990?

15 Who has recorded with Barry Gibb, Neil Diamond and Don Johnson?

16 Who released the album *Jagged Little Pill*?

17 How is Yvette Stevens better known?

18 What were Ant and Dec previously known as?

19 Who sang "I'd Really Love to See You Tonight"?

20 What was Gary Barlow's first solo single after leaving Take That?

Quiz 52 The Beatles
Answers – see page 158

1 What is Paul McCartney's first name?

2 What were the Beatles known as immediately before acquiring their final famous name?

3 Who was their bass player in the early 60s?

4 Who did Ringo replace as drummer?

5 Where did they have their first gig as the Beatles?

6 To 100 either way, how many people went to the Beatles' first gig in southern England?

7 What completes the LP title *A Collection of Beatles Oldies...*?

8 What was the name of their first EP?

9 Which song was the group's first US No. 1?

10 Which song did the Beatles perform first on nationwide TV?

11 Who sang lead vocal on "Yellow Submarine"?

12 In which film did John Lennon play the role of Private Gripweed?

13 In 1969 John changed his middle name from what to what?

14 George and Patti Harrison were arrested for marijuana possession in 1969 on which special day for Paul McCartney?

15 Who was the first ex-Beatle to have a No. 1 album?

16 What was the Beatles' second album?

17 Which children's TV series did Ringo begin narrating in 1984?

18 Which previously unreleased Beatles single came out in the mid 90s?

19 Who did Ringo marry in 1981?

20 Which album was the first to have track lyrics on the sleeve?

Quiz 53 Pot Luck 27

Answers – see page 163

1   How is Marie McDonald McLaughlin Lawrie better known?

2   Who plays Magaldi in the film *Evita*?

3   Which musical instrument does Ravi Shankar play?

4   Who was Johnny Kidd's backing group?

5   What does UHF mean on a radio dial?

6   Which group was often known as P.I.L.?

7   In which decade was Lionel Richie born?

8   Who starred as Bongo Herbert in a film?

9   Who had an album called *My People Were Fair and Had Sky in their Hair But Now They're Content to Wear Stars on their Brows*?

10   Which song title links Cars and R.E.M.?

11   Which comic chat show host used an Abba song for his show's title?

12   What could Barry Manilow not do in 1978?

13   Who were the "Top of the Pops" dancers for nine years until 1976?

14   How were Danny, Joe, Donnie, Jon and Jordan better known?

15   Whose first album was *Born to Run*?

16   What is the surname of the Spice Girls' Geri?

17   Which number links a 70s hit by Ringo Starr and a 60s hit by Neil Sedaka?

18   Which "drink" was the Four Seasons' first hit?

19   Which Wet Wet Wet single has "Home and Away" in brackets?

20   In which decade was Chris Rea's first Top Ten hit?

Answers

Pot Luck 28 (see Quiz 55)
1 1950s. 2 Rod Argent. 3 The Pharaohs. 4 Roy Orbison. 5 France. 6 Cat Stevens. 7 Bacharach and David. 8 Robin Sarstedt. 9 "Every Loser Wins". 10 French. 11 1950s. 12 *Bad*. 13 His daughter Lisa Marie. 14 Psychedelic colours. 15 Lionel Richie. 16 The Jukebox. 17 "Top of the Pops". 18 Mike Oldfield. 19 Tony Ferrino. 20 Sinead O'Connor.

Quiz 54 Cover Versions

Answers – see page 164

LEVEL 2

1 Which 60s Beatles song was a chart hit for the Overlanders?

2 Who took "No Woman No Cry" into the charts in 1996?

3 Who had the first hit with "Walk On By"?

4 Who covered "Strawberry Fields Forever" in 1990?

5 What was an important date for Donny Osmond and Cliff Richard?

6 Which song has been a hit for Bing Crosby and Jim Davidson?

7 Who got higher in the charts first time out with "My Girl" – Otis Redding or the Temptations?

8 Who covered Roy Orbison's "A Love So Beautiful"?

9 Who had the UK version and covered "Singing the Blues"?

10 Who had the original version of Boyzone's "Father and Son"?

11 Which Tommy Roe song was covered by Vic Reeves and the Wonder Stuff?

12 Which female sang on "I Got You Babe" in 1985?

13 Who had a hit with "Everything I Own" in the 80s?

14 Which instrumental was a 50s hit for Perez Prado and Eddie Calvert?

15 Which song has been a hit for Elvis Presley and the Stylistics?

16 Who covered Jennifer Rush's "The Power of Love" in 1994?

17 Which song links Willie Nelson and the Pet Shop Boys?

18 Who had the original "This Wheel's On Fire", covered by Siouxie and the Banshees in 1987?

19 Which Kinks song did the Stranglers cover in 1988?

20 Who had the original version of "Love Is All Around"?

Quiz 55 Pot Luck 28

Answers – see page 161

LEVEL 2

1 In which decade was Prince born?

2 Who recorded with San José calling himself Rodriguez Argentina?

3 Who was Sam the Sham's backing group?

4 Whose first chart album was *In Dreams*?

5 Which country is Johnny Halliday from?

6 How was Yusef Islam known when he was in the pop charts?

7 How are the pop composers Burt and Hal better known?

8 What did Clive Sarstedt change his name to for the pop charts?

9 Which Nick Berry single was the best seller of 1986?

10 The Singing Nun had a hit record in which language?

11 In which decade were LPs first sold in the UK?

12 Which Michael Jackson album was the best-selling album of 1987?

13 Who did Elvis Presley name his private jet after?

14 What was special about the paintwork of John Lennon's 1965 Rolls-Royce?

15 Who had the best-selling 1984 album *Can't Slow Down*?

16 What was first unveiled at the Palais Royal Saloon in San Francisco in 1889?

17 In which show did Samantha Juste play the records?

18 Whose 70s instrumental album sold over two million copies in the UK?

19 Which Portuguese singing sensation was created by Steve Coogan?

20 Which Irish singer released "Don't Cry For Me Argentina" as a single in 1992?

Quiz 56 Stage Show Hits

Answers – see page 162

LEVEL 2

1 Which show does "Love Changes Everything" come from?

2 Who had a hit with "I Don't Know How to Love Him" in 1972?

3 Which show does the song come from?

4 Which musical includes the classic "Send in the Clowns"?

5 "One" comes from which long-running stage show?

6 Who had a hit single with "All I Ask of You" but did not star in the show?

7 Who had a hit with "As If We Never Said Goodbye" in 1994?

8 "With One Look" features in which West End and Broadway show?

9 Which show features "Let the Sun Shine In"?

10 What are the nationalities of the Elaine Paige and Barbara Dickson characters portrayed in "I Know Him So Well"?

11 Who duetted with Diana Morrison on "The First Man You Remember"?

12 In which musical does Mrs Johnstone sing "Tell Me It's Not True"?

13 Which song from *Oliver!* did Shirley Bassey take into the charts?

14 Who had a hit with "If I Were A Rich Man" in 1967?

15 Who sang "Wishing You Were Somehow Here Again" in 1987?

16 Which musical does "You'll Never Walk Alone" come from?

17 Which *Evita* song provided Barbara Dickson with a Top Twenty hit?

18 Which show does "Your the One That I Want" come from?

19 Who had a hit with "Aquarius" in 1969?

20 Who had chart success with "Oh What A Circus" in 1978?

Cover Versions (see Quiz 54)

1 "Michelle". 2 The Fugees. 3 Dionne Warwick. 4 Candy Flip. 5 The Twelfth of Never. 6 "White Christmas". 7 Otis Redding. 8 Michael Bolton. 9 Tommy Steele. 10 Cat Stevens. 11 "Dizzy". 12 Chrissie Hynde. 13 Boy George. 14 "Cherry Pink and Apple Blossom White". 15 "Can't Help Falling in Love". 16 Celine Dion. 17 "Always On My Mind". 18 Julie Driscoll, Brian Auger and the Trinity. 19 "All Day and All of the Night". 20 The Troggs.

Answers

Quiz 57 Pot Luck 29

LEVEL 2

1   What was the Bob Marley hit compilation album called?

2   In which decade did Olivia Newton-John have her first hit record?

3   Who had the best-selling album *Oxygène*?

4   Which was the only group to have an album among the top ten of the decade in the 70s and the 80s?

5   How much did an LP measure across?

6   In which language was Falco's "Rock Me Amadeus" sung?

7   "Money For Nothing" and "So Far Away" featured on which album?

8   Which Boys featured on the Fat Boys' "Wipe Out" in 1987?

9   Which record label used by Daniel O'Donnell shares its name with a famous London Hotel?

10 In which decade was Neil Diamond born?

11 Who had the best-selling record of 1974 with "You Won't Find Another Fool Like Me"?

12 Which pop show did Cathy McGowan regularly present?

13 Who recorded the Grammy-winning "Don't Worry Be Happy"?

14 Who was B. Bumble's backing group?

15 How was the controversial James Marcus Smith better known?

16 Who sang with Paul Miles-Kingston on "Pie Jesu"?

17 Who had a 1996 hit with "Mysterious Girl"?

18 Which group did Paul Heaton form after the Housemartins?

19 What is Leonard Cohen's home country?

20 Who teamed up with Natalie Cole on a 1983 tribute album to her father?

Pot Luck 30 (see Quiz 59)

Answers
1   Art Garfunkel. **2** 1980s. **3** David Bowie. **4** Donna Summer.
5 Glenn Medeiros. **6** Ken Dodd. **7** "Day Tripper". **8** "Mull of Kintyre". **9** Human League. **10** Jennifer Rush, Stevie Wonder.
11 Dire Straits. **12** Philip. **13** 1980s. **14** Ricky Valance.
15 "When the Girl In Your Arms Is the Girl in Your Heart". **16** 33 1/3. **17** Phil Collins. **18** Marianne Faithfull. **19** 1950s.
20 Perry Como.

Quiz 58 Place the Place

Answers – see page 168

LEVEL 2

1 Who were going to Barbados in 1975?

2 Which Asian country provided Kim Wilde with an 80s hit?

3 In which US state might you be Dreamin' of Girls or a Man in a Hotel?

4 Patsy Gallant was From where to where in 1977?

5 Which city was the title of a Simple Minds EP in 1989?

6 Which geographical group had China, Tokyo and Cantonese in chart titles?

7 Who had a 60s hit with "Do You Know the Way to San Jose?"?

8 Which city has given hit songs to Frank Sinatra, Gerard Kenny and Sting?

9 Who was in Africa in 1983?

10 It was a Rainy Night and The Devil Went Down to where?

11 Who was Leavin' Durham Town in 1969?

12 Wichita and Galveston provided hits for whom?

13 Which location was a hit for Bobby Bloom in 1970?

14 Where was Michael Jackson a Stranger in 1996?

15 Which Queen was a hit for Billy Ocean?

16 Where did Tony Christie ask the Way To in the 70s?

17 Which US city links Elton John and Bruce Springsteen in song?

18 Which tropical paradise was the subject of a David Essex hit?

19 Which US state was a 70s hit for Pussycat?

20 Who were All the Way From Memphis in 1973?

Quiz 59 Pot Luck 30

Answers – see page 165

1 Who sang the theme song from *Watership Down*?

2 In which decade did CDs first go on sale in Europe?

3 Which pop star called his son Zowie?

4 How is LaDonna Andrea Gaines better known?

5 Who had a hit with "Nothing's Gonna Change My Love for You" aged 18?

6 Which comedian had the best-selling record of 1965?

7 What was on the other side of the Beatles' "We Can Work It Out"?

8 Which single of 1977 was the first ever to sell two million in the UK?

9 Who sang "Do You Want Me?" in 1981?

10 Who were the only two Americans to have million-selling singles in the 80s in the UK?

11 Who made Private Investigations in 1982?

12 What is Mick Jagger's middle name?

13 In which decade did John Lennon's "Imagine" hit the top spot?

14 Whose "Tell Laura I Love Her" was banned in 1960?

15 Which Cliff Richard record before 1997 has the longest title?

16 How many r.p.m. did an LP have?

17 Who had the 1981 album *Face Value*?

18 What is Marianne Faithfull's real name?

19 In which decade was Bryan Adams born?

20 Which veteran had a 70s album *And I Love You So*?

Quiz 60 The Bee Gees

Answers – see page 166

LEVEL 2

1 Which Gibb brothers are twins?

2 Where in the UK were the Gibbs born?

3 What was their first UK hit?

4 What was the sleeve to "Odessa" made from?

5 Who did Maurice marry in 1969?

6 In 1969 which brothers did the Bee Gees consist of?

7 Which song is about a man about to be electrocuted on death row?

8 Which song from *Saturday Night Fever* did Yvonne Elliman record?

9 How many Bee Gees songs were in *Saturday Night Fever*?

10 Which Barry Gibb song was a hit for Frankie Valli in 1979?

11 Who had a No. 1 UK and US hit with Barry Gibb's "Woman in Love"?

12 What was their last No. 1 of the 70s and their last for eight years?

13 Which 80s hit meant they were the first group to have a No. 1 in each of three decades?

14 Which of their songs was a hit for Dionne Warwick in 1982?

15 What was the sequel to *Saturday Night Fever*?

16 Which Bee Gee had a solo album called *Secret Agent*?

17 Which cricketer contributed to "We Are the Bunburys" about a group of cricket-mad rabbits?

18 Which Gibb made a cameo appearance in "Only Fools and Horses"?

19 Which group used a Gibb song as their swan song?

20 Who did they pay tribute to in "Tapestry Revisited"?

Answers

Place the Place (see Quiz 58)

1 Typically Tropical. 2 Cambodia. 3 California. 4 From New York to LA. 5 Amsterdam. 6 Japan. 7 Dionne Warwick. 8 New York. 9 Toto. 10 Georgia. 11 Roger Whittaker. 12 Glen Campbell. 13 Montego Bay. 14 Moscow. 15 Caribbean. 16 Amarillo. 17 Philadelphia. 18 Tahiti. 19 Mississippi. 20 Mott the Hoople.

Quiz 61 Pot Luck 31

Answers – see page 171

1   Which religious political leader were the Clash referring to in "Rock The Casbah"?

2   Which group received a gold record for "Baby I'm A Want You" in 1972?

3   Which No. 1 for the Platters was a hit for Brian Ferry in 1974?

4   Who had the original hit in 1963 with "It's My Party"?

5   Who duetted with Georgio Moroder on "Together In Electric Dreams"?

6   Who sang "Wonderful World Beautiful People" in 1969?

7   Who was the manager of the Dave Clark Five?

8   Which John Cougar hit has the lyric "two American kids growin' up in the heartland"?

9   What is Ringo Starr holding on the cover of the *Sgt Pepper* album?

10   What was the title of Freda Payne's No. 1 from 1970?

11   Which breakfast cereal was advertised with the song "Spirit in the Sky" in early 1997?

12   In which decade was Tori Amos born?

13   Who is Bobby Boris Pickett's backing group?

14   Whose first hit was "Can't Stand Losing You" in the 70s?

15   Which drink was Berni Flint singing about in 1977?

16   Who spent her early years in radio in "Meet The Huggetts"?

17   Whose second manager and first husband is Bobby Willis?

18   What was Andy Newman's nickname?

19   What is Love according to Pat Benatar in 1984?

20   Who was the Man with the Golden Trumpet?

Pot Luck 32 (see Quiz 63)
1 Marguerita Time. 2 Andrew Lloyd Webber. 3 Chic. 4 The Fugees. 5 Fox. 6 Guy Mitchell. 7 Nerves and brain. 8 Old-fashioned boxing gloves. 9 Howard Keel. 10 San Fernando. 11 1950s. 12 New York. 13 Of '69. 14 ABC. 15 Davy. 16 Barry Green. 17 Bette Midler. 18 The Pretenders. 19 The Culprits. 20 Deep Blue Something.

Quiz 62 Christmas Records

Answers – see page 172

1 What did Dora Bryan want for Christmas in 1963?

2 In which decade did Bing Crosby's "White Christmas" first enter the UK charts?

3 What did John Lennon's "Happy Christmas" have in brackets in 1980?

4 According to Adam Faith what was in a Christmas Shop in 1960?

5 Who said "Please Come Home for Christmas" in 1994?

6 Which Christmas Rock has been a hit for Max Bygraves and Chubby Checker with Bobby Rydell?

7 Who wished It Could Be Christmas Every Day in 1973?

8 What was Johnny Mathis's 1976 Christmas hit?

9 What kind of Merry Christmas did a band of environmentalists wish us in 1974?

10 Who said "All I Want For Christmas is You" in 1994?

11 Which comedian was "Rockin' Around the Christmas Tree" in 1987?

12 Which Snowman did the Cocteau Twins sing about in 1993?

13 Who covered the Carpenters' "Santa Claus is Comin' To Town" in 1985?

14 Where was Santa Claus according to Spitting Image in 1986?

15 Who pleaded with Santa Baby?

16 Who sang with the Smurfs on "Christmas in Smurfland" in 1978?

17 Whose "Christmas Alphabet" went to No. 1 in 1955?

18 Who had a Wonderful Christmas Time in 1979?

19 What is the theme song from *The Snowman*?

20 Who had "White Christmas" on the other side of "Too Risky"?

Answers

I Write the Songs (see Quiz 64)

1 Gerry Goffin. 2 Burt Bacharach and Hal David. 3 Tim Rice. 4 David Cassidy. 5 Reg Presley. 6 Gary Barlow. 7 Andrew Lloyd Webber. 8 Prince. 9 Cook and Greenaway. 10 Nicky Chinn. 11 The Bee Gees. 12 Tom. 13 "Living Doll". 14 "You'll Never Walk Alone". 15 Bjorn Ulvaeus, Benny Andersson. 16 Neil Diamond. 17 Barry Manilow. 18 Pomus and Shuman. 19 Billy J Kramer and the Dakotas. 20 Dolly Parton.

Quiz 63 Pot Luck 32

Answers – see page 169

Answers – see page 169

LEVEL 2

1   What time was it for Status Quo in a 1983 No 3 hit?

2   Who launched The Really Useful company in 1986?

3   Which disco group was formed by Nile Rodgers and Bernard Edwards?

4   Who were Ready Or Not in 1996?

5   What was On the Run for Manfred Mann in 1968?

6   Who was No. 1 with "Singing the Blues" in 1956?

7   What are shaking and rattling in "Great Balls of Fire"?

8   What is David Bowie wearing on his hands on the cover of the *Let's Dance* album?

9   Which "Dallas" star released his *And I Love You So* album in 1984?

10   Where was Johnny Duncan's Last Train going to in 1957?

11   In which decade was Joan Armatrading born?

12   Which city features in the title of the 1978 Darts hit?

13   Which Summer was a 1985 hit for Bryan Adams?

14   Whose first album was *The Lexicon of Love*?

15   Who's On the Road Again according to Manfred Mann's Earth Band in 1978?

16   What is Barry Blue's real name?

17   Who is known as the Divine Miss M?

18   Whose first hit was "Stop Your Sobbing" in the 70s?

19   Who are Craig McLachlan's backing group?

20   Who had Breakfast at Tiffany's in 1996?

Answers

Pot Luck 31 (see Quiz 61)

1 Ayatollah Khomeini. 2 Bread. 3 "Smoke Gets In Your Eyes".
4 Lesley Gore. 5 Phil Oakey. 6 Jimmy Cliff. 7 Dave Clark.
8 "Jack and Diane". 9 Trumpet. 10 "Band of Gold". 11
Kellogg's Bran Flakes. 12 1960s. 13 The Crypt-Kickers. 14 The
Police. 15 Southern Comfort. 16 Petula Clark. 17 Cilla Black.
18 Thunderclap. 19 A Battlefield. 20 Eddie Calvert.

1   Who was Carole King's songwriting partner?

2   Who wrote "Anyone Who Had a Heart" which was a Cilla Black hit?

3   Who was the lyricist on "A Whole New World" from *Aladdin*?

4   Who had a hit with "I Write the Songs" in 1975?

5   Who wrote "Love Is All Around"?

6   Which member of Take That also wrote "Everything Changes"?

7   Who wrote the music for Phillip Schofield's first hit single?

8   Which singer wrote Sinead O'Connor's "Nothing Compares 2 U"?

9   Which two Rogers' many hits include "Something's Gotten Hold of My Heart"?

10   Who co-wrote with Mike Chapman on over 50 Top Ten hits of the 70s?

11   Who wrote "Chain Reaction" for Diana Ross?

12   Who was Dusty Springfield's song-writing brother?

13   Which Cliff Richard No. 1 was written by Lionel Bart?

14   Which 1985 No. 1 was written by Rodgers and Hammerstein?

15   Who co-wrote "I Know Him So Well" with Tim Rice?

16   Whose first No. 1 as a writer was with the Monkees' "I'm A Believer"?

17   Which singer/songwriter was Bette Midler's pianist and arranger?

18   How are songwriters Doc and Mort better known?

19   Who was the first act, other than the Beatles, to take a Lennon and McCartney composition to No. 1?

20   Who wrote Whitney Houston's "I Will Always Love You"?

Quiz 65 Pot Luck 33

Answers – see page 175

LEVEL 2

1 Who had a 1996 hit with "Flava"?

2 Who joined East 17 on "If You Ever" in 1996?

3 What nickname did the DJ Steve Wright give Prince?

4 What is Andy Summers doing on the cover of the *Synchronicity* LP?

5 What did Mrs Brown have according to Herman's Hermits?

6 Which Rod Stewart album had "Blondes" in the title?

7 What was a hit for Neil Sedaka and then the Partridge Family?

8 In which city was Eartha Kitt Under the Bridges Of in 1955?

9 What was the title of Paul McCartney's first solo album?

10 Who sang "Unbreak My Heart" in 1997?

11 In which decade was Michael Bolton born?

12 Whose first hit was "Letter From America" in the 80s?

13 Who was told Don't Be A Hero by Paper Lace in 1974?

14 Which type of Summer was an 80s hit for the Style Council?

15 Whose first album was *Soul Provider*?

16 Whose nickname was Lady Leather?

17 Which country star's initials are J.R.?

18 How is Christopher Geppert better known?

19 Which city features in the title of the Clash hit?

20 Who is Harold Melvin's backing group?

Pot Luck 34 (see Quiz 67)

1 Evita. 2 Daniel. 3 Jennifer Warnes. 4 Your Love.
5 Foreigner. 6 Georgia . 7 Blondie. 8 *Synchronicity*.
9 "Vincent". 10 Status Quo. 11 Doris Day. 12 Laurie
Anderson. 13 Chuck E. 14 The Communards. 15 Tokyo
(Olympics). 16 The Bunnymen. 17 Billy Joel. 18 "Cruel
Summer". 19 The Real Thing. 20 1960s.

Answers

Quiz 66 Glam Rock

Answers – see page 176

LEVEL 2

1   Who was lead singer with the Sweet?

2   Which dance-hall group banned the Sweet due to their suggestive stage act?

3   What was Marc Bolan's real name?

4   Which former glam rocker is the father of the producer Paul Gadd Junior?

5   Whose second album was *Rock 'N' Roll Dudes*?

6   What was Alvin Stardust's first No. 1?

7   What was T. Rex's first No. 1 album?

8   For which song did the Sweet dress up in native American costumes and make up?

9   What was David Bowie's first hit with "star" in the title?

10   Which song did Bowie give to Mott the Hoople?

11   Who wrote an autobiography called *Leader*?

12   Who did Alvin Stardust feature as in the charts in 1961?

13   Which glam rock writers were referred to as Chinnichap?

14   What was Mud's first No. 1?

15   Who was Mud's lead singer?

16   What was the debut single of Tyrannosaurus Rex?

17   Who played Leather Tuscadero in the TV series "Happy Days"?

18   Which band had two each of vocalists, drummers, guitarists and bass players?

19   Mickey Finn was part of which band?

20   Who took "The Cat Crept In" to No. 2?

Answers

Frank Sinatra (see Quiz 68)
1 1910s (1915). 2 Ole Blue Eyes. 3 1980s. 4 "Three Coins in the Fountain". 5 Albert. 6 *From Here To Eternity*. 7 Reprise.
8 "Strangers in the Night". 9 "Nancy (With the Laughing Face)".
10 Paul Anka. 11 "I've Got You Under My Skin". 12 *Pal Joey*.
13 Grace Kelly. 14 Mia Farrow. 15 1960s. 16 Frank Junior.
17 Chicago. 18 New York. 19 Al Martino. 20 *It Might As Well Be Swing*.

174

1 Which film heroine was born in 1919 and died in 1952?

2 Who is "a star in the face of the sky" in an Elton John hit?

3 Who joined Jo Cocker in the 1983 hit "Up Where We Belong"?

4 What couldn't Petula Clark Live Without in her 1966 hit?

5 Which group had a No. 1 in 1985 with "I Wanna Know What Love Is"?

6 What did Ray Charles have "on his mind" in the 1960 hit?

7 What group went Atomic in 1980?

8 Which Police album cover had coloured stripes superimposed with photos?

9 Which No. 1 is sometimes referred to as "Starry Starry Night"?

10 Who had a No. 1 hit with "Down Down"?

11 How is Doris Kappelhoff better known?

12 Who had a hit with "Oh Superman" in 1981?

13 Who's In Love according to Rickie Lee Jones in 1979?

14 Who had the 1987 hit "Never Can Say Goodbye"?

15 Which city features in the title of the 1964 hit with a sporting link by Helmut Zacharias?

16 Who is Echo's backing group?

17 Whose first Top Ten album was *52nd Street*?

18 Which Summer was an 80s hit for Bananarama?

19 Whose first hit was "You To Me Are Everything" in the 70s?

20 In which decade was Jon Bon Jovi born?

Quiz 68 Frank Sinatra

LEVEL 2

1   In which decade was Sinatra born?

2   What is his nickname?

3   Which is the only decade in which Sinatra has not had a Top Ten album?

4   What was his first UK No. 1 in 1954?

5   What is Sinatra's middle name?

6   For which 50s film did Sinatra win an Oscar?

7   What was Sinatra's own record label, set up in 1961?

8   Which 1966 hit won a Grammy that year?

9   Which song was dedicated to his elder daughter?

10 Who wrote the English lyric for Sinatra's signature tune "My Way"?

11 Which song did he take into the charts with Bono in 1993?

12 In which film did Sinatra sing his famous "The Lady Is A Tramp"?

13 Of which co-star did he say on her death, "She was a princess from the day she was born"?

14 Which of Sinatra's wives went on to marry Andre Previn?

15 In which decade was "My Way" first released?

16 Which of Sinatra's children was kidnapped?

17 Which city gave Sinatra a 50s hit?

18 Which city gave him a hit single 23 years later?

19 Who played the character loosely based on Sinatra in *The Godfather*?

20 In addition to *Sinatra-Basie* which album did he make with Count Basie in 1964?

Answers

Glam Rock (see Quiz 66)
1 Brian Connolly. 2 Mecca. 3 Mark Feld. 4 Gary Glitter.
5 The Glitter Band. 6 "Jealous Mind". 7 *Electric Warrior*.
8 "Wig Wam Bam". 9 "Starman". 10 "All The Young Dudes".
11 Gary Glitter. 12 Shane Fenton. 13 Chapman and Chinn.
14 "Tiger Feet". 15 Les Gray. 16 "Debora". 17 Suzi Quatro.
18 Showaddywaddy. 19 T. Rex. 20 Mud.

176

Quiz 69 Pot Luck 35

Answers – see page 179

LEVEL 2

1 Which group had a hit with "Rag Doll" in 1964?

2 Which 1977 hit told of "four hungry children and a crop in the field"?

3 Which song was highest in the charts for the Spice Girls at the beginning of 1997?

4 In which month was Pat Boone in love, in a 1957 song title?

5 What is on the cover of the *Brothers In Arms* album?

6 Which female was Shakin' Stevens singing about in his 1982 No. 1?

7 What sort of wind did Frank Ifield and Jimmy Young sing about?

8 What was Blur's first No. 1 of 1997?

9 Which Small Faces song asks "What did you do there?"?

10 What did Guy Mitchell have "by the number" in his final hit in 1959?

11 Which Summer was a 1990 hit for Belinda Carlisle?

12 Which Michael Jackson/Paul McCartney hit is one word three times?

13 In which decade was Bob Geldof born?

14 What game were the Pet Shop Boys Dancing to in 1988?

15 Which late singer was born Ellen Naomi Cohen?

16 Who was Dear according to Siouxsie and the Banshees in 1983?

17 Whose first album was *Heaven On Earth*?

18 Which town features in the title of the 1988 Four Tops hit?

19 Whose first hit was "Daddy Cool" in the 70s?

20 Who is Eddie's backing group?

Answers

Pot Luck 36 (see Quiz 71)
1 "Talk to the Animals". 2 Mary. 3 1952. 4 A tubular bell.
5 Stewart Copeland. 6 Andy Stewart. 7 Good Vibrations.
8 *Elton John's Greatest Hits*. 9 Peter Noone. 10 Jamiroquai.
11 The Heartbreakers. 12 Boyz II Men. 13 1960s. 14 New York. 15 Marti Pellow. 16 Marilyn Martin. 17 Violin.
18 Cher. 19 Darren Day. 20 Lynda.

1 Which ballad began life as "Comme D'Habitude"?

2 Which song has charted for Frankie Laine, plus Robson and Jerome ?

3 Which 50s singer of big ballads was nicknamed the Sultan of Sob?

4 Connie Francis had a 1958 No. 1 with "Who's Sorry Now?", but in which decade was the song written?

5 Who had a 60s hit with "As Long As He Needs Me"?

6 Which song from *La Cage Aux Folles* was a hit for Gloria Gaynor?

7 Which Platters hit begins "They asked me how I knew"?

8 Which song charted for Doris Day and Kathy Kirby?

9 Which two acts have had a No. 1 with "You'll Never Walk Alone"?

10 Who got to No. 2 with "You've Lost That Lovin' Feeling", pipped at the post by the Righteous Brothers?

11 Who had a UK No. 1 with the English version of a French hit "La Dernière Valse"?

12 Which 6' 9" chart topper sang "Let The Heartaches Begin"?

13 Which 1970 No. 1 for Elvis was recorded live in Las Vegas?

14 Which writer did not live to see Mariah Carey's version of his song reach the top in 1994?

15 Which Diana Ross ballad reached No. 1 after Tony Blackburn played it every day of his breakfast show in 1971?

16 What was Madonna's first hit of 1997?

17 Who had a 1965 No. 1 with "Where Are You Now (My Love)?"?

18 Which song took Whitney Houston to the top of the charts in 1988?

19 Which ballad first took the Walker Brothers to No. 1 in the mid 60s?

20 Which 1996 album did Celine Dion's "All By Myself" come from?

Answers

Novelty Songs (see Quiz 72)
1 Hylda Baker. 2 The Frog Chorus. 3 Arthur Daley. 4 The Goodies. 5 Trigger. 6 Kinky Boots. 7 The Ugly Duckling. 8 Margate. 9 Fred Wedlock. 10 John McEnroe and Pat Cash. 11 The Brownies. 12 "Ballad of Spotty Muldoon". 13 "It's 'Orrible Being In Love (When You're 8 And A Half)". 14 Ray Moore. 15 Dick Emery. 16 Haysi Fantayzee. 17 "I Am a Cider Drinker". 18 "Whispering Grass". 19 Laurel and Hardy. 20 Bobby Boris Pickett and the Crypt-Kickers.

Quiz 71 Pot Luck 36

Answers – see page 177

LEVEL 2

1 What song from *Dr. Dolittle* won an Oscar in 1967?

2 Who did the Everly Brothers ask a message to be taken to in 1959?

3 In which year was the first UK record chart published: 1952, '53 or '54?

4 What, on the cover of *Tubular Bells,* is set against the sky?

5 Who was the tallest member of the Police?

6 Who had "A Scottish Soldier" in the charts for nine months in 1961?

7 What do the Beach Boys get from "the way sunlight plays upon her hair"?

8 Which Elton John album cover shows him sitting in a white suit at a piano?

9 Who was Herman's Hermits' lead singer?

10 Who had a 1996 album called *Travelling Without Moving*?

11 Who is Tom Petty's backing group?

12 Whose first hit was "End of the Road" in the 90s?

13 In which decade was Boy George born?

14 Which city features in the title of the 1988 Sting hit?

15 How is Mark McLoughlin better known?

16 Who sang with Phil Collins on the 1985 hit "Separate Lives"?

17 Which musical instrument does Stephane Grappelli play?

18 Whose first album was *All I Really Want to Do*?

19 Who starred in the 1996 revival of *Summer Holiday* on stage?

20 Who were Hue and Cry Looking for in 1989?

Answers

Pot Luck 35 (see Quiz 69)
1 The Four Seasons. 2 "Lucille". 3 "2 Become 1". 4 April.
5 A steel guitar. 6 Oh Julie. 7 A wayward wind.
8 "Beetlebum". 9 "Itchycoo Park". 10 Heartaches.
11 "Summer Rain". 12 "Say Say Say". 13 1950s. 14 Domino.
15 Mama Cass. 16 Prudence. 17 Belinda Carlisle.
18 Acapulco. 19 Boney M. 20 The Hotrods.

Quiz 72 Novelty Songs

Answers – see page 178

LEVEL 2

1 Who sang with Arthur Mullard on "You're the One That I Want"?

2 Who backed Paul McCartney on "We All Stand Together"?

3 Who were the Firm singing about when they said " 'E's Alright"?

4 Who sang about the Funky Gibbon in 1975?

5 What was the name of Ernie the fastest milkman's horse?

6 Which clothes were Honor Blackman and Patrick MacNee singing about in 1990?

7 Which song did the adult comedian Mike Reid take into the pop charts?

8 Which seaside resort provided Chas and Dave with a 1982 hit?

9 Who was The Oldest Swinger in Town in 1981?

10 Which two 80s Wimbledon champions were backed by the Full Metal Rackets on their 1991 record?

11 Which all-girl pack was Billy Connolly in, in 1979?

12 Which Ballad was a 1965 hit for Peter Cook?

13 Which record did Claire and Friends chart with in 1986?

14 Which late radio DJ recorded "O' My Father Had a Rabbit" in 1986?

15 Who used his catchphrase "You Are Awful" in a chart hit?

16 Who announced "John Wayne is Big Leggy" in 1982?

17 Which song did the Wurzels record to "Paloma Blanca"?

18 Which record has the line "Sing Lofty"?

19 Which comedy duo were on the Trail of the Lonesome Pine in 1975?

20 Who sang the Monster hit which begins "I was working in the lab late one night"?

Big Ballads (see Quiz 70)

Quiz 73 Pot Luck 37

Answers – see page 183

1 Who was "bound to die" in Lonnie Donegan's 1958 hit?

2 Whose names also feature on the album title *Two Rooms*?

3 Who took "Bye Bye Baby" to the top in 1975?

4 What instrument is on the back cover of Stevie Wonder's *Hotter Than July* LP?

5 Who was singing about "My Guy" in 1964?

6 What Buddy Holly song goes: "Oh misery, misery, what's gonna become of me"?

7 Who narrated Jeff Wayne's *War Of The Worlds* album?

8 What sort of entertainment were Simply Red enjoying in 1995?

9 Which group made No. 5 with "De Do Do Do, De Da Da Da"?

10 Who told us he was An Innocent Man?

11 Who took "Two Can Play at That Game" to No. 2 in the charts?

12 Which George Michael video featured the supermodel Linda Evangelista?

13 How is Roberta Streeter better known?

14 What was Jimi Hendrix's first Top Ten hit in the UK?

15 Who had Something In Common in 1994?

16 Who said "Don't Turn Around" in 1988?

17 What did Bobby Goldsboro say Hello to in 1974?

18 Which colours did Michael Jackson take to the top in 1991?

19 Who had a hit with "The Fly" the same year?

20 Which song begins "Close your eyes and I'll kiss you, Tomorrow I'll miss you"?

Answers

Pot Luck 38 (see Quiz 75)
1 Brand New. 2 Dr Hook. 3 "Tune In, Cop Out". 4 "Annie's Song". 5 "Can't Get Used To Losing You". 6 Jane Asher. 7 Big Dee Irwin. 8 Daryl Hall. 9. Whisky and rye. 10 A Moon Shadow. 11 Neville. 12 "Aquarius". 13 1950s. 14 Alison Moyet. 15 Petula Clark. 16 Holland Dozier and Holland. 17 Peter Sellers. 18 Limmie and the Family Cookin'. 19 Matt Bianco. 20 Billy Idol.

Quiz 74 Dance & Disco

Answers – see page 184

LEVEL 2

1   Which Patrick Swayze film had a top-selling soundtrack album in 1987?

2   Who took "Dr Love" into the Top Ten in 1976?

3   In which decade were the *Dance Mix* albums first released?

4   Who had a 1986 album called *Disco*?

5   Who sang "He's The Greatest Dancer" in 1979?

6   Who took "Yes Sir I Can Boogie" to the top of the charts?

7   Who was Dancing on a Saturday Night in 1973?

8   Who sang with the Sex-O-Lettes?

9   Who was heard to Rock his Baby in 1974?

10 Who was Happy Just to Be With You in 1995?

11 Who had an 80s hit with "Ooh La La La (Let's Go Dancin')"?

12 Who were in a "Gangsta's Paradise" in 1995?

13 What completes the title of Chic's "Dance Dance Dance"?

14 Who had a 1995 hit with "Cotton Eye Joe"?

15 Which Brothers went "Boom Boom Boom" in the 90s?

16 Which Donna Summer disco hit was at No. 1 when Elvis Presley died?

17 Who were a Sight For Sore Eyes in the 90s?

18 Which dance record was the Bee Gees' first 70s No. 1?

19 Which Bee Gees song did N Trance take to the charts nearly 20 years after the original?

20 Who had a 1974 No. 1 with "You're The First The Last My Everything"?

Status Quo (see Quiz 76)

Answers
1 1960s. **2** Marty Wilde. **3** "The Wanderer". **4** "Rockin' All Over the World". **5** South Africa. **6** *Piledriver*. **7** "Anniversary Waltz" – Part 1 and Part 2. **8** "Running All Over the World". **9** NEC. **10** Porsche. **11** Rugby League Cup Final. **12** *Hello*. **13** 1985. **14** "TOTP2". **15** Francis Rossi. **16** Manchester United. **17** "Burning Bridges (On and Off and On Again)". **18** *In the Army Now*. **19** Radio 1FM. **20** Parfitt and Rossi.

Quiz 75 Pot Luck 38

Answers – see page 181

LEVEL 2

1 What do You Make Me Feel according to the Stylistics?

2 Who had "Sexy Eyes" at No. 4 in 1980?

3 What did Freak Power do after "Turn On" in 1995?

4 What was John Denver's only solo hit single in the UK?

5 What was a No. 2 hit for Andy Williams and a No. 3 for the Beat?

6 Who was Paul McCartney's girlfriend from 1963 to 1966?

7 Who sang with the uncredited Little Eva on "Swinging on a Star"?

8 Who partnered John Oates on "Maneater"?

9 What were them "good ole boys drinkin'" in "American Pie"?

10 What is following Cat Stevens in his 1971 hit?

11 What is the real first name of Noddy Holder of Slade?

12 Which song begins "When the moon is in the seventh house, and Jupiter aligns with Mars"?

13 In which decade was Steve Harley born?

14 Who was lead vocalist with Yazoo?

15 Which recording and musical star has written under the pseudonym of Al Grant?

16 How were the Motown writers Eddie, Lamont and Brian better known?

17 Who recited "A Hard Day's Night" dressed as Richard III?

18 How were Limmie, Jimmy and Martha Snell known?

19 Whose first hit was "Get Out of Your Lazy Bed"?

20 How is William Broad better known?

Pot Luck 37 (see Quiz 73)

Answers

1 Tom Dooley. 2 Elton John and Bernie Taupin. 3 Bay City Rollers. 4 A Piano. 5 Mary Wells. 6 "Raining In My Heart". 7 Richard Burton. 8 Fairground. 9 The Police. 10 Billy Joel. 11 Bobby Brown. 12 "Too Funky". 13 Bobby Gentry. 14 "Hey Joe". 15 Bobby Brown and Whitney Houston. 16 Aswad. 17 Summertime. 18 "Black or White". 19 U2. 20 "All My Loving".

Quiz 76 Status Quo

Answers – see page 182

LEVEL 2

1 In which decade did Status Quo have their first Top Ten hit?

2 Which 50s/60s singer co wrote "Ice in the Sun"?

3 Which Dion hit did they record in 1984?

4 Which song did they open the Live Aid concert with in 1985?

5 In 1988 Status Quo apologized to the UN for performing where?

6 What was Status Quo's first UK hit album?

7 What were their 1990 medleys of rock 'n' roll classics called?

8 Which rerecorded song was used for the Race Against Time in 1988?

9 Where was their 1982 hit "Caroline" recorded live?

10 What sort of car was Rick Parfitt driving when he was involved in an accident in 1995?

11 Which game between England and Australia was about to be played when they sang "Rockin' All Over the World" in 1995?

12 What was the title of their first No. 1 album?

13 In which year did they release no singles, breaking a run of a Top 20 single per year for 12 years ?

14 Which first BBC 2 pop show did they appear on in 1994?

15 Who has been with Quo from the beginning along with Rick Parfitt?

16 Which soccer team did Quo help to the top of the charts in 1994?

17 Which Quo song was the football song based on?

18 What was the name of a single and an album in 1986?

19 Who refused to play Status Quo in 1996 saying they were too old?

20 Who wrote the Status Quo autobiography in 1993?

Dance & Disco (see Quiz 74)

Answers

1 *Dirty Dancing*. 2 Tina Charles. 3 1980s. 4 The Pet Shop Boys.
5 Sister Sledge. 6 Baccara. 7 Barry Blue. 8 Disco Tex.
9 George McCrae. 10 Michelle Gayle 11 Kool and the Gang.
12 Coolio Featuring L.V. 13 "(Yowsah Yowsah Yowsah)".
14 Rednex. 15 Outhere Brothers. 16 "I Feel Love". 17 M
People. 18 "Night Fever". 19 "Stayin' Alive". 20 Barry White.

1 Which song begins "Why do birds suddenly appear, ev'ry time you are near"?

2 Who had the No. 1 "Don't Give Up On Us"?

3 What is the logo of the British record label Parlophone?

4 Who had the first instrumental No. 1 hit in 1953?

5 Who resigned as a Radio 1 DJ when he couldn't have Fridays off?

6 In which decade was Roberta Flack born?

7 Who was Dancing on the Ceiling according to his 1986 hit?

8 Who was a "junkie" according to Bowie's "Ashes to Ashes"?

9 On which tube station were the New Vaudeville Band in 1967?

10 Which *Mary Poppins* song won an Oscar in 1964?

11 Which bathroom item was advertised by "Raindrops Keep Falling on My Head" in 1997?

12 Which song has been a hit for Doris Day and Tracey Ullman?

13 Which part of which day features in song titles by Cat Stevens and Barry Blue?

14 What was the Miami Sound Machine's first UK hit?

15 Which country does Eddy Grant originate from?

16 Which London store refused Jason Donovan entry because he was improperly dressed?

17 Who were Frankie Lymon's youthful backing group?

18 In which country was Peter Andre brought up outside the UK?

19 Who is Tom Petty's backing group?

20 Who sang about The Living Years in 1989?

Answers

Pot Luck 40 (see Quiz 79)
1 Lieutenant Pigeon. 2 Johnny Cash. 3 Mary Hopkin. 4 Diana.
5 A Painted Smile. 6 Dave Edmunds. 7 "I'm Still Waiting".
8 *Yellow Submarine*. 9 "Apache". 10 Charlie Drake. 11 1960s.
12 Def Leppard. 13 Cliff Richard. 14 Maria Nayler. 15 3T.
16 Virgin. 17 "Can't Help Falling in Love". 18 Deep Blue
Something. 19 Bangers and Mash. 20 Antonio Banderas.

Quiz 78 Country Style

Answers – see page 188

LEVEL 2

1 Which song begins "Trailer for sale or rent, Rooms to let 50 cents"?

2 What is Johnny Cash's singing daughter called?

3 Which three country stars feature on "Honky Tonk Angels"?

4 Who had a 60s hit with "Harper Valley P.T.A."?

5 What was Garth Brooks's first UK Top Ten album?

6 Who wrote Emmylou Harris's only UK hit, "Here, There and Everywhere"?

7 Whose life was portrayed in the film *Your Cheatin' Heart*?

8 Whose first album hit in the UK was *Good 'N' Country* in 1964?

9 Which country singer wrote a piece for the soundtrack of *Dead Man Walking*?

10 Who recorded the album *Images*?

11 Who is Loretta Lynn's youngest sister?

12 Who did Don Williams Recall in his UK hit?

13 Who wrote "By the Time I Get To Phoenix"?

14 Who sang "Thank God I'm A Country Boy" in the 70s?

15 Whose "The Battle" in 1975 told of the split from his wife Tammy Wynette?

16 Whose "Red River Valley" topped the album charts in 1977?

17 Whose "I'm a Lonesome Fugitive" reflected his life in prison and on the run?

18 Who are referred to as the "first family" of American country music?

19 Which specialist type of singing is Slim Whitman famous for?

20 Which country star recorded an album of ballads called *Time Piece*?

Answers

Stateside (see Quiz 80)

1 "White Christmas". 2 Four. 3 Little Eva. 4 Debby Boone.
5 Mariah Carey. 6 "I Want to Hold Your Hand". 7 "I Will Always Love You" – Whitney Houston. 8 Debbie Gibson.
9 Tiffany. 10 Boston. 11 "Hound Dog". 12 America.
13 Johnny Mathis. 14 1980s. 15 Billy Preston. 16 Ella Fitzgerald. 17 Bacharach and David. 18 Texas. 19 Tennessee.
20 Elvis Presley.

Quiz 79 Pot Luck 40

Answers – see page 185

LEVEL 2

1 Who had a hit with "Mouldy Old Dough"?

2 Which country star is backed by the "Tennessee Two"?

3 Which Welsh singer stipulated that two songs per album be recorded in Welsh?

4 Who does Paul Anka ask "Oh, please, stay with me"?

5 What were the Isley Brothers behind in the title of a hit from 1969?

6 Who had a 1970 hit with a cover version of "I Hear You Knocking"?

7 What was the first UK No. 1 hit for Diana Ross as a solo artist?

8 Which Beatles LP includes "Only A Northern Song" and "Hey Bulldog"?

9 Which single gave the Shadows their first hit without Cliff Richard?

10 Which comedian had a hit with "Splish Splash" in 1958?

11 In which decade was M.C. Hammer born?

12 Who sang "Let's Get Rocked" in 1992?

13 Whose *Private Collection* album consisted of hits from 1977–1988?

14 Who featured with Robert Miles on the 1996 hit "One and One"?

15 Whose 1996 debut single was "Anything"?

16 Which record label do the Spice Girls record on?

17 Which song begins "Wise men say only fools rush in"?

18 Who had Breakfast at Tiffany's in 1996?

19 Which food was a 60s hit for Peter Sellers and Sophia Loren?

20 Who plays Che in the film *Evita*?

Pot Luck 39 (see Quiz 77)

Answers

1 "Close to You". 2 David Soul. 3 A pound sterling.
4 Mantovani. 5 Chris Evans. 6 1930s. 7 Lionel Richie.
8 Major Tom. 9 Finchley Central. 10 "Chim Chim Cheree".
11 Carex Body Wash. 12 "Move Over Darling". 13 Saturday
night. 14 "Dr Beat". 15 Guyana. 16 Harrods. 17 The
Teenagers. 18 Australia. 19 The Heartbreakers. 20 Mike and
the Mechanics.

Quiz 80 Stateside

Answers – see page 186

LEVEL 2

1 Which song has been a bestseller in the US every year since 1942?

2 How many members of Boyz II Men are there?

3 Who was only 17 when she had a US hit with "The Locomotion"?

4 Who had the 70s US best seller "You Light Up My Life"?

5 Who sang with Boyz II Men on "One Sweet Day"?

6 What is the Beatles' best-selling single in the US?

7 Which song was the first to top 4 million US sales in the 1990s?

8 Which American starred as Sandy in *Grease* in London in the 90s?

9 Whose debut single was "I Think We're Alone Now"?

10 Which US group are named after a US town and had a debut album of the same name in 1977 and another in 1981?

11 What is on the other side of Elvis's "Don't Be Cruel"?

12 Who recorded "A Horse With No Name"?

13 Who had a 50s album called *Heavenly*?

14 In which decade did Garth Brooks first top the US country charts?

15 Which American joined the Beatles on "Get Back"?

16 Which US jazz singer recorded "Can't Buy Me Love" as a single?

17 Which Americans wrote "Walk On By", a 90s hit for Gabrielle?

18 In which US state was The Best Little Whorehouse in the musical film?

19 What was Ernie Ford's nickname?

20 Who has had most chart albums in the US?

Answers

Country Style (see Quiz 78)

1 "King of the Road". 2 Roseanne. 3 Dolly Parton, Loretta Lynn, Tammy Wynette. 4 Jeannie C. Riley. 5 *In Pieces*. 6 Lennon and McCartney. 7 Hank Williams. 8 Jim Reeves. 9 Johnny Cash. 10 Don Williams. 11 Crystal Gayle. 12 A Gypsy Woman. 13 Jimmy Webb. 14 John Denver. 15 George Jones. 16 Slim Whitman. 17 Merle Haggard. 18 The Carter Family. 19 Yodelling. 20 Kenny Rogers.

1 Which playing card gave Lonnie Donegan a hit in 1957?

2 Who was born Wynette Pugh in 1942?

3 Which religious ballad was a No. 1 for Elvis in 1965?

4 Who was doing A Whole Lotta Shakin in 1957?

5 What album did "Candle In The Wind" come from?

6 Whose only UK No. 1 was "She"?

7 What is Herb Alpert's home country?

8 What type of soldier was a hit for the Small Faces?

9 In which decade was Marvin Gaye born?

10 Who else is mentioned by name in "Eleanor Rigby"?

11 On which ill-fated flight was the Everly Brothers' Ebony Eyes?

12 Which husband-and-wife team wrote "Don't Sleep in the Subway"?

13 What was the name of the biopic about Tina Turner?

14 Whose first No. 1 was "Go Now" in 1964?

15 Which comedy group invited us to Always Look on the Bright Side of Life in 1991?

16 Which 1989 film was the Oscar-winning "Under the Sea" from?

17 Whose recording names have included Bonnie Jo Mason and Cherilyn?

18 Which veteran released the album *Strong Love Affair* in 1996?

19 Which half of a duo celebrated his 60th birthday on February 1, 1997?

20 What was the name of the film in which Elvis Presley appeared as himself?

Pot Luck 42 (see Quiz 83)
Answers

1 *The Young Ones.* 2 Doris Day. 3 King. 4 Gary Puckett.
5 "Don't You Want Me?". 6 1960s. 7 Scarlet. 8 "The Way We Were". 9 White. 10 Carol. 11 "With a Little Help From My Friends". 12 Slim Whitman. 13 Righteous Brothers. 14 "Romeo and Juliet". 15 English. 16 Jim Reeves. 17 Rover. 18 *The Third Man.* 19 Muddy Waters. 20 Ragtime.

Quiz 82 Michael Jackson

Answers – see page 192

1 What is the name of Jackson's second wife?

2 Which part in *The Wiz* was Jackson chosen to play in 1977?

3 What was his first solo No. 1?

4 Which record label did he move to with his brothers after leaving Motown?

5 What was the first hit he had with Paul McCartney?

6 Who is credited with Jackson on the sleeve of "I Can't Stop Loving You" but not on the label?

7 What type of creature is his pet Muscles?

8 "Happy" was the love theme from which film?

9 Which horror film actor raps on the album *Thriller*?

10 Which particular item of clothing did the Michael Jackson doll have?

11 What is the name of Jackson's pet chimpanzee?

12 What was his autobiography called?

13 What was Jackson's next No. 1 album after *Bad*?

14 Which film were "Scream" and "Childhood" from?

15 Who duetted with Michael on "Scream"?

16 What were Lisa Marie Presley's grounds for divorce from Jackson?

17 Which other male vocalist appears on the *...Very Best Back to Back* album?

18 Who else is on the 1983 Greatest Hits album?

19 What was his 1995 No. 1 album called?

20 What is the youngest Jackson brother called?

Quiz 83 Pot Luck 42

Answers – see page 189

LEVEL 2

1   Which film gave Cliff Richard his first lead role and fifth British No. 1?

2   Who had a No. 1 in 1954 with "Secret Love"?

3   What was "your love" according to Sade?

4   Who was the lead singer with the Union Gap on "Young Girl"?

5   What Human League hit was the only single to sell over a million in the UK in 1981?

6   In which decade was k.d. lang born?

7   What colour ribbons was Harry Belafonte singing about in 1957?

8   Which Barbra Streisand hit starts "Memories light the corners of my mind"?

9   What colour suit is Michael Jackson wearing on the cover of the *Thriller* album?

10   Who treated Neil Sedaka "cruel" in his No. 3 hit from 1959?

11   Which song begins "What would you do if I sang out of tune"?

12   Who had a No. 1 hit with "Rose Marie"?

13   Whose combined age was over 100 when they had a hit with "Unchained Melody"?

14   Which Dire Straits hit is the title of a Shakespeare play?

15   In which language did Charles Aznavour sing his only UK No. 1?

16   Who had a hit with "Distant Drums"?

17   Which make of car does Sting's "Englishman in New York" advertise?

18   Which film did "The Harry Lime Theme" come from?

19   Whose "Mannish Boy" was used in a jeans ad?

20   What type of music was Scott Joplin famous for?

Answers

Pot Luck 41 (see Quiz 81)
1 The Jack of Diamonds. 2 Tammy Wynette. 3 "Crying In The Chapel". 4 Jerry Lee Lewis. 5 *Goodbye Yellow Brick Road.*
6 Charles Aznavour. 7 USA. 8 Tin Soldier. 9 1930s.
10 Father Mackenzie. 11 12.03. 12 Jackie Trent and Tony Hatch.
13 *What's Love Got to Do With It?* 14 The Moody Blues.
15 Monty Python. 16 *The Little Mermaid.* 17 Cher. 18 Ray Charles. 19 Don Everly. 20 *This is Elvis.*

Quiz 84 Folk Roots

Answers – see page 190

1   Who felt we were on the "Eve of Destruction" in 1965?

2   Which Joan Baez hit became a civil rights anthem?

3   Maddy Prior has been linked with which band since the 70s?

4   In which language did Fairport Convention sing their first UK hit?

5   How are Yarrow, Stookey and Travers better known?

6   Who wrote "Leaving on a Jet Plane"?

7   In which decade was Pete Seeger born?

8   What was Joan Baez's first UK Top Ten hit?

9   Which song with words from the Old Testament was a 60s hit for the Byrds?

10   Who wrote the 1965 No. 1 for the Byrds, "Mr Tambourine Man"?

11   Who wrote "Streets of London"?

12   Whose first hit was "Meet Me on the Corner" in 1972?

13   Which Rainy Day Women were a hit for Bob Dylan in 1966?

14   Which musical instrument did Martin Carthy play?

15   Who had a UK Top Ten hit with "Both Sides Now"?

16   What is the nationality of Leonard Cohen?

17   Who wrote "The Last Thing On My Mind"?

18   What was Simon and Garfunkel's first UK Top Ten hit?

19   Which folk singer's songs feature on the Joan Baez album *Any Day Now*?

20   Which five-piece group recorded "Light Flight"?

Quiz 85 Pot Luck 43

Answers – see page 195

1   What was George Michael's first solo album?

2   Who won the British Rock and Pop Best Female Singer award in 1978 and 1979?

3   Which word links a Sinatra hit and an instrumental by Acker Bilk?

4   Who is on the cover of the *Guilty* album with Barbra Streisand?

5   What was Tommy Steele's first No. 1?

6   Who was Twistin' the Night Away in 1962?

7   What Connie Francis hit says: "Yours was red, mine was baby pink"?

8   What group's first No. 1 was "True"?

9   What is a beguine in the classic "Begin the Beguine"?

10 How many tears did the Goombay Dance Band sing about in 1982?

11 Who was the only American to have a UK No. 1 in 1963?

12 Who had a 70s No. 1 with "The Streak"?

13 Who had the original hit with "Matthew and Son"?

14 Which song begins "Desmond has a barrow in the market place"?

15 Who had a 1996 album called *A Different Beat*?

16 Which fictional doctor did Andy Stewart sing about?

17 What did Stephen Stills suggest doing if you "couldn't be with the one you love"?

18 Whose first hit was "Second Hand Rose"?

19 Who had a 1996 album called *Take Two*?

20 Which Simon and Garfunkel song was a 1996 hit for Suggs?

Answers

Quiz 86 David Bowie

Answers – see page 196

LEVEL 2

1 In which part of London was David Bowie born?

2 What was the name of his first No. 1 album?

3 Which novelty disc did he make imitating Anthony Newley?

4 Which new record label turned down Bowie in 1968?

5 In which important space year was "Space Oddity" first released?

6 Who was his first wife?

7 Which Bowie song was a hit for Lulu?

8 Which stage persona did Bowie introduce in 1972?

9 Why did Bowie leave on the *QE2* for the US in 1973?

10 Which Lou Reed hit was co-produced by David Bowie?

11 Which model appears on the album cover of *Pin-Ups*?

12 What was his son Joe originally called?

13 In which film did he play the title role in 1975?

14 Which role did he play on Broadway in 1980?

15 Which film did he make with Tom Conti?

16 Which song did he record for the Band Aid Trust?

17 In which film did he play the Goblin King?

18 Which record label did he sign to in 1995?

19 Which model did he marry in 1992?

20 Which music industry charity did he become patron of in 1994?

Answers

Tom Jones (see Quiz 88)
1 1940s. 2 16. 3 *Along Came Jones*. 4 "Thunderball".
5 Detroit. 6 Art of Noise. 7 The Talk of the Town. 8 Investiture of the Prince of Wales. 9 "Green Green Grass of Home".
10 *Delilah*. 11 Las Vegas. 12 "I (Who Have Nothing)".
13 Dave Stewart. 14 The Chippendales. 15 Pony tail. 16 El Cordobes. 17 "Move Closer". 18 "The Boy From Nowhere".
19 *Under Milk Wood*. 20 13.

Quiz 87 Pot Luck 44

Answers – see page 193

LEVEL 2

1   What is step three in "Three Steps to Heaven"?

2   Who have all the luck according to a Rod Stewart 1984 hit?

3   Who was backed by the Raelettes?

4   Which Boomtown Rats song goes "Walk, don't walk, talk, don't talk"?

5   Who is on the inside cover of the Who's *Quadrophenia* album?

6   In which decade was Des O'Connor born?

7   Which 70s band had an album called *Crepes and Drapes*?

8   Whose first chart hit was "Mandinka"?

9   What was Joe Cocker's first No.1?

10 Who did Buddy Holly love with a heart so rare and true?

11 Who was the only American soloist to have a UK No. 1 in 1964?

12 Who in 1968 were the second married couple to have a No. 1 hit?

13 Who were Dion's backing group?

14 Who were Young At Heart in 1993?

15 In which decade was Jose Feliciano born?

16 Which Brothers were Ronald, Rudolph and O'Kelly?

17 Which country is the orchestra leader Bert Kaempfert from?

18 Which "Fantasy League" stars featured on "Three Lions"?

19 Who was behind Sakkarin with the 70s hit "Sugar Sugar"?

20 Who represented the UK in the Eurovision Song Contest in 1996?

Answers

Pot Luck 43 (see Quiz 85)
1 *Faith*. 2 Kate Bush. 3 Strangers. 4 Barry Gibb. 5 "Singing The Blues". 6 Sam Cooke. 7 "Lipstick On Your Collar". 8 Spandau Ballet. 9 A dance. 10 Seven. 11 Elvis Presley. 12 Ray Stevens. 13 Cat Stevens. 14 "Ob-La-Di, Ob-La-Da". 15 Boyzone. 16 Dr Finlay. 17 "Love the One You're With". 18 Barbra Streisand. 19 Robson and Jerome. 20 "Cecilia".

195

Quiz 88 Tom Jones

Answers – see page 194

1 In which decade was Tom Jones born?

2 How old was he when he first married?

3 What was his first album called?

4 Which song did he sing for a James Bond film?

5 Which city was the subject of a 1967 hit?

6 Who also features on his 1988 hit "Kiss"?

7 At which venue was he on a Live 1967 album?

8 Which Royal event was he invited to sing at in 1969?

9 What was his second chart-topper?

10 What was his first No. 1 album?

11 He produced a live album from which US city in 1969?

12 Which 70s hit had previously been recorded by Ben E. King and Shirley Bassey?

13 Who did he record "All You Need is Love" with in aid of Childline?

14 According to an American critic, Tom Jones made which act possible?

15 In which style did he wear his hair in the early days?

16 Who was the projected musical *Matador* about?

17 Which Phyllis Nelson hit did he record in the 80s?

18 Which hit single came from *Matador*?

19 Which George Martin-produced recording did he feature on with other Welsh performers?

20 How many Smash Hits were on his 1967 album?

1 What were the Moody Blues "in search of" in 1968?

2 Who produced the 1984 Lionel Richie hit "Hello"?

3 What was the Who's first Top 10 LP in the USA?

4 What group suggested "a great big melting pot"?

5 Who was the first on-stage Evita?

6 What does "everybody" have according to Bruce Springsteen?

7 What is on the front cover of the *Out Of The Blue* album by ELO?

8 Which movie had "Up Where We Belong" as its theme?

9 Whose face is on the cover of the *No Jacket Required* album?

10 There "ain't no way to hide" what according to the Eagles?

11 Who had an album called *Love Over Gold*?

12 Who was a Professional Widow in 1997?

13 Sheila Ferguson was vocalist with which group?

14 What was Fiddler's Dram's destination in 1979?

15 Who had a 1983 No. 1 with "Only You"?

16 Which number *Now That's What I Call Music!* topped the compilation charts at the beginning of 1997?

17 Which manager promoted the Four Tops on their early 60s visits to the UK?

18 What is Boris Gardiner's home country?

19 What was Art Garfunkel's first solo No. 1?

20 In which decade was Natalie Cole born?

Quiz 90 And I Quote

Answers – see page 200

1 Who was described as, "the tacky tattooed terror of the 20th century"?

2 Who said, "I would not want to be Bach, Mozart, Tolstoy ... or James Dean."?

3 Who said, "I can't picture Jesus doing a whole lotta shakin'"?

4 What did John Lennon tell people in expensive seats to do at a Royal Show?

5 Who said, "Hair today gone tomorrow" when he joined the army?

6 Who said, "I really wanted to be a soccer star."?

7 How did Elton John finish "I haven't met anyone I'd like to settle down with…"?

8 Who said, "I never had any problems with drugs, only with policemen"?

9 Who said, "If we hadn't been related we would probably never have gotten back together"?

10 Who said on announcing his second retirement, "I've rocked my roll."?

11 Who said about her early career, "I must have been a revolting little cow"?

12 Which rock star said, "People like their blues singers dead"?

13 Who dedicated his first solo record to his parents: "5 minutes … for 21 years"?

14 On whose death was the statement made, "As soon as we are able, we would like to celebrate his life in the style to which he was accustomed"?

15 Which band was Mick Taylor referring to when he said he left them because he wanted to be a rock-and-roll star?

16 Who said he let Frank Sinatra have "My Way" because he didn't want to find a horse's head in his bed?

17 Who said, "Marriage is a wonderful invention but so is the bicycle repair kit"?

18 Who was Marvin Gaye referring to when he said, "If he refuses to release me then you'll never hear any more music from Marvin Gaye"?

19 Which female singer said in a song, "Mother stands for comfort"?

20 Who said, "It costs a lot to make me look so cheap"?

Answers

Queen (see Quiz 92)
1 "Seven Seas of Rhye". 2 John Deacon. 3 *Queen 2*. 4 "Fat Bottomed Girl". 5 EMI. 6 *Sheer Heart Attack*. 7 Six minutes. 8 *A Night at the Opera*. 9 Roger Taylor. 10 "A Whiter Shade of Pale". 11 Lonnie Donegan. 12 *Flash Gordon*. 13 South America. 14 Shell. 15 ANC. 16 "We Are the Champions". 17 *Mr Bad Guy*. 18 "The Great Pretender". 19 "These Are the Days of Our Lives". 20 *Made in Heaven*.

Quiz 91 Pot Luck 46

Answers – see page 197

LEVEL 2

1 What word begins song titles that end with "Daddy," "Shack" and "Sugar" ?

2 Which city does the song "Three Coins in a Fountain" refer to?

3 Which Merseyside group got to No. 1 one month before the Beatles in 1963?

4 Who had a No. 1 hit with "Back Home" in 1970?

5 Which pop programme first appeared on screen in November 1982?

6 Which drink did Bob Geldof advertise in 1987?

7 Where, according to Ben E. King, is there a rose?

8 What word begins song titles that end "That a Shame" and "No Sunshine"?

9 On which record label did Cat Stevens record all but one of his LPs?

10 Which pianist had a fifties chart success with "Party Pops"?

11 How many bottles do the Police find "washed up" on the shore?

12 What girl is "always window-shopping but never stopping to buy"?

13 What was Tina Turner's autobiography called?

14 Which song has been a hit for George Michael and Bobbie Williams?

15 Who was the oldest Beatle?

16 In which decade was Noel Gallagher born?

17 Who had a live album *Under A Blood Red Sky*?

18 Which country does Enigma come from?

19 How is Leslie Sebastian Charles better known?

20 Which band did Frank Zappa establish in 1966?

Pot Luck 45 (see Quiz 89)

1 The Lost Chord. 2 Lionel Richie. 3 *Tommy*. 4 Blue Mink.
5 Elaine Paige. 6 A Hungry Heart. 7 A flying saucer. 8 *An Officer and A Gentleman*. 9 Phil Collins. 10 Your lyin' eyes.
11 Dire Straits. 12 Tori Amos. 13 Three Degrees. 14 Bangor.
15 The Flying Pickets. 16 35. 17 Brian Epstein. 18 Jamaica.
19 "I Only Have Eyes For You". 20 1950s.

1 What was Queen's first hit single?

2 Who was the band's bass player?

3 What was the band's first hit album?

4 What was on the other side of "Bicycle Race" in 1978?

5 On which record label did they make their early recordings?

6 Which album was "Killer Queen" on originally?

7 "Bohemian Rhapsody" lasts just under how many minutes?

8 Which album followed *Sheer Heart Attack*?

9 Who was the first member of the group to release a solo disc?

10 Which record tied with "Bohemian Rhapsody" as best-selling single of the period of the Queen's reign, 1952–77, honouring her Silver Jubilee?

11 Freddie Mercury contributed to whose album *Puttin' On the Style*?

12 Which film soundtrack did they record in 1980?

13 Which continent did they visit on their Gluttons For Punishment tour?

14 Who used their "I Want to Break Free" for TV commercials?

15 Which South African political group also used "I Want to Break Free"?

16 What was on the other side of "We Will Rock You"?

17 What was Freddie Mercury's first solo album called?

18 Which song did he take to No 5 in March 1987?

19 What was on the other side of "Bohemian Rhapsody" after its rerelease following Freddie Mercury's death?

20 Which album topped the charts in its first week in 1995?

1 What was "all over the world" according to the Carpenters in 1976?

2 Who had a hit in 1984 with "You Take Me Up"?

3 Which rock-and-roll classic opens with: "Get out in that kitchen and rattle those pots and pans"?

4 Who had a No 5 with "Sugar Me" in 1972?

5 In which film did the Platters perform "Only You" and "The Great Pretender"?

6 Which Chicago hit gave them a Grammy award in 1976?

7 What group consisted of Godley, Creme, Stewart and Gouldman?

8 Which two Williamses had No. 1 hits with "Moon River"?

9 Which song by Barry Manilow starts: "I've been alive forever"?

10 Where were the lights brighter for Petula Clark?

11 Whose autobiography was called *Is That It?*?

12 Who were All Right Now in the 70s and again in the 90s?

13 How was the 50s/60s star Ronald Wycherly better known?

14 Which film featured the music "Lara's Theme" which was used in the song "Somewhere My Love"?

15 What was Telly Savalas's only UK No. 1?

16 Whose first album was called *City to City*?

17 Who asked, "Ullo John, Got a New Motor?" in 1984?

18 What was Seal's first UK hit?

19 Whose first No. 1 was "Ebeneezer Goode"?

20 What was on the other side of the Sex Pistols's "No One is Innocent"?

Quiz 94 60s Revisited

Answers – see page 204

LEVEL 2

1 Who had a 1969 hit with "Frozen Orange Juice"?

2 What was Procul Harum's follow-up to "A Whiter Shade of Pale"?

3 Which solo singer had the best-selling single of 1966?

4 Which Georgie Fame hit was the first No. 1 of 1968?

5 Which group was Paul McCartney's brother in?

6 Which tearjerker was on the other side of "Walk Right Back"?

7 In "A Whiter Shade of Pale" who were leaving for the coast?

8 What was the longest No. 1 single of the 60s?

9 Which song includes the lines "I could be handy mending a fuse, When your lights have gone"?

10 Which two cities are mentioned in "Trains and Boats and Planes"?

11 In which TV show did Mary Hopkin find fame?

12 Who had 1969's best seller "Sugar Sugar"?

13 Who are the two main characters in "Ob-La-Di, Ob-La-Da"?

14 How was "Je ne regrette rien" known in English?

15 What comes after "I've lived a life that's full" in "My Way"?

16 Who did Steve Winwood have a No. 1 with in 1966?

17 Who had a No. 1 "With A Girl Like You"?

18 Which song did the Hollies take to the top twice in 1965?

19 What was on the other side of Cliff Richard's "The Next Time"?

20 Who wrote Petula Clark's "This is My Song"?

Answers

70s Revisited (see Quiz 96)
1 Simon and Garfunkel. 2 Norman Greenbaum. 3 *Paint Your Wagon*. 4 Mungo Jerry. 5 "The Wonder of You". 6 George Harrison. 7 *Don't Shoot Me I'm Only the Piano Player*. 8 Edison Lighthouse. 9 "I Love You Love Me Love". 10 Joni Mitchell. 11 Clive Dunn – Jones in "Dad's Army". 12 Perry Como. 13 Tony Orlando. 14 Middle of the Road. 15 *Breakfast in America*. 16 "I'd Like To Buy the World a Coke". 17 Peters and Lee. 18 The Carpenters. 19 Nottingham. 20 "The Streak".

1   Which word starts song titles which end in "Surrender" and "Music"?

2   Who made his stage debut in 1980 as the Elephant Man?

3   Which sixties TV pop show was co-hosted by the boxer Freddie Mills?

4   What sleeps tonight according to the Tokens and Tight Fit?

5   Who was the lead singer for the Bay City Rollers?

6   Who was a Woman In Love according to her 1980 No. 1 hit?

7   What was the title of Chicago's 13th album?

8   Who took "Donna" to No. 3 in 1959?

9   Which Beatles song goes "sont les mots qui vont très bien ensemble"?

10   Who wrote "It Doesn't Matter Anymore"?

11   Stevie Nicks and Christine McVie were in which band in the 70s?

12   Who won the Grammy award for Best Soul Singer from 1967 to 1974?

13   Who had a 90s album called *Bilingual*?

14   How is John Beverly better known?

15   In which decade was the ex-Shadow Jet Harris born?

16   Which actress has been married to recording stars Don Johnson and Antonio Banderas?

17   Who sang about the Jean Genie in 1972?

18   How many *letters* are there in the title of Kirsty MacColl's first Top Twenty hit?

19   Which soundtrack was the top-selling album of 1965, '66 and '68?

20   Who sang "I Could Be So Good For You" from "Minder"?

Quiz 96 70s Revisited

Answers – see page 202

LEVEL 2

1 Which duo's album was the bestseller of 1970 and 1971?

2 Who had a 1970 No. 1 with "Spirit in the Sky"?

3 Which musical did Lee Marvin's "Wandrin' Star" come from?

4 Whose lead singer was Ray Dorset?

5 What was Elvis's first 70s No. 1?

6 Which Beatle had the bestselling single of 1971?

7 What was Elton John's top-selling album of 1973?

8 Who had a hit with "Love Grows (Where My Rosemary Goes)"?

9 What was Gary Glitter's bestseller of 1973?

10 Who wrote *Woodstock* though she only watched the festival on TV?

11 Which chart-topper's catchphrase was "They don't like it up 'em"?

12 Whose album *And I Love You So* was a 1973 best seller?

13 Who was born Michael Anthony Orlando Cassavitis?

14 Who had a No. 1 with "Chirpy Chirpy Cheep Cheep"?

15 What was Supertramp's best-selling 70s LP?

16 What was "I'd Like To Teach the World To Sing" originally called?

17 Who were Lennie and Di?

18 Who had a compilation LP of their singles from 1969–1973?

19 Which city was home to Paper Lace and gave them their name?

20 Which song had the line "Don't look, Ethel"?

60s Revisited (see Quiz 94)

Answers

1 Peter Sarstedt. 2 "Homburg". 3 Tom Jones – "Green Green Grass of Home". 4 "Ballad of Bonnie and Clyde". 5 Scaffold. 6 "Ebony Eyes". 7 16 vestal virgins. 8 "Hey Jude". 9 "When I'm Sixty Four". 10 Paris, Rome. 11 "Opportunity Knocks". 12 The Archies. 13 Desmond and Molly Jones. 14 "No Regrets". 15 "I travelled each and every highway". 16 Spencer Davis Group. 17 The Troggs. 18 "I'm Alive". 19 "Bachelor Boy". 20 Charlie Chaplin.

Quiz 97 Pot Luck 49

Answers – see page 206

LEVEL 2

1 What type of vehicle is featured on the album sleeve of Meat Loaf's *Bat Out Of Hell*?

2 Which African River gave a hit title to Lou Busch and Eddie Calvert?

3 Who once performed as Artie Garr?

4 EMI used the record-number prefix "Marc" from 1972–77 for which group's releases?

5 Who accompanied Bing Crosby with a 1956 Top Ten hit "True Love"?

6 What did Lily the Pink invent?

7 Whose first hit which reached No. 1 in 1974 was "Sugar Baby Love"?

8 What is the main colour of the *Brothers In Arms* album cover?

9 Which group got to the top of the charts with "Start"?

10 Who was married in silk taffeta before 3,000 Mormons in June 1982?

11 Which major 60s event was held at the farm of Max Yasgur?

12 Which Pilot hit reached No. 1 on February 1, 1975?

13 Which chart-topper's catchphrase was "Who loves ya, baby?"?

14 How many marriages had Tammy Wynette had when she advised "Stand By Your Man"?

15 Who were the first male/female vocal duo to have two No. 1 hits?

16 "My Sweet Lord" was accused of being like which Chiffons hit?

17 Which Jackie Wilson hit topped the charts two years after his death?

18 Which band was named after a song by Bernard Cribbins?

19 What did Free's "All Right Now" advertise in 1991?

20 Which Rolling Stones hit has the longest title?

Answers

Pot Luck 50 (see Quiz 99)
1 The Equals. **2** "Singing the Blues". **3** Seventh Heaven. **4** Lucille. **5** Manfred Mann. **6** The Kinks. **7** The Police. **8** Keith, Greg, Carl. **9** "Back In The USSR". **10** "Get Back". **11** Oleta Adams. **12** 1940s. **13** The Beach Boys. **14** 32. **15** Michael Caine. **16** The Overlanders. **17** Supremes, Bananarama. **18** Paul McCartney. **19** "You've Got A Friend". **20** Two Pints of Lager and a Packet of Crisps Please.

Quiz 98 80s Revisited

Answers – see page 207

LEVEL 2

1 Who had the album *Eat to the Beat*?

2 Who sang "Together We Are Beautiful"?

3 Who was the Police's drummer?

4 What was the No. 1 sung by St Winifred's School Choir?

5 What was Roxy Music's first No. 1?

6 How many members of Bucks Fizz were there?

7 Which 80s No. 1 was recorded in Spanish?

8 Who wrote and produced "Under Pressure"?

9 Which Motown trio wrote Phil Collins chart topper "You Can't Hurry Love"?

10 How many members of Kajagoogoo were there?

11 Whose second album was *Cargo*?

12 What was David Bowie's first No. 1 not to mention Major Tom?

13 Which band included the Kemp brothers?

14 Who sang "I Want to Know What Love Is" in 1985?

15 Who duetted with Philip Bailey on "Easy Lover"?

16 Which single referred to the average age of US soldiers in the Vietnam War?

17 Who were Pal, Mags and Morgen?

18 Which part did Nick Berry play in "EastEnders"?

19 What was Madonna's third No. 1?

20 What was the nationality of Aneka who had a hit with "Japanese Boy"?

Answers

Pot Luck 49 (see Quiz 97)

1 A motorcycle. 2 The Zambesi. 3 Art Garfunkel. 4 T. Rex's. 5 Grace Kelly. 6 Medicinal Compound. 7 The Rubettes. 8 Blue. 9 The Jam. 10 Marie Osmond. 11 Woodstock. 12 "January". 13 Telly Savalas. 14 Five. 15 John Travolta, Olivia Newton-John. 16 "He's So Fine". 17 "Reet Petite". 18 Right Said Fred. 19 Chewing gum. 20 "Have You Seen Your Mother Baby Standing in the Shadow?".

1 Which group were asking "Baby Come Back" in 1968?

2 Which song was a No. 1 for both Tommy Steele and Guy Mitchell in 1956?

3 Where does Bill Haley want to be "when the chimes ring five and six and seven"?

4 Which girl's name gave Kenny Rogers a Grammy Award in 1977?

5 Who started Manfred Mann's Earth Band in 1971?

6 Who, in 1965, got Tired Of Waiting For You?

7 Who released an album entitled *Outlandos d'Amour*?

8 What were the first names of Emerson, Lake and Palmer?

9 Which Beatles record begins and ends with the sound of a jet?

10 Which song includes the lines "Sweet Loretta Martin thought she was a woman, but she was another man"?

11 Who had the album *Circle of One*?

12 In which decade was Bryan Ferry born?

13 Who had a 60s hit with "God Only Knows"?

14 How old was Karen Carpenter when she died?

15 Which film star was the title of a single by Madness?

16 Who had a 60s hit single with "Michelle"?

17 Which two groups had hits with "Nathan Jones"?

18 Who was on Junior's Farm in 1974?

19 Which song title links James Taylor, and Big Fun and Sonia?

20 What did Splodgenessabounds ask for in 1980?

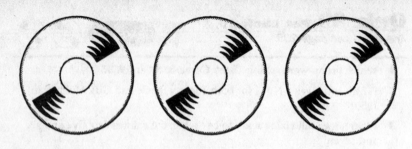

The Hard Questions

If you thought that this section of this book would prove to be little or no problem, or that the majority of the questions could be answered and a scant few would test you then you are sorely mistaken. These questions are the *hardest* questions *ever*! So difficult are they that any attempt to answer them all in one sitting will addle your mind and mess with your senses. You'll end up leaving the pub via the window while ordering a pint from the horse brasses on the wall. Don't do it! For a kick off there are 2,000 of them, so at 20 seconds a question it will take you over 10 hours – and that's just the time it takes to read them. What you should do instead is set them for others – addle your friends' minds.

Note the dangerous nature of these questions though. These are you secret weapons use them accordingly unless, of course, someone or some team is getting your back up. In which case you should hit them hard and only let up when you have them cowering under the bench whimpering "Tom Jones".

These questions work best against league teams, they are genuinely tough and should be used against those people who take their pub quizzes seriously. NEVER use these questions against your in-laws.

Quiz 1 Pot Luck 1

Answers – see page 211

1 In the 1990s Sweet's Brian Connolly discovered which TV detective was his natural brother?

2 In which film did Elvis play the role of Clint Reno?

3 Who released an album entitled *The Dream of the Blue Turtles*?

4 What was Russ Conway's second No. 1?

5 Who wrote "World Without Love" for Peter and Gordon?

6 Who was Capital Radio's choice as Best London Artist from 1978–80?

7 Who is the biopic *La Bamba* about?

8 Who played the heavy-metal guitar on Michael Jackson's "Beat It"?

9 Who had a hit in 1981 with "Shaddap you face"?

10 Who wrote the lyric to the theme from Exodus?

11 Who said, "If music be the food of love, let's have a Beethoven butty"?

12 In which town was Marc Almond born?

13 Who backed Graham Parker?

14 What was Glenn Medeiros's debut album called?

15 Why did Donovan spend two weeks in Strangeways Prison in Manchester in the early 60s?

16 In which sport did Billy Joel excel when at school?

17 Which band was once called the Ravens?

18 Which group's name is the German for "power plant"?

19 Who won the Logie Award for Best New Talent in Australia in 1987?

20 Which two bands have President Bill Clinton's middle name in their names?

Pot Luck 2 (see Quiz 3)
1 Bette Midler. 2 *Led Zeppelin II*. 3 *Reckless*. 4 Roy Wood.
5 Yellow. 6 "Get Off Of My Cloud". 7 Dave Berry. 8 The
Police. 9 The Applejacks. 10 "Poison Ivy". 11 Meat Loaf.
12 Melanie. 13 Jan and Dean. 14 Charlotte Rampling.
15 Ottawa. 16 The Detroit Wheels. 17 Paul McCartney.
18 Barclay. 19 Jerome. 20 Japan (David Sylvian and Steve
Jansen are David and Jansen Batt).

Answers

Quiz 2 The 50s

Answers – see page 212

LEVEL 3

1 Where was Emile Ford born?

2 Which chart topper appeared on BBC TV's "Drumbeat"?

3 Who had a 50s No. 1 with "Here Comes Summer"?

4 Who played the piano on Bobby Darin's "Dream Lover"?

5 How was Terence Perkins better known?

6 What was Marty Wilde's highest chart hit?

7 Which female singer starred in "It's Trad Dad"?

8 What was Cliff Richard's middle name when he was Harry Webb?

9 Who was the first solo instrumentalist to have consecutive No. 1 hits?

10 Which female had four Top Ten hits in 1952?

11 Who sang the English version of "Le Jour Où La Pluie Viendra"?

12 Who was the resident band on "Oh Boy"?

13 Who had the 50s hit with "It's All in the Game"?

14 Which brothers replaced which brothers at No. 1 in 1958?

15 Which Cherokee Indian was in the charts in 1958?

16 Which 1950s artist had a TV show "Relax With Mike"?

17 Who was the first British female singer to have a No. 1 in the 50s and what was it called?

18 What was Conway Twitty's real name?

19 How many records made up the charts in 1952 and 1953?

20 Which song was recorded by Al Hibbler, Les Baxter, Liberace and Jimmy Young?

The 60s (see Quiz 4)

Answers

1 Cliff Richard. 2 John F. Kennedy was assassinated. 3 The Searchers. 4 Cream. 5 Nothing. 6 *Catch Us If You Can*. 7 The Bachelors. 8 *Aftermath*. 9 Peter Asher. 10 Blackburn. 11 The Honeycombs. 12 Sandie Shaw. 13 30. 14 The Walker Brothers. 15 Val Doonican. 16 From The Small Faces to Humble Pie. 17 Two – Beatles and Rolling Stones. 18 "Out of Time" – Chris Farlowe. 19 "In the Year 2525". 20 Union Gap.

Quiz 3 Pot Luck 2

Answers – see page 209

1 Who won the 1973 Grammy for Best New Artist?

2 What album contains the tracks "Whole Lotta Love" and "The Lemon Song"?

3 What was Bryan Adams's debut album called?

4 Who wrote "Blackberry Way"?

5 What colour was the MGM label in the sixties?

6 What was the follow-up single to the Rolling Stones' "(I can't get no) Satisfaction"?

7 How is David Grundy better known?

8 Which group released an album titled *Outlandos d'Amour*?

9 Whose only UK Top Ten hit was "Tell me When"?

10 Which song by the Coasters recommends "Calamine Lotion"?

11 Who starred as Ulysses S. Grant in *Hair* in Los Angeles in 1969?

12 Which singer, known only by her first name, has the surname Safka?

13 How were Berry and Torrence better known?

14 Which actress married Jean-Michel Jarre?

15 In which city was Paul Anka born?

16 Who backed Mitch Ryder?

17 Who wrote under the pseudonym of Bernard Webb?

18 Which record label did Charles Aznavour have his hit records on?

19 What was "Doc" Shuman's real first name?

20 Which group included the Batt brothers?

Quiz 4 The 60s
Answers – see page 210

1 Who had a 1961 album called *21 Today*?

2 Which major world event took place when Gerry and the Pacemakers were at No. 1 with "You'll Never Walk Alone"?

3 Which was the most successful Mersey group not managed by Brian Epstein?

4 Whose 1969 album was called *Goodbye*?

5 What did the J. stand for in Billy J. Kramer's name?

6 Which film did the Dave Clark Five make?

7 Who were originally called the Harmonichords?

8 Which Stones album was No. 1 in the album charts in 1966?

9 Which 60s chart topper went on to manage James Taylor and Linda Ronstadt?

10 Which town did the Four Pennies come from?

11 What was the drummer Ann Lantree's group?

12 Who was originally offered "It's Not Unusual" before Tom Jones?

13 How old was Sonny when he had his first No. 1 record with Cher?

14 Who were Messrs Engel, Maus and Leeds?

15 Who had a 1968 album, ...*Rocks But Gently*?

16 Which group did Steve Marriott leave to form which band in 1969?

17 How many different bands had a No. 1 album in 1964?

18 Which single topped the charts when England won the World Cup?

19 Which song was subtitled "Exordium and Terminus"?

20 Which group sold more singles than the Beatles in the US in 1968?

The 50s (see Quiz 2)

Answers

1 The Bahamas. 2 Adam Faith. 3 Jerry Keller. 4 Neil Sedaka.
5 Craig Douglas. 6 "Teenager in Love". 7 Helen Shapiro.
8 Roger. 9 Russ Conway. 10 Vera Lynn. 11 Jane Morgan.
12 Lord Rockingham's XI. 13 Tommy Edwards. 14 The Kalin Twins replaced the Everly Brothers. 15 Marvin Rainwater.
16 Michael Holliday. 17 Lita Roza, "How Much Is That Doggy in the Window?". 18 Harold Jenkins. 19 12. 20 "Unchained Melody".

Quiz 5 Pot Luck 3

Answers – see page 215

LEVEL 3

1 Who is Bob Dylan arm in arm with on the cover of *The Freewheelin' Bob Dylan*?

2 Who backed Gary Lewis?

3 At whose party did Rod Stewart meet Britt Ekland?

4 On what single and album did Marc Almond join Bronski Beat?

5 Which music paper published Britain's first-ever record chart?

6 What was Tori Amos's debut album called?

7 What was Matt Monro's first UK hit?

8 Which guitarist formed a group called the Band of Gypsies?

9 Who did Sid Vicious replace in the Sex Pistols in 1977?

10 Which group included Derek Leckenby and Keith Hopwood?

11 In which town was Rick Astley born?

12 How are the Bramlett family duo better known?

13 Which song won the first Grammy Record of the Year in 1958?

14 Which TV show did Al Jarreau's "Since I Fell For You" feature in?

15 Which musical instrument did Jethro Tull's Ian Anderson play?

16 Who complete Grandmaster Flash's group?

17 Which two artist's have recorded albums called *Tapestry*?

18 Who left home to hitch-hike through Canada with her dog Sparkle?

19 Where did John Lennon marry Yoko Ono?

20 Which group previously called themselves History of Headaches?

Answers

Pot Luck 4 (see Quiz 7)
1 *Innervisions.* 2 The Tremeloes. 3 The Spectres. 4 Denny Laine. 5 Bruce Springsteen. 6 T. Rex. 7 *Not Satisfied.* 8 Cyndi Lauper. 9 Mike Oldfield. 10 *Absolute Beginners.* 11 Iraq. 12 Ella Fitzgerald. 13 The Temptations. 14 Phil Lynott. 15 Jim Capaldi. 16 JFK Stadium, Philadelphia. 17 The Juniors. 18 *Loving You.* 19 Cher. 20 The Turtles.

1　Which duo had the first reggae No. 1 in 1971?

2　Which ex-Hoochie Coochie Men vocalist went on to have great success in the 70s and beyond?

3　Which 1972 single was the first major hit to feature a synthesizer?

4　Which singer/songwriter was "Killing Me Softly" written about?

5　Which song was about babysitting for the singer's manager?

6　Which hit featured Rob and Hilda Woodward?

7　Which 70s group leader died on February 10, 1997?

8　What was the first No. 1 for Jonathan King's UK record label?

9　Who accompanied Nottingham Forest FC on "We've Got the Whole World in Our Hands" in 1978?

10　Which group was famous for its white berets in 1974?

11　Who was the "Queen of the Blues" in the 1971 hit by Ray Stevens?

12　Who was mentioned in a 1974 song title but not in the song itself?

13　Which part did David Essex play in *That'll Be The Day*?

14　Which was the third of Mud's three 70s No. 1s?

15　Which group were Jeffrey Calvert, Max West plus session musicians?

16　Whose version of "No Charge" was called "No Chance"?

17　Who was the heaviest individual chart topper in the 70s?

18　What was Elton John's first release on Rocket?

19　What nationality were Pussycat?

20　What was Deniece Williams's profession before singing?

1   Which Stevie Wonder LP won a 1973 Grammy for Album of the Year?

2   Who had a million-seller in 1967 with "Here Comes My Baby"?

3   What were Status Quo originally called prior to 1968?

4   Who is on the cover of the *Band on the Run* album apart from Paul and Linda McCartney?

5   Who married Julianne Phillips in Oregon in May 1985?

6   Who had hit albums called *The Slider* and *Futuristic Dragon*?

7   What was Aswad's debut album called?

8   Who beat Madonna to take the 1985 Best New Artist Grammy award?

9   Who recorded under the name Sallyangie?

10 What soundtrack album from 1986 showed a black-and-white photo of David Bowie?

11 Other than the USA, in which country was Joan Baez brought up?

12 Who won four out of the first five Grammy awards for Best Pop Female Vocal Performance?

13 Who were originally known as the Elgins?

14 Whose book of poems was called *Songs For While I'm Away*?

15 Who was drummer/vocalist with Traffic?

16 Where did the US part of the Live Aid concert take place?

17 Who backed Danny?

18 In which film did Elvis play the role of Deke Rivers?

19 Who said, "The trouble with some women is they get all excited about nothing – then they marry him"?

20 Howard Kaylan was lead vocalist with which group?

Pot Luck 3   (see Quiz 5)

Answers

1 Suzie Rutollo. 2 The Playboys. 3 Joni Mitchell's. 4 *Love to Love You Baby*. 5 *The New Musical Express*. 6 *Little Earthquakes*.
7 "Portrait of My Love". 8 Jimi Hendrix. 9 Glen Matlock.
10 Herman's Hermits. 11 Warrington. 12 Delaney and Bonnie.
13 "Nel Blu Dipinto Di Blu" (Volare). 14 "Moonlighting".
15 Flute. 16 Melle Mel and the Furious Five. 17 Carole King, Don McLean. 18 Cyndi Lauper. 19 Gibraltar. 20 Tears For Fears.

1 Which was the largest group to have a chart-topper in 1981?

2 Who played the Fairy Godmother on Adam and the Ants' "Prince Charming" video?

3 In which decade was Julio Iglesias's first solo hit written?

4 Which band included Philip Oakey and Susanne Sulley?

5 How did Demis Roussos hit the headlines in 1985?

6 Which double-sided No. 1 replaced which double-sided No. 1 in 1982?

7 Which 80s hit was based on a Zulu folk tune?

8 How did Mark Chapman find notoriety in the 1980s?

9 Which video by which band featured Ian McKellen as Dracula?

10 Which band's name means "black" in Arabic?

11 How is the American Ms Darwisch better known?

12 Which album was T'Pau's "China In Your Hand" from?

13 What was the Bee Gees' first 80s No. 1?

14 Which country are Europe from?

15 How was Ray Burns known as an 80s soloist?

16 What did the Real Thing's Chris Amoo win in 1987?

17 Which country were the Goombay Dance Band based in?

18 Who, in which song, sang "I've been undressed by kings and I've seen some things a woman ain't supposed to see"?

19 Which city are Berlin from?

20 Which Radio 1 DJ first refused to play Frankie Goes to Hollywood's "Relax"?

Quiz 9 Pot Luck 5

Answers – see page 219

1 In which town was Barry Gibb born?

2 What is in the baby's mouth on the cover of Van Halen's 1984 album?

3 Who organizes Buddy Holly Week each year?

4 What type of car was used by Madness in their video for "Driving in My Car"?

5 Which fifties singer married Millicent Martin?

6 What label did the Police record all their hit albums on?

7 What Beatles movie was originally going to be called *Eight Arms to Hold You*?

8 Which California group toured with Maharishi Mahesh Yogi?

9 Who backed Captain Beefheart?

10 What shape is the sleeve of the Rolling Stones' *Through the Past Darkly* album?

11 Who is lead singer with UB40?

12 Which Steve Winwood song was Grammy Record of the Year in 1986?

13 Who were first formed as Tiger Lily in 1973?

14 Which veteran was behind the US fundraiser by USA for Africa?

15 Which role did Tina Turner play in *Mad Max: Beyond Thunderdome*?

16 Who was President Reagan writing to when he said, "Your deep faith in God and adherence to traditional values is an inspiration to us all"?

17 How is Jiles Perry Richardson better known?

18 What was Bananarama's debut album called?

19 What were the Troggs initially called?

20 What is U2's the Edge's real name?

Pot Luck 6 (see Quiz 11)

Answers

1 A circle. 2 The Fish. 3 A cat. 4 Mitch Murray. 5 The Commotions. 6 The Spencer Davis Group. 7 His left elbow. 8 Frank Ifield. 9 Mary Hopkin. 10 Las Vegas. 11 Gudmundsdottir. 12 Playboy Bunny. 13 Whitechapel. 14 "Wind Beneath My Wings". 15 Paul Hewson. 16 Guitar. 17 Ritchie Valens. 18 Vangelis. 19 Pornographic paperback. 20 *Precious Time*.

Quiz 10 The 90s

Answers – see page 220

LEVEL 3

1 Which band was started with a loan from the alleged Mafia member James Martorano?

2 Which band presented the 1994 Christmas edition of "Top of the Pops"?

3 Who did the 52-year-old manager Rene Angelil marry in 1994?

4 Who went on a "Zoo TV Tour" in 1992?

5 Where was it suggested Elton John be listened to through headphones otherwise noise regulations could be broken?

6 Who was the album *No Prima Donna* a tribute to?

7 Why didn't Englandneworder make a follow-up to the 1990 "World in Motion"?

8 What are the first names of the Spice Girls?

9 Which album was Madonna's "Vogue" taken from?

10 Which band included Keymaster Snow and MC Golden Voice?

11 Who was named as executive producer of "Itsy Bitsy Teeny Weeny Yellow Polka Dot Bikini"?

12 Who was the first female vocalist with Beautiful South?

13 Which two movies did "The One And Only" feature in?

14 How is Jim Moir better known?

15 Who, in the early 1990s, would make records only in aid of charities?

16 Who featured on the soundtrack of *In the Name of the Father*?

17 How many weeks was Wet Wet Wet's "Love Is All Around" at No. 1?

18 Which 90s band included Wanya and Nathan Morris?

19 Who made the album *Growing Up in Public*?

20 Whose suicide note said, "It's better to burn out than to fade away"?

Answers

Madonna (see Quiz 12)
1 Louise Veronica. 2 *Desperately Seeking Susan*. 3 Madonnaland. 4 Bette Midler. 5 Husband Sean Penn. 6 Sir John Mills. 7 Meryl Streep. 8 Breathless Mahoney. 9 Jean Paul Gaultier. 10 Her hedge blocked his view. 11 "Justify My Love". 12 Cannes Film Festival. 13 Maverick. 14 *Erotica*. 15 Bullfighting. 16 Personal trainer, father to her daughter. 17 Alan Parker. 18 Drums. 19 George Harrison. 20 *True Blue*.

Quiz 11 Pot Luck 6

Answers – see page 217

1 What shape was the Small Faces' *Ogden's Nut Gone Flake* album cover?

2 Who backed Country Joe?

3 Which animal appears on the cover of Tina Turner's *Private Dancer* album?

4 Who wrote the first two No. 1 songs for Gerry and the Pacemakers?

5 Who backed Lloyd Cole?

6 What group was Steve Winwood a member of before joining Traffic?

7 What is Michael Jackson leaning on, on the cover of *Thriller*?

8 Who was the first artist to have three consecutive UK No. 1 singles?

9 Who did Lennon and McCartney write "Goodbye" for?

10 Which city saw the most Elvis performances?

11 What is Björk's surname?

12 What type of waitress was Debbie Harry?

13 In which part of London was Damon Albarn born?

14 What was Bette Midler's 1989 Grammy Record of the Year for?

15 What is the real name of Bono of U2?

16 What is a Fender Stratocaster?

17 Who did Buddy Holly's guitarist Tommy Allsup give up his seat for on the ill-fated last flight?

18 How is Evangelos Papathanassiou better known?

19 How did the Velvet Underground get their name?

20 What was Pat Benatar's debut album called?

Pot Luck 5 (see Quiz 9)
1 Douglas, IOM. 2 Cigarette. 3 Paul McCartney. 4 Morris 1000.
5 Ronnie Carroll. 6 A & M. 7 *Help!* 8 Beach Boys. 9 The
Magic Band. 10 Octagonal. 11 Ali Campbell. 12 "Higher
Love". 13 Ultravox. 14 Harry Belafonte. 15 Aunty Entity.
16 Michael Jackson. 17 The Big Bopper. 18 *Deep Sea Skiving*.
19 The Troglodytes. 20 David Evans.

Quiz 12 Madonna

Answers – see page 218

LEVEL 3

1 What are Madonna's two middle names?

2 What was her first major film role?

3 What name was given to the clothing outlet in Macy's US stores?

4 Who described Madonna as "a woman who pulled herself up by her bra straps"?

5 Who did Madonna describe as "the coolest guy in the universe"?

6 Which knight did Madonna star with in *Who's That Girl*?

7 Who was said to have beaten Madonna to the *Evita* role in 1988?

8 Which role did Madonna play in *Bugsy Malone*?

9 Who designed her clothes for the Blonde Ambition tour?

10 Why was Madonna sued by her neighbour in 1990?

11 Which 1991 video shows a steamy bedroom scene filmed in black and white?

12 Where was Madonna when she was interviewed on "Wogan"?

13 What was the name of her company founded in 1992?

14 What was her first album on her own record label?

15 Which controversial "sport" features in her "Take A Bow" and "You'll See" videos?

16 Which two roles did Carlos Leon have in Madonna's life?

17 Who directed Madonna in *Evita*?

18 Which instrument did Madonna play in the rock band Breakfast Club?

19 Who produced "Shanghai Surprise"?

20 Which album was "Papa Don't Preach" originally on?

The 90s (see Quiz 10)
1 New Kids on the Block. 2 Take That. 3 Celine Dion. 4 U2.
5 Hong Kong. 6 Van Morrison. 7 They did not qualify for the
1994 World Cup. 8 Mel B, Mel C, Victoria, Geri and Emma. 9 *I'm
Breathless.* 10 Partners in Kryme. 11 Andrew Lloyd Webber.
12 Briana Corrigan. 13 *Buddy's Song, Doc Hollywood.* 14 Vic
Reeves. 15 George Michael. 16 Sinead O'Connor. 17 15. 18
Boyz II Men. 19 Jimmy Nail. 20 Kurt Cobain.

Quiz 13 Pot Luck 7

Answers – see page 223

Answers – see page 223

LEVEL 3

1   Whose stabbed head appears on the cover of her first solo album?

2   Which country pioneered pirate radio ships in the late fifties?

3   Which guitarist went from Barnstorm to the Eagles?

4   What was Manfred Mann's last single with Paul Jones on vocals?

5   Who started his career with "I Go Ape" in 1959?

6   Who composed the soundtrack for *Deathwish II*?

7   Who backed Archie Bell?

8   Who did Jerry Hall have a long relationship with before Mick Jagger?

9   What is Mike Oldfield standing on, on the *Incantations* album cover?

10 Who formed the Straight and Barking Pumpkin labels?

11 What was Boy George's debut album called?

12 Whose autobiography was called *X-Ray*?

13 Who were made up of a cowboy, an Indian, a policeman, a biker, a GI and a builder?

14 How was Vincent Eugene Craddock better known?

15 In which year was Bert Weedon born?

16 In which film did Elvis play the role of Vince Everett?

17 In 1997 who issued Bonds in his name for people to invest in?

18 What relation is Pat Boone to the Western pioneer Daniel Boone?

19 In which part of Manchester was Elkie Brooks born?

20 In which immortalized road in Woking did Paul Weller live as a child?

Quiz 14 Karaoke

Answers – see page 224

LEVEL 3

1 Which song has a line based loosely on one from Shakespeare's *As You Like It*, "You know someone said that all the world's a stage"?

2 What does Celine Dion sing after "I think of all the friends I've known" in "All By Myself"?

3 How many times does Gabrielle sing "Walk on By" in the first chorus?

4 Which song has the line "Will all those having relatives on Flight 1203 please report to the chapel across the street"?

5 Which 1960s song has the line "Wearing smells from lab'ratories, facing a dying nation of moving paper fantasy"?

6 Who does Bob Dylan tell "Don't block up the hall" in "The Times They Are A'Changin'"?

7 Which song starts, "What goes up must come down"?

8 Which month is it in Paul Simon's "I Am a Rock"?

9 In "My Way" what goes before "I did what I had to do"?

10 Which song says "I love your chin-ey chin chin"?

11 Which line follows the unforgettably tasteless "I'm as serious as cancer"?

12 Which island does Madonna lament in "La Isla Bonita"?

13 What colour did Vincent "paint his palette" in the Don McLean hit?

14 Which song goes "I've never done good things, I've never done bad things"?

15 Where would you find the lines "Ev'ry summer we can rent a cottage in the Isle of Wight"?

16 Which song has the lines "I got up to wash my face, When I come back to bed, Someone's taken my place"?

17 Which song starts "When I was a little girl I had a rag doll"?

18 Where will you hear the line "Tried to hitch a ride to San Francisco"?

19 Which song says "the world is like an apple whirling silently in space"?

20 What is the answer to "What do you see when you turn out the light?"

Answers

Groups (see Quiz 16)
1 Bay City Rollers. 2 The Seekers, The New Seekers. 3 Canada. 4 "Looking After No. 1". 5 Bacharach and David. 6 Left Depeche Mode for Yazoo. 7 Dr Hook. 8 "The Cover of *Radio Times*". 9 Errol Brown. 10 Siobhan Fahey. 11 Hull. 12 Level 42. 13 Sigue Sigue Sputnik. 14 Three. 15 U2. 16 Wet Wet Wet. 17 Fine Young Cannibals. 18 R.E.M. 19 Jackson Five. 20 A fire engine.

Quiz 15 Pot Luck 8

Answers – see page 221

1   Who had a No. 1 hit with "Young Love" 16 years before Donny Osmond?

2   Who took the cover photo for Paul McCartney's first solo album?

3   In which city was Joe Cocker born?

4   Who had a 1973 hit with "Gaye"?

5   Who married the heiress Anne Friedman in 1984?

6   Which Rod Stewart album cover features him sitting in an armchair?

7   What was Boyz II Men's debut album called?

8   What rag was Winifred Atwell celebrating in 1953?

9   What did Ringo Starr have removed in November 1964?

10   How many albums did David Bowie have in the charts in July 1983?

11   Which Doobie Brothers song was Grammy Record of the Year in 1979?

12   An imitator of which pop star won the 1996 "Stars in Their Eyes"?

13   Why was Barry White imprisoned in 1960?

14   Which vocalist links Deep Purple and Whitesnake?

15   Who backed Mike Batt on "Summertime City"?

16   Who said, "Too much of a good thing is simply wonderful"?

17   Who was brought up in the bordello run by his aunt Handsome "Honey" Washington?

18   Which singer shares her birthday with Emily Brontë?

19   Which band includes Bob "The Bear" Hite and Al "Blind Owl" Wilson?

20   Who was the youngest-ever recipient of the Songwriter of the Year trophy at the Ivor Novello awards in 1985?

Answers

Pot Luck 7 (see Quiz 13)
1 Debbie Harry. 2 Denmark. 3 Jo Walsh. 4 "Pretty Flamingo".
5 Neil Sedaka. 6 Jimmy Page. 7 The Drells. 8 Bryan Ferry.
9 A beach. 10 Frank Zappa. 11 *Sold*. 12 Ray Davies.
13 Village People. 14 Gene Vincent. 15 1921. 16 *Jailhouse Rock*. 17 David Bowie. 18 Great-great-great-great-grandson.
19 Salford. 20 Stanley Road (album title).

Quiz 16 Groups

Answers – see page 222

1 Who were originally called the Saxons?

2 Which group was Keith Potger in and which group did he form?

3 What was the home country of Bachman-Turner Overdrive?

4 What was the Boomtown Rats' first hit?

5 Whose songs are on Deacon Blue's 1990 EP?

6 Vince Clarke left one successful band for another in 1981–82. Which?

7 Whose single "The Cover of *Rolling Stone*" was banned by the BBC because they said it was advertising?

8 What did the group change the title to?

9 Who was Hot Chocolate's lead vocalist?

10 Who links Bananarama and Shakespear's Sister?

11 What was the home town of the Housemartins?

12 Which band took its name from *The Hitch-Hiker's Guide to the Galaxy* and the answer to the question "What is the meaning of life?"?

13 Whose first Top Ten hit was "Love Missile F1–11"?

14 How many Stray Cats were there?

15 Whose first album was called *Boy*?

16 Who signed a deal to sponsor Clydebank Football Club in 1993?

17 Roland Gift was lead singer with which group?

18 Which group released "Songs in the Key Of X" in 1996?

19 Who first performed as Ripples and Waves plus Michael?

20 What did Reo Speedwagon name themselves after?

Quiz 17 Pot Luck 9

Answers – see page 227

LEVEL 3

1 In which country was Chris de Burgh born?

2 What label did Buddy Holly record on?

3 How old was Bobby Darin when he found out that the woman he thought was his mother was his sister?

4 What is the Yardbirds' only hit to get in the Top 10 in the US and UK?

5 Who left Roxy Music to form Obscure Records?

6 Who left the Go Go's to go solo?

7 Whose alter ego was The Thin White Duke?

8 Which Stones' album commences with "Sympathy For The Devil"?

9 Who backed Freddy Bell on "Giddy-Up-A-Ding-Dong"?

10 What record label was founded by Ahmet Ertegun and Herb Abramson?

11 What was Billy Bragg's debut album called?

12 Who won the Grammy Record of the Year in 1967 with "Up Up and Away"?

13 Who were called the High Numbers in their early days?

14 Which UK vocalist joined Michael Jackson on his Bad tour in Europe?

15 How is Roberta Anderson better known?

16 In which city was Steve Winwood born?

17 Which band has Fish on lead vocals?

18 What is Bob Marley's eldest son called?

19 What was Barry Manilow's "Mandy" originally called in the US?

20 Which 1977 chart topper was sung in French?

Pot Luck 10 (see Quiz 19)

Answers
1 13. 2 Shirley Owens. 3 Apple. 4 His Rockets. 5 Ray Hildebrand and Jill Jackson. 6 Bad. 7 Marc Bolan. 8 The Rolling Stones. 9 A Train. 10 Lonnie Donegan. 11 *Ropin' The Wind*. 12 Phil Collins. 13 "Wipe Out" by the Surfaris. 14 Madstock. 15 Little Richard. 16 Bo Diddley. 17 Glasgow. 18 *King Creole*. 19 Dave Stewart. 20 Their window-cleaner.

Quiz 18 Dance

Answers – see page 228

LEVEL 3

1 Penny Ford and Turbo B were vocalists in which 90s dance group?

2 In which city did House Music originate?

3 Where is Perez "Guaglione" Prado from?

4 Whose first single was "Dance Stance"?

5 Which Madonna dance hit was her first No. 1?

6 What follows the Outhere Brothers' "Don't stop"?

7 Who had a party hit about "Atmosphere"?

8 Whose "Sideboard Song" was subtitled "Got My Beer in the Sideboard Here"?

9 Who sang about "Reggae Like It Used to Be"?

10 What gave the Brothers Johnson their first Top Ten hit?

11 Ottawan who had an 80s hit with "D.I.S.C.O" were from where?

12 Who sang "I Haven't Stopped Dancing Yet" in 1989?

13 Who are credited with "Boogie Wonderland" in 1979?

14 Who said Dance Yourself Dizzy in 1980?

15 Which disco queen's first album was *Heart and Soul*?

16 In which year did Barry White's "You're the First the Last, My Everything" hit the top?

17 Whose first album was *Party Party 16 Great Party Icebreakers*?

18 What did the party hit "Hoots Mon" advertise when it was rereleased in 1993?

19 Which disco band included Maizie Williams, Bobby Farrell and Marcia Barrett?

20 Which two stars are credited on the cover of *Dirty Dancing*?

No. 1s (see Quiz 20)

1 Al Martino. **2** "One Night"/"I Got Stung". **3** The Big Bopper. **4** "I Love You". **5** "Lady Madonna". **6** "Don't Stand So Close to Me". **7** Robin Beck. **8** "Mistletoe and Wine". **9** "Bohemian Rhapsody". **10** "Rock And Roll Waltz". **11** "Let The Heartaches Begin". **12** Charles and Eddie. **13** Michael Jackson. **14** Boyzone, Robson and Jerome. **15** "Whispering Grass". **16** "That'll be the day". **17** The Temperance Seven 18 Puppy. **19** From "Miss Grace" to "Ms Grace". **20** The Stargazers – "Broken Wings".

Answers

Quiz 19 Pot Luck 10

Answers – see page 225

LEVEL 3

1 How many older brothers and sisters does Celine Dion have?

2 Who was the lead singer of the Shirelles?

3 Which label's first releases included Mary Hopkin and James Taylor?

4 Who backed Boyd Bennett on "Seventeen"?

5 What were the real names of Paul and Paula?

6 What is George Benson's nickname?

7 Who made his mark in the 60s act John's Children?

8 Which group's own record label uses the reference number prefixes COC and CUN?

9 What type of transport was on Elton John's Rocket record label?

10 Who had Britain's first-ever double-sided No. 1 in the 1950s?

11 What was Garth Brooks's debut album called?

12 Who won the Grammy award for Best Male Vocal Performance in 1984 and 1985?

13 What did "5-4-3-2-1" replace as theme music for "Ready Steady Go!"?

14 What name was given to the open-air concerts by Madness at Finsbury Park in 1992?

15 Who said, "I'm the innovator. I'm the emancipator. I'm the originator. I'm the architect of rock 'n' roll"?

16 How is Otha Ellas Bates better known?

17 In which city was Mark Knopfler born?

18 In which film did Elvis play the role of Danny Fisher?

19 Who formed the Spiritual Cowboys?

20 Who did Joe Cocker's parents name him after?

Pot Luck 9 (see Quiz 17)
1 Argentina. 2 Coral. 3 32. 4 "For Your Love". 5 Brian Eno.
6 Belinda Carlisle. 7 David Bowie's. 8 *Beggars' Banquet*. 9 The
Bell Boys. 10 Atlantic. 11 *Life's A Riot With Spy vs Spy*. 12 5th
Dimension. 13 The Who. 14 Kim Wilde. 15 Joni Mitchell.
16 Birmingham. 17 Marillion. 18 Ziggy (real name David).
19 "Brandy". 20 Manhattan Transfer's "Chanson d'Amour".

Quiz 20 No. 1s

Answers – see page 226

1 Who was the only performer to have a No. 1 in 1952?

2 What was Elvis Presley's first double-sided No. 1?

3 Who sings the backing "ook-a-chunka, ook-a-chunka" with George Jones on Johnny Preston's "Running Bear"?

4 With which record did Cliff first replace Elvis at the No. 1 spot?

5 What was the Beatles' last No. 1 on Parlophone?

6 Which 80s No. 1 was about the love between a teacher and pupil?

7 Who recorded the 1988 No. 1 which advertised Coca-Cola?

8 What was Cliff Richard's first self-produced No. 1?

9 What was the first record to be No. 1 over two separate Christmases?

10 What was the first No. 1 with "rock and roll" in the title?

11 What was at No. 1 when the first heart transplant took place in 1967?

12 Who were Messrs Pettigrew and Chacon who had a No. 1 in 1992?

13 Who had a record go straight to No. 1 in 1995 while in hospital?

14 Which two acts had No. 1s with cover versions in autumn 1996?

15 What was a No. 1 for Sargeant Major Williams and Private Sugden?

16 Which phrase used by John Wayne in *The Searcher* inspired a 50s No. 1 hit?

17 Which chart toppers had Canon Colin Bowles and Sheikh Haroun Wadi el John R.T. Davies among their number?

18 Which animal was in the title of No. 1s by David Cassidy and Donny Osmond?

19 How did Women's Lib change the title of the 1975 hit by the Tymes?

20 Who was the first British act to have a No. 1 and what was it called?

Quiz 21 Pot Luck 11

Answers – see page 231

LEVEL 3

1 What producer's label had the slogan "Tomorrow's Sound Today"?

2 What was the lady wearing on the front and back covers of Rod Stewart's *Blondes Have More Fun* album?

3 Who recorded "Daydream Believer (Cheer Up Peter Reid)" in 1996?

4 Who was the first group at No. 1 with Roman numerals in its name?

5 What did Pink Floyd's 1977 Animals tour feature an inflatable of?

6 Whose first album was *Natty Dread*?

7 Whose deaths were recalled in the Stones' "Sympathy for the Devil"?

8 Which group was formerly Linda Ronstadt's backing band?

9 Who wrote Lulu's hit "The Boat that I Row"?

10 Which British female singer had three song titles on the first UK chart?

11 How is Michael Lubowitz better known?

12 What do the Beverley Sisters, the Bee Gees and the Shangri-Las have in common?

13 Who links the Beatles in Hamburg, Elvis's "Wooden Heart" and "Strangers in the Night"?

14 How is the US producer Jazzie B better known?

15 What are the grandchildren called in "When I'm Sixty-Four"?

16 Who was the first female performer to have four UK No. 1s?

17 What did the Bluebells' "Young At Heart" advertise in 1993?

18 Who were John McGeoch, Steve Severin and Budgie?

19 Who are the five named people in "Fifty Ways to leave Your Lover"?

20 Which 50s chart topper was at one time Paul Simon's father-in-law?

Pot Luck 13 (see Quiz 23)
1 Paul Kossoff. 2 The Rolling Stones. 3 Jennifer Rush. 4 The Performing Right Society. 5 "Dragnet". 6 A Doll's House. 7 Russ Conway. 8 "Green Door". 9 Their feet. 10 Kalin Twins. 11 Ricky Valance. 12 "Hey Joe". 13 Canada. 14 "Punky's Dilemma". 15 Melissa Manchester. 16 Grateful Dead. 17 Paul Jones. 18 Chicago Transit Authority. 19 Ronald Reagan. 20 The National Academy of Recording Arts and Sciences.

Quiz 22 Instrumentals

Answers – see page 232

LEVEL 3

1 Which instrumental was the first to have a mother and son at No. 1?

2 Which orchestra leader recorded as Manuel and his Music of the Mountains?

3 What was the guitarist John Williams's first solo single?

4 Who had an album called *Rockin' With Curly Leads*?

5 Which group included the music writer Benny Green?

6 Which film theme was the first to top the charts in 1953?

7 Who played "A Taste of Honey" with the Leon Young String Chorale?

8 Which city were Doop from?

9 In which year did Fleetwood Mac's "Albatross" enter the charts?

10 Which musical instrument did Floyd Cramer play?

11 Which instrumental took over from which instrumental at the top of the charts in 1962?

12 Whose backing group had the Tornados been?

13 Who had a 1960s instrumental hit with "Love is Blue"?

14 On which album did "Amazing Grace" first appear?

15 Which hit included electric violin, ocarina, piccolo, trumpet and electronic harmonica?

16 What was the first TV theme to be a chart topper?

17 Who had a 1997 Top Ten hit with "Toxygene"?

18 Which Kenny Ball hit had an oriental-sounding title?

19 Who was the first person to have a hit with "Classical Gas"?

20 Who had the album *Music From Riverdance – The Show*?

Solo Singers (see Quiz 24)

Answers

1 Frankie Avalon. 2 Otis Redding. 3 Carly Simon. 4 Sandie Shaw. 5 "634–5789". 6 Bryan Adams. 7 Van Morrison. 8 Fell from a hotel bedroom window. 9 Gene Pitney. 10 Neil Diamond. 11 Chris De Burgh. 12 Camille, Spooky Electric. 13 Matt Monro. 14 Adam Faith. 15 Mary Hopkin. 16 Piano. 17 John Lee Hooker. 18 Julio Iglesias. 19 "Being With You". 20 Des O'Connor.

Quiz 23 Pot Luck 12

Answers – see page 229

1 Which Free member was brought back to life after 35 minutes in 1975?

2 Which group had three members pay £5 fines for urinating against a London petrol station?

3 Who followed up her No. 1 hit with a song called "Ring of Ice"?

4 Which society collects performance royalties for British composers?

5 Which TV cop series theme tune was a hit in 1953 for Ray Anthony?

6 Which gift to the royal family inspired HMV to manufacture the world's smallest working gramophone records?

7 How is Trevor Sandford DSM better known?

8 Which song begins "Midnight, one more night without sleeping"?

9 What do drummers play the high hat cymbals with?

10 Which brothers are singing on the flip side of Cliff Richard's "Saviour's Day" in 1990?

11 How is David Spencer better known?

12 Which song title links Frankie Laine and Jimi Hendrix?

13 Which country are Crash Test Dummies from?

14 Which Paul Simon song begins "Wish I was a Kellogg's Corn Flake"?

15 Who won a 1982 Grammy as Best Pop Female Vocal Performance for "You Should Hear How She Talks About You"?

16 Which band included Ron "Pigpen" McKernan?

17 Which singer/presenter/actor is also the name of a Victorian dance?

18 What were Chicago called on their first album?

19 Who has not made an album – Ronald Reagan, Pope John Paul II, or Winston Churchill?

20 Who organizes the Grammy awards?

Answers

Pot Luck 11 (see Quiz 21)
1 Phil Spector's. 2 A leopard-skin jumpsuit. 3 Simply Red and White. 4 Lord Rockingham's XI. 5 A huge pig. 6 Bob Marley. 7 John and Bobby Kennedy's. 8 The Eagles. 9 Neil Diamond. 10 Vera Lynn. 11 Manfred Mann. 12 They all contain twins. 13 Bert Kaempfert (producer, writer, writer respectively). 14 Soul II Soul. 15 Vera, Chuck and Dave. 16 Madonna. 17 Volkswagen. 18 The Banshees. 19 Jack, Stan, Roy, Gus, Lee. 20 Eddie Fisher.

Quiz 24 Solo Singers

Answers – see page 230

LEVEL 3

1 Who sang "Beauty School Dropout" in the film *Grease*?

2 Which fellow singer did Bryan Ferry name his son after?

3 Who wrote the children's opera Romulus Hunt?

4 Who celebrated her 21st birthday party in the Chamber of Horrors in 1968?

5 Which number was a Top Forty hit for Wilson Pickett?

6 Whose second album was called *You Want It, You Got It*?

7 Who made the album *Irish Heartbeat* with the Chieftains?

8 What was Donny Hathaway's cause of death?

9 Whose first UK hit was "I Wanna Love My Life Away"?

10 Which singer starred in a film with Laurence Olivier in 1979 and received the largest-ever fee for a debut role?

11 Who had a 1980s album called *Spanish Train and Other Stories*?

12 What are the forces of good and evil called on Prince's "Lovesexy"?

13 Who was the first person to take "Yesterday" into the Top Ten?

14 Which singer was Leo Sayer's manager?

15 Who made a comeback album *Spirit* in 1989?

16 Which musical instrument does Oleta Adams play?

17 Which singer's supposed 75th birthday was commemorated on a Tanzanian stamp in 1994?

18 In 1980 who did CBS say was the world's top-selling male singer?

19 What was Smokey Robinson's first solo No. 1 single?

20 Which 60s chart topper compered Buddy Holly's only UK tour?

Answers

Instrumentals (see Quiz 22)
1 "Mouldy Old Dough". 2 Geoff Love. 3 "Cavatina". 4 The Shadows. 5 Lord Rockingham's XI. 6 *Moulin Rouge*. 7 Acker Bilk. 8 The Hague. 9 1968. 10 Piano. 11 "Nut Rocker" took over from "Wonderful Land". 12 Billy Fury's. 13 Paul Mauriat. 14 *Farewell to the Greys*. 15 "The Good, The Bad and the Ugly". 16 "Eye Level". 17 Orb. 18 "Sukiyaki". 19 Mason Williams. 20 Bill Whelan.

1 Which group's first UK hit was called "Candida"?

2 Which Rolling Stone plays dulcimer on "Lady Jane"?

3 Which Janis Joplin album was posthumously released?

4 Who was the only British girl singer to have three No. 1 hits in the 1960s?

5 What is Cliff Richard sporting on the cover of his *I'm No Hero* album?

6 Who did Brian Bennett replace in which group in 1961?

7 Whose *Bop Til You Drop* was the first digitally recorded rock album?

8 Which was the second group with Roman numerals in its name to have a No. 1?

9 Who was the first British artist to enter the US Top Twenty?

10 Whose debut album was called *Tops With Me*?

11 In which decade was David Bowie's "Laughing Gnome" recorded?

12 Which TV series did the 1981 No. 2 hit "Chi Mai" come from?

13 What was the name of the group made up of Mary Hopkin, Peter Skellern and Julian Lloyd Webber?

14 What was Barry Manilow's first Top Ten hit?

15 What did Shakin' Stevens call himself between his real name Michael Barratt and his later stage persona?

16 Who other than Michael Ball had a hit called "Love Changes Everything"?

17 Whose first solo album was *Talk Is Cheap*?

18 Which item of Jimi Hendrix's was auctioned at Sotheby's for £14,300?

19 How is Frederick Heath better known?

20 In which film did Elvis play the role of Tulsa McLean?

Quiz 26 Stateside

Answers – see page 236

Answers – see page 236

LEVEL 3

1 Who were at No. 1 when Princess Margaret married Anthony Armstrong-Jones?

2 Which US band featured on the first-ever "Old Grey Whistle Test"?

3 Who were Chynna, Carnie and Wendy?

4 Which first name did Jackie Wilson use as an amateur boxer?

5 What is Bobby Vinton's real first name?

6 Who was criticized for singing "The Star-Spangled Banner" in a Latin style before a baseball match in 1968?

7 Whose only UK hit was "Time For Living"?

8 How is Kevin Donovan better known?

9 Which vocalist is a former Miss America?

10 Which musical instrument did Connie Francis perform with as a child?

11 In which country was Fugee Clef Jean born?

12 What was Bill Haley's follow-up to "Rock Around the Clock" after it had first been No. 1?

13 Who established their own Brothers record label?

14 Who made the double album *Black Moses*?

15 Whose debut album was *Stompin' At the Savoy*?

16 Which band was Kim Carnes a member of in the late 60s?

17 Which film did Brenda Lee's "Speak to Me Pretty" come from?

18 Which group's name is Spanish for Wolves?

19 Before 1997 which was the best-selling UK album in the US charts?

20 Who named their group after a steamroller they had seen repairing a road?

Answers

Singers (see Quiz 28)

1 Gallagher and Lyle. 2 Gerry Goffin and Carole King. 3 *Mud Slide Slim and the Blue Horizon*. 4 "Love on the Rocks". 5 Marvin Hamlisch and Carole Bayer Sager. 6 Neil Sedaka. 7 Neil Young. 8 "Hold Me Close". 9 Freddie Mercury. 10 Melanie. 11 A Fortnight. 12 Ian Dury. 13 Gary Numan. 14 Kris Kristofferson. 15 Elvis Presley – he died. 16 "Oh Julie". 17 Dave Stewart. 18 Ann Orson and Carte Blanche. 19 Joni Mitchell. 20 Tim Hardin.

1　Who did Jon Landau produce in the 1970s and call the "future of rock 'n' roll"?

2　Which blues artist died in July 1959 of liver failure?

3　Who did the Chieftains record with on their first album?

4　Who's dancing in a red dress on the LP cover of *She's So Unusual*?

5　Peter Cetera was vocalist with which band?

6　Who had a 1960s album called *Blues Breakers*?

7　Which Elvis movie featured "Can't Help Falling In Love"?

8　Which British group's US LP cover was deemed in such bad taste in 1966 that 750,000 copies were recalled?

9　Which song refers to a bloody rose lying crushed and broken in the virgin snow?

10　Who signed James Taylor to Apple in 1968?

11　Who were Graham Russell and Russell Hitchcock?

12　Whose debut album was *Isn't It Grand Boys* in 1966?

13　Which forename is shared by Paul McCartney's father and son?

14　Which group takes its name from a 1950s Bette Davis film?

15　Who is the songwriting brother-in-law of the 1960s singer Julie Rogers?

16　Which country were Teach-In from?

17　Which concert was a follow-up to Live Aid and raised funds for the unemployed in the Irish Republic?

18　What were Roxy Music named after?

19　Whose son is called Edan?

20　How is Vito Farinola better known?

Quiz 28 Singers

Answers – see page 234

1 Which duo were resident songwriters with McGuinness Flint?

2 Which singer/songwriter did Little Eva babysit for?

3 On which album was James Taylor's "You've Got a Friend"?

4 What was Neil Diamond's best-selling single from *The Jazz Singer*?

5 Who was the musical "They're Playing Our Song" based on?

6 Whose autobiography was called *Laughter in the Rain*?

7 Whose album *Out of the Blue* was a reaction to punk rock?

8 Which David Essex song was his last No. 1 of the 70s?

9 Who started out with the group Smile in the early 70s?

10 Who wrote the music for the Worzels' "Combine Harvester"?

11 How long were the Bee Gees given to come up with the songs for *Saturday Night Fever*?

12 Who was leader of Kilburn and the High Roads?

13 How is Gary Webb better known?

14 Who wrote "One Day at a Time", a 1970s hit for Lena Martell?

15 Who did Mungo Jerry's Ray Dorset write "Feels Like I'm In Love" for and why did he not record it?

16 What was Shakin' Stevens's first No. 1 that he wrote himself?

17 Who was Guiot who co-wrote "Stay" for Shakespear's Sister?

18 Who are credited with writing "Don't Go Breaking My Heart"?

19 Who wrote "Both Sides Now", a hit for Judy Collins?

20 Who died of a heroin overdose the same month as John Lennon was murdered?

Answers

Stateside (see Quiz 26)

1 Everly Brothers. 2 America. 3 Wilson Phillips. 4 Sonny. 5 Stanley. 6 Jose Feliciano. 7 The Association. 8 Afrika Bambaataa. 9 Vanessa Williams. 10 Accordion. 11 Haiti. 12 "Rock-A-Beatin' Boogie". 13 The Beach Boys. 14 Isaac Hayes. 15 Rufus and Chaka Khan. 16 New Christy Minstrels. 17 *Two Little Bears*. 18 Los Lobos. 19 *Rumours* – Fleetwood Mac. 20 Buffalo Springfield.

1   Which Beatles album includes "Eight Days A Week"?

2   What is Diana Ross's middle name?

3   Who starred in the Western featuring the No. 1 "Man From Laramie"?

4   Who was chosen to play a classical concert by Arthur Rubenstein?

5   What does the instrumentalist in Captain and Tenille play?

6   Who persuaded Connie Francis to update "Who's Sorry Now?"?

7   Which Beach Boys single took six months, 90 hours of tape and four studios to make?

8   Who was the first woman to study philosophy at the Gukushuin University?

9   Who wrote "The First Cut Is The Deepest" for P.P. Arnold?

10 What was Roy Orbison's last No. 1 in his lifetime?

11 Which was the third group with Roman numerals in its name to have a No. 1?

12 Which chart topper was in *Sister Act II*?

13 Which group was made up of Maria Mendiola and Mayte Mateus?

14 Which word was in both Art Garfunkel's No. 1 hits?

15 According to "19" what was the average age of a soldier in World War II?

16 How is Arthur Kelm better known?

17 Who worked at Luton's Vauxhall car plant and was a member of Kat Kool and the Kool Kats?

18 What is Dave Stewart's middle initial on some songwriting credits?

19 In UB40's "If It Happens Again" what was "It"?

20 Who played guitar on "Wuthering Heights"?

Pot Luck 16 (see Quiz 31)
Answers
1 B.J. Thomas. 2 Pink. 3 Frank Sinatra. 4 Chicago. 5 "The Last Waltz". 6 *Blackboard Jungle*. 7 *The Poseidon Adventure*. 8 "Diane". 9 The Who. 10 White. 11 Johnny Otis. 12 Van McCoy. 13 Motown. 14 Freddy Cannon. 15 Burl Ives. 16 Twiggy. 17 *Flaming Star*. 18 Del Shannon. 19 South Africa. 20 "Dreadlock Holiday".

Quiz 30 Soul

Answers – see page 240

LEVEL 3

1 What did "Three Times A lady" replace as Motown's UK best seller?

2 Which instrument did Lionel Richie play with the Commodores?

3 Who was Linda Womack's father?

4 Which group was Ronnie White in?

5 Who appeared in the films *Muscle Beach Party* and *Bikini Beach*?

6 Who was the eldest Jackson brother?

7 Who did Berry Gordy sell Motown to in 1988?

8 Where was Gamble and Huff's record label based in the 70s?

9 Which record label did Lionel Richie go to after leaving Motown?

10 Which Jackson's real name was Toriano Adaryll?

11 Who was the first major star to leave Motown in 1964?

12 Which song did Lou Rawls make after the Budweiser beer he advertised?

13 Who left Motown in 1967 to set up their own labels?

14 Where in the US were Gladys Knight and the Pips all from?

15 Who made an album called *The Wildest Organ in Town*?

16 Where did Motown relocate to in 1971?

17 Who did Randy Taraborelli write a biography of in 1991?

18 Who wrote "Reet Petite" with Jackie Wilson's cousin?

19 Who was Miss Wright – and Miss Right – for Stevie Wonder in 1970?

20 Which song did Lionel Richie write for Kenny Rogers?

Answers

Novelty Songs (see Quiz 32)
1 Laurel and Hardy. 2 Cadillac. 3 Anthony Newley, Joan Collins.
4 *The Millionairess*. 5 Roland Rat Superstar. 6 Wink Martindale. 7 Kevin Keegan. 8 "My Old Man's A Dustman". 9 Joan Collins Fan Club (Julian Clary). 10 Craig Johnston. 11 Harry Secombe, Peter Sellers and Spike Milligan. 12 "You're a Pink Toothbrush, I'm a Blue Toothbrush". 13 Barron Knights. 14 "No Chance". 15 René and Yvette ("Allo Allo"). 16 The Krankies. 17 The Archies.
18 "Bloodnok's Rock 'N' Roll". 19 "The Old Payola Roll Blues".
20 Kevin the Gerbil.

Quiz 31 Pot Luck 16

Answers – see page 237

LEVEL 3

1 Who sang "Raindrops Keep Falling on My Head" in the film?

2 What colour was the Island 45 record label in the 60s?

3 Who was the first artist to have two Oscar-winning songs in the same decade?

4 Whose first UK hit was "I'm A Man"?

5 What was Engelbert Humperdinck's last No. 1 in the 60s?

6 From which film did "Rock Around The Clock" come from?

7 Which film had the song "The Morning After"?

8 What was the Bachelors' only No. 1?

9 Which London group failed an EMI audition and had 15 Top 10 hits?

10 What is the main colour on the *Beggar's Banquet* album?

11 Who was known as the Godfather of Rhythm and Blues?

12 Who wrote Jackie Wilson's "The Sweetest Feeling"?

13 On which label was Lionel Richie's 1992 album *Back To Front*?

14 Who was the first solo artist to have a No. 1 album?

15 Whose real surname was Ivanhoe?

16 Who had a 60s album called *Please Get My Name Right*?

17 In which film did Elvis play the role of Pacer Burton?

18 How is Charles Westover better known?

19 In which country was Danny Williams born?

20 Which hit was based on a stay by Justin Hayward in Jamaica?

Answers

Pot Luck 15 (see Quiz 29)

1 *Beatles For Sale*. 2 Ernestine. 3 James Stewart. 4 Neil Sedaka.
5 Keyboards. 6 Her Father. 7 "Good Vibrations". 8 Yoko Ono.
9 Cat Stevens. 10 "(Oh) Pretty Woman". 11 Boyz II Men.
12 Lauryn "L" Hill of the Fugees. 13 Baccara. 14 Eyes. 15 26.
16 Tab Hunter. 17 Paul Young. 18 A. 19 Margaret Thatcher's re-election. 20 Dave Gilmour.

Quiz 32 Novelty Songs

Answers – see page 238

1   Which duo sang with the Avalon Boys featuring Chill Wills on their 1975 hit?

2   What type of car did that Old Fashioned Girl Eartha Kitt want that would accommodate a bowling alley?

3   Which husband-and-wife team were on the album *Fool Britannia* about the Profumo affair?

4   Which film inspired the novelty hit "Goodness Gracious Me"?

5   Whose *Cassette of the Album* reached 67 in the album charts?

6   Who had "Deck of Cards" in the charts five times in 14 years?

7   Who was Head Over Heels in Love in 1979?

8   Which song had the lines "[It's] full of toadstools – How do you know? – There's not mushroom inside!"?

9   Who was Leader of the Pack in 1988?

10 Which Australian was credited on Englandneworder's "World In Motion"?

11 Who had an album called *How To Win an Election* in 1964?

12 Which song ends with "When we both use the same toothpaste"?

13 Who had a hit with "Pop Go the Workers" in 1965?

14 What was Billy Connolly's response to J.J. Barrie's "No Charge"?

15 Who had a hit with "Je t'aime" in 1986?

16 Who had a hit with "Fan'Dabi'Dozi" twice in 1981?

17 Whose first song "Bang-Shang-A-Lang" launched their US TV show?

18 What was on the other side of the Goons' "Ying Tong Song" in 1956?

19 In which song did Stan Freberg introduce Clyde Ankle?

20 Who had a hit with "Summer Holiday" in 1984?

Quiz 33 Pot Luck 17

Answers – see page 243

LEVEL 3

1 Whose last hit was "Cowboy Jimmy Joe"?

2 What song from *Dr Dolittle* won an Oscar in 1967?

3 Which David Bowie video was censored because of nudity?

4 Which Rolling Stone produced "The Art Of Chris Farlowe"?

5 Who made a comeback in 1979 with her album *Broken English*?

6 What is Neil Young wearing on the album cover of *After The Goldrush*?

7 What 50's song goes: "Oo-ee oo-ah-ah ting tang walla bing bang"?

8 Whose first hit was "Leaving Las Vegas"?

9 What was the first song ever to win an Oscar?

10 Which Orchestra did Procul Harum make an album with in 1972?

11 Which country did Plastic Bertrand come from?

12 Who was lead singer with the Floaters?

13 How many No. 1 hits did Elvis Presley have before 1997?

14 Where did Marc Almond study music?

15 How old was Bryan Hyland when he had a US No. 1 with "Itsy Bitsy Teeny Weeny Yellow Polka Dot Bikini"?

16 Which Lisa Stansfield song was on the soundtrack of *Indecent Proposal*?

17 Where did Black Box come from?

18 Who had a 60s hit with "Don't Jump Off the Roof Dad"?

19 Which sitcom did Sonia appear in?

20 Which group was Michael Steele in in 1989?

Answers

Pot Luck 18 (see Quiz 35)
1 "All Along The Watchtower". 2 Milkman. 3 Israel. 4 The Beatles. 5 Clannad. 6 The Hollies. 7 "Love Letters". 8 Ted Heath's. 9 Bobby Crush. 10 Motorhead. 11 *Towering Inferno*. 12 Otis Clay. 13 Mark Moore. 14 Derek Jarman. 15 The Specials. 16 "Those Were The Days". 17 Russian. 18 "Lily the Pink". 19 Marmalade. 20 Soft Cell.

Quiz 34 Elvis

Answers – see page 244

LEVEL 3

1 What was Graceland before it was a mansion?

2 What was the band with Elvis, Scotty Moore and Bill Black called?

3 The *Young World* newspaper of which country declared Elvis Public Enemy No. 1 in 1960?

4 Why did Americans put the wrong address on letters in 1993?

5 Which annual Ball commemorates Elvis in Memphis?

6 Who hosted the "Welcome Home Elvis" Show in 1960?

7 Who played the older Elvis in the 1996 revival of *Elvis* in London?

8 Which Harold Robbins novel was *King Creole* based on?

9 What was given away with the album *A Date With Elvis* in 1959?

10 Which Elvis magazine was first published in February 1960?

11 Who played the title role in the TV film *Elvis* in 1979?

12 Which was Elvis's only million seller between 1962 and 1969?

13 What was Peter Guralnick's biography about Elvis called?

14 Which was the only Elvis single between November 1960 and May 1962 not to reach No. 1?

15 Who with Elvis made up the so-called Million Dollar Quartet?

16 Which Elvis No. 1 is the only one for which he is credited with the writing?

17 Which Elvis hit was the first record ever to go straight to No. 1?

18 What did Elvis buy with the $5,000 he received on signing with RCA?

19 What was the first private record Elvis made in 1954?

20 What was Elvis's first hit after he left the army?

DJs (see Quiz 36)

1 Kenny Everett. 2 Radio Atlantis. 3 "Too Much Gravy". 4 John Peel. 5 Jimmy Savile. 6 Paul Jones. 7 Simon Mayo. 8 Mark Goodier. 9 Jimmy Young. 10 Jive Bunny and London Beat. 11 Radio 1 DJ Posse. 12 The Big Bopper. 13 Ravenscroft. 14 Noel Edmonds. 15 Chris Tarrant. 16 Jimmy Savile. 17 Tony Prince. 18 Phillip Schofield. 19 Emperor Rosko. 20 Kenny Everett.

Answers

Quiz 35 Pot Luck 18

Answers – see page 241

1 What song sees the joker tell the thief, "There must be some way out of here"?

2 What was Craig Douglas's occupation before "Only Sixteen"?

3 Where did the singers of "Cinderella Rockefella" come from?

4 Who backed Tony Sheridan on "My Bonnie (Lies Over The Ocean)"?

5 Which band consisted of the Duggans and the Brennans?

6 Which group was made up of Allan, Graham, Tony, Eric and Bobby?

7 Which hit links Ketty Lester and Elvis Presley?

8 Whose orchestra had a 1950s hit with "The Faithful Hussar"?

9 Who wrote "Orville's Song" for Keith Harris?

10 What group is Lemmy's group?

11 Which film had the Oscar-winning song "We May Never Love Like This Again"?

12 Who had the original "The Only Way is Up"?

13 Which DJ was behind S Express?

14 Which director's film backed stage performances of the Pet Shop Boys' "Heart"?

15 Which group were at No. 1 when Charles and Diana got married?

16 Which Mary Hopkin song was originally called "Darogoi Dlimmoyo"?

17 What language was it originally in?

18 Other than the Hollies hit, where else does Jennifer Eccles appear?

19 Who were originally Dean Ford and the Gaylords?

20 Which group had their own Big Frock record label?

Pot Luck 17 (see Quiz 33)
1 Alma Cogan. 2 "Talk To The Animals". 3 "China Girl". 4 Mick Jagger. 5 Marianne Faithfull. 6 A Donkey Jacket. 7 "Witchdoctor". 8 Sheryl Crow. 9 "The Continental". 10 Edmonton Symphony Orchestra. 11 Belgium. 12 Larry Cunningham. 13 17. 14 Leeds Polytechnic. 15 16. 16 "All the Right Places". 17 Italy. 18 Tommy Cooper. 19 "Bread". 20 The Bangles.

Answers

243

LEVEL 3

1 Who was sacked from Radio 1 because he said the Transport Minister's wife had probably passed her driving test by slipping the examiner a fiver?

2 Which Belgian station did Steve Wright work for?

3 What was Chris Evans's 1992 Sunday show on Radio 1 called?

4 Who has a wife Sheila, four children and lives near Stowmarket?

5 Who was the first Radio 1 DJ to be knighted in 1990?

6 Which 60s singer presents a radio R&B show?

7 Which Radio DJ presented "Confessions" on TV?

8 Who presented the UK Top Forty show on Radio 1 at the start of 1997?

9 Who is the only BBC national daily radio DJ to have had a No. 1 hit?

10 Who sang with Liz Kershaw and Bruno Brookes on "It Takes Two Baby"?

11 Who sang with Bruno and Liz on "Let's Dance"?

12 How was the former DJ J.P. Richardson better known?

13 What is John Peel's real surname?

14 Who presented the Radio 1 Breakfast Show between 1973 and 1978?

15 Who has been called the instigator of so called "zoo-radio"?

16 Who introduced Radio Luxembourg's "Under The Bedclothes Club"?

17 Whose catchphrase was "Your royal ruler, I wouldn't fool ya"?

18 Who was born on April Fool's Day in Oldham and has been a Capital Radio and Radio 1 DJ?

19 How was Michael Pasternak better known?

20 Whose autobiography was called *The Custard Stops at Hatfield*?

Answers

Elvis (see Quiz 3 4)
1 Church. 2 The Blue Moon Boys. 3 East Germany. 4 It would show the new Elvis stamp and read "Return to Sender". 5 Dead Elvis Ball. 6 Frank Sinatra. 7 P.J. Proby. 8 *A Stone for Danny Fisher*. 9. A Calendar counting Elvis's release from the army. 10 *Elvis Monthly*. 11 Kurt Russell. 12 "Return to Sender". 13 *Last Train to Memphis*. 14 "Wild in the Country"/"I Feel So Bad". 15 Johnny Cash, Carl Perkins, Jerry Lee Lewis. 16 "All Shook Up". 17 "Jailhouse Rock". 18 Pink Cadillac. 19 "My Happiness". 20 "Stuck On You".

Quiz 37 Pot Luck 19

Answers – see page 247

1   Who designed the album covers for Velvet Underground and Nico?

2   Which song links Elvis, Dorothy Squires and the Sex Pistols?

3   Who got to No. 18 with "Shifting Whispering Sands" in 1956?

4   What Stones album cover shows them dressed as sorcerers?

5   Who co-wrote "Fame" with John Lennon?

6   Which Paul Simon song begins "When I think back on all the crap I learned in high school"?

7   What is Chet Atkins's real first name?

8   Which film did the Oscar-winning "I'm Easy" come from?

9   What former Bee Gees manager produced the film *Saturday Night Fever*?

10   What is Pete Townshend holding on the cover of *The Who Sell Out* album?

11   What is Nana Mouskouri's only chart hit up to 1997?

12   Whose final album was *Message From the Country*?

13   Whose first band was Vance Arnold and the Avengers?

14   Who did Billy J. Kramer work for before entering the music business?

15   Which poet was part of a 1969 No. 1 hit?

16   Which country were Mouth and MacNeal from?

17   Whose unsuccessful follow-up to a No. 1 was called "Accidents"?

18   Which group was named after characters in "Tin Tin"?

19   Who has starred as Frank N Furter in *The Rocky Horror Show*, and in "Neighbours" and *Grease*?

20   How was William Howard Ashton better known?

Quiz 38 Keyboards

Answers – see page 248

1 Who was the organist on "A Whiter Shade of Pale"?

2 Who left the Strawbs to join Yes?

3 Which band was Gary Brooker in before founding Procul Harum?

4 Who played keyboards with Erasure?

5 How is Rod Argent credited on San José's 1978 "Argentine Melody (Cancion de Argentina)"?

6 Which 1978 Elton John hit was an instrumental?

7 Which suitably titled album did Billy Joel make in the US in 1974 although it was 10 years later that it was a minor UK hit?

8 Which band did Rod Argent found while still at school?

9 Who was keyboards player with the Doors?

10 Which pianist was one of the first Western musicians to visit China in 1991 with his Oriental Melody tour?

11 Who won a piano scholarship to the Juilliard School of Music in 1957?

12 Which jazz pianist had hits with "Take Five" and "Unsquare Dance"?

13 Who was keyboard player with the Moody Blues on "Go Now"?

14 Which Hammond organ specialist became Van Morrison's musical director in the early 90s?

15 Who was the original keyboard player with Pink Floyd?

16 Whose debut solo album was *Between Today and Yesterday*?

17 How is Silsoe better known?

18 Which theme music did Silsoe record for ITV's coverage of the 1986 World Cup Finals?

19 Which 70s David Bowie album did Rick Wakeman work on as a backing session musician?

20 How is Ferdinand la Menthe Morton better known?

Answers

Cliff (see Quiz 40)

1 *The Young Ones*. 2 *Good News*. 3 *When in Spain*. 4 "Oh Boy".
5 One. 6 Minnie Caldwell. 7 Bill Latham. 8 *Aladdin, Cinderella*.
9 50s clothes. 10 *Serious Charge*. 11 *Single-Minded*. 12 Cilla
Black's. 13 Rolf Harris. 14 Tim Brooke-Taylor. 15 "Daddy's
Home". 16 *Five Finger Exercise*. 17 Wembley Stadium. 18 Van
Morrison. 19 Singing at Wimbledon. 20 His fan club.

Quiz 39 Pot Luck 20

Answers – see page 245

LEVEL 3

1   Where did the Beatles stay in New York in their first week in the US?

2   Who did Bing Crosby Zing a Little Zong with in 1952?

3   What follows "I don't want to talk about it", in Rod Stewart's 1977 hit?

4   Whose *Imperial Bedroom* album has a Picasso-styled front cover?

5   Which song has the chorus "Lie la lie…"?

6   Who wrote the soundtrack for the Francis Ford Coppola film *Rumblefish*?

7   Which record label was used by the Kinks throughout the sixties?

8   What soundtrack album was the best-selling album of the fifties?

9   What stands where "the Palais used to stand" in the 1980 Kinks hit?

10 Whose debut album was *Child is the Father of the Man*?

11 Who was Larry Cunningham's backing group?

12 Which group named themselves after a 1956 John Wayne film?

13 Whose first hit was "Endless Sleep"?

14 Who was the only non-Londoner in the Kinks?

15 How was Dino Paul Crocetti better known?

16 Who wrote a children's book called *The Saga of Baby Divine*?

17 Which US group's only hits mention Tracy then Julie?

18 What injuries did James Taylor sustain in a 1969 motorbike accident?

19 Which singer/actor was Great Britain Irish Dance Champion at the age of 14?

20 Whose first album was called *God Shuffled His Feet*?

Quiz 40 Cliff

Answers – see page 246

LEVEL 3

1   Which Cliff film was called *Wonderful to be Young* in the USA?

2   What was Cliff's first religious album called?

3   Which album was recorded completely in Spanish?

4   Which show saw Cliff's TV debut?

5   How many weeks was "Bachelor Boy" in the charts in the US?

6   Which "Coronation Street" character was responsible for Cliff going on a diet – describing him as "that chubby Cliff Richard"?

7   Who is Cliff's manager who co-wrote "Which One's Cliff" with him?

8   Which two pantomimes did Cliff record soundtracks of in the 60s?

9   In the "Cliff Richard Rock Special" in 1981, what did the audience wear?

10   What was Cliff's first film?

11   What was Cliff's autobiography called?

12   On whose show in 1973 did Cliff sing possible Eurovision songs for viewers to vote for?

13   When Cliff fell ill at the Palladium in 1974 who took over for three shows?

14   Which Goodie starred with *Cliff in The Case* in 1972?

15   Which 1981 hit was first recorded by Shep and the Limelites in 1961?

16   In which Peter Shaffer play did Cliff make his straight stage debut in 1970?

17   Where did "Cliff Richard – The Event" take place in 1989?

18   Who duetted with Cliff on 'Whenever God Shines His Light' in 1989?

19   In 1996 what did the *Daily Telegraph* refer to as "Cliffstock"?

20   Who decided to release 'Please Don't Tease' as a single in 1960?

Answers

Keyboards (see Quiz 38)
1 Matthew Fisher. 2 Rick Wakeman. 3 The Paramounts. 4 Vince Clarke. 5 Rodriguez Argentina. 6 "Song For Guy". 7 *Piano Man*. 8 The Zombies. 9 Ray Manzarek. 10 Richard Clayderman. 11 Neil Sedaka. 12 Dave Brubeck. 13 Mike Pinder. 14 Georgie Fame. 15 Rick Wright. 16 Alan Price. 17 Rod Argent. 18 "Aztec Gold". 19 *Hunky Dory*. 20 Jelly Roll Morton.

LEVEL 3

1 Who played in the group Aphrodite's Child with Demis Roussos?

2 Which Rolling Stone served for two years in the RAF?

3 Who had a hit in 1956 with "Moonlight Gambler"?

4 Which boxer appeared on the album cover of *Band On The Run*?

5 Who had the original version of "Na Na Hey Hey Kiss Him Goodbye"?

6 Who were described as a "con" by Pete Murray on "Juke Box Jury"?

7 Which Ken Dodd hit was the third-biggest-selling UK 1960s single?

8 Which former Animal managed and produced Slade?

9 Which Canadian gave EMI their biggest-ever hit in 1957?

10 Which Gallagher and Lyle album shows them on rollerskates?

11 How is Florencia Bisenta de Casillas Martinez Cardona better known?

12 What was the Oscar-winning song from the 1976 film *A Star is Born*?

13 A recording of whose singing at a 1957 church fête was sold at Sotheby's for £78,000?

14 Who were the first Scottish band to have three No. 1s?

15 Which town does Tony Di Bart come from?

16 Which song title links a hit by Kool and the Gang and the Gap Band?

17 Who was Tommy Bruce's backing group?

18 What was Joe Henderson's nickname?

19 Why was Wilson Pickett arrested in New York in November 1974?

20 Which raunchy dance troupe appeared on "The Kenny Everett Video Show"?

1 In which year was the so-called Summer of Love?

2 Whose only hit was "Let's Go To San Francisco"?

3 Which song described the history of the Mamas and Papas?

4 Whose melody was "A Whiter Shade of Pale" based on?

5 On which show did the Beatles sing "All You Need is Love" live to five continents?

6 Who did the Mamas and Papas back on their first recordings?

7 Where did the Beatles plus Mick Jagger and Marianne Faithfull first attend one of the Maharishi's courses?

8 What did Ringo Starr compare to a Butlin's holiday camp in February 1968?

9 What colour jacket is John Lennon wearing on the Sgt Pepper cover?

10 Who recorded "Like An Old Time Movie" in November 1967?

11 Who was paid the most to play at Woodstock?

12 Who took their name from the punchline to the joke "What's purple and lives at the bottom of the sea?"?

13 Where in San Francisco was the first "Human Be-In"?

14 Who enjoyed San Franciscan Nights in 1967?

15 Who wrote "San Francisco (Be Sure to Wear Some Flowers in Your hair)"?

16 Which band had Grace Slick on lead vocals?

17 How was Ellen Cohen better known?

18 Who wrote "A Whiter Shade of Pale"?

19 What was Scott McKenzie's real name?

20 Which politician sued the Move over a promotional postcard for "Flowers in the Rain" which had a caricature of him in the nude?

Answers

Girl Groups (see Quiz 44)

1 Shakespeare's Sister. 2 Pointer Sisters. 3 The Shangri-Las.
4 Holland. 5 "Early to Bed". 6 The Caravelles. 7 Dawn French, Jennifer Saunders, Kathy Burke. 8 The Bangles. 9 The Nolans.
10 "All's well that ends well". 11 Kaye Sisters. 12 Three Degrees.
13 TLC. 14 Shirelles. 15 Ronettes. 16 The Dixie Cups. 17 Mary Wilson. 18 McGuire Sisters. 19 *It's About Time*. 20 Tamla Motown.

Quiz 43 Pot Luck 22

Answers – see page 249

LEVEL 3

1 What is on David Bowie's face on the album cover of *Aladdin Sane*?

2 Which instrumental group had a hit with "Perfidia" in the 1960s?

3 Who played bass on Manfred Mann's "Pretty Flamingo"?

4 Who first played Dorothy and the Scarecrow in *The Wiz* on Broadway?

5 Which Isley Brothers song was recorded by the Beatles?

6 Which British trio released the gold album *Brain Salad Surgery*?

7 What was the first-ever UK Reggae No. 1, in 1969?

8 Who wrote "Baby Come Back" for the Equals?

9 Who was the first French solo singer to get to No. 1 in the UK?

10 Which Stones album cover had peel-off sticky labels on the front?

11 Who recorded the title track for *Twins* with Philip Bailey?

12 What is Evelyn King's middle nickname?

13 Who had a minor hit with "Gin and Juice" in 1994?

14 Whose first album was called *Postcard*?

15 Which British pop festival was founded in 1968?

16 What was the Oscar-winning song from the 1985 film *White Nights*?

17 How is Apollo C. Vermouth, producer of "The Urban Spaceman" by the Bonzo Dog Doo-Dah Band better known?

18 About whom did John Lennon say "We might have had him in the group"?

19 Which severe illness did Joni Mitchell suffer from when she was nine?

20 Which song title links the Supremes and Danii Minogue?

1 Who had an album called *Hormonally Yours*?

2 Who were only the second all-girl group to receive a star on the Hollywood Hall of Fame?

3 Which group was made up of the Weiss sisters and the Ganser twins?

4 Which country were Mai Tai from?

5 What was the Poni-Tails' follow-up to "Born Too Late"?

6 Whose only hit was "You Don't have to be a Baby to Cry"?

7 Who were La Na Nee Nee Noo Noo, who sang "Help!" with Bananarama in 1989?

8 Who had their own Downkiddie record label?

9 Who had a 1992 album called *Portrait*?

10 Which quotation did Shakespear's Sister use to announce their break up?

11 Who joined Frankie Vaughan on "Gotta Have Something in the Bank Frank"?

12 Who had an album *Gold* in 1980?

13 Whose debut single was "Ain't 2 Proud 2 Beg"?

14 Who were originally called the Poquellos?

15 Who interviewed the Beatles on their first US tour?

16 Who were provisionally called Little Miss and the Muffets?

17 Whose autobiography was called *Dreamland*?

18 Who were Phyliss, Dorothy and Christine?

19 What was S.W.V.'s debut album?

20 On which record label did the Marvelettes record on?

1 What is on the back cover of Bridge Over Troubled Water?

2 Which song title links Tears For Fears and Lulu?

3 Which UK record label was the first to have 50 No. 1 hits?

4 What did Frank Sinatra lose at the Copacabana on April 26, 1950?

5 Who had a No. 10 hit with "Heaven Knows I'm Miserable Now"?

6 What is Duane Eddy standing beside on the album cover *Twangin' the Golden Hits*?

7 Which Buddy Holly hit exclaims "My love's bigger than a Cadillac"?

8 Who had four No. 1's between February 1971 and May 1972?

9 Who was originally a drummer for Curved Air?

10 What are the celebrities standing in front of on the *Band On The Run* cover?

11 Who played Paul McCartney's grandfather in *A Hard Day's Night*?

12 Where did Madonna's Blonde Ambition tour begin?

13 What was the title of the Eagles' 1994 reunion album?

14 Who was Michael Jackson's song "Ben" originally intended for?

15 Which US soccer team was co-owned by Paul Simon, Mick Jagger, Rick Wakeman and Peter Frampton?

16 Which song did Dusty Springfield record for *Casino Royale*?

17 Whose 1991 autobiography was called *And the Beat Goes On*?

18 What was the Oscar-winning song from the 1988 film *Working Girl*?

19 Where were the group Mezzoforte from?

20 Why did Harry Connick Jr walk out of a benefit concert in 1995?

Pot Luck 24 (see Quiz 47)
Answers
1 "This is the World Calling". 2 *Electric Ladyland*. 3 Horst Jankowski . 4 Gerry Monroe. 5 Two. 6 "I Am A Rock". 7 A Gun and A Guitar. 8 Synthesizer. 9 Granada. 10 Ryan O'Neal, Diana Ross. 11 Hot Chocolate. 12 Blackpool. 13 Ireland. 14 Barry Manilow. 15 Royal Guardsmen. 16 "How Much is That Doggy in the Window". 17 FBI. 18 Sweden. 19 Keith Michell. 20 "(I've Had) The Time of My Life".

Quiz 46 Queen

LEVEL 3

1 Which band did Brian May and Roger Taylor form in 1967?

2 How was Freddy Mercury billed on "I Can Hear Music" in 1973?

3 Which album did "Las Palabras de Amor" come from?

4 Which song mentions Kruschev and Kennedy?

5 Which organization owned the record company Queen signed with in 1990?

6 Which band had Freddy Mercury been singing with before he joined May and Taylor in 1970?

7 What did Brian May study at Imperial College London in the 60s?

8 Where did Freddy Mercury study graphic art and design?

9 Who did Queen support on their first US tour?

10 Who was "Bohemian Rhapsody" leaked to when EMI were reluctant to release it as it was too long?

11 Which album featured "Radio Gaga"?

12 Which record had been longest at No. 1 before the nine-week run of "Bohemian Rhapsody"?

13 Which Queen film supported *The Hustle* in UK cinemas?

14 What was Queen's follow-up to "Bohemian Rhapsody"?

15 Who supported Queen at their free Hyde Park concert in 1976?

16 Where did Freddy Mercury appear with Wayne Eagling and Derek Dean in July 1979?

17 Who played rhythm guitar on "Crazy Little Thing Called Love"?

18 Who was Roger Taylor's band on his solo album *Shove It*?

19 Whose 1985 No. 3 hit was produced by Roger Taylor?

20 Which album featured "I Want It All"?

2's Company (see Quiz 48)

Answers

1 Sonny and Cher. 2 Shellie and Karen. 3 Sale sign in a furniture shop in Hull. 4 1984 miners' strike. 5 *It's Time*. 6 Baccara. 7 Bellamy Brothers. 8 Esther and Abi Ofarim. 9 Was (Not Was). 10 Nightcrawlers featuring John Reid. 11 Soft Cell – "Tainted Love". 12 Michael Bolton. 13 Brian and Michael. 14 Bardo. 15 Jon and Vangelis. 16 Elton John. 17 Nightcrawlers. 18 Outhere Brothers. 19 Germany. 20 Justin Hayward and John Lodge.

1 What was Bob Geldof's first solo single called?

2 Which Jimi Hendrix album cover shows a group of naked women?

3 Who took a walk in The Black Forest in 1965?

4 Who had a 1970 hit with "Sally"?

5 How many million sales constitute a platinum single in the USA?

6 Which song says "I have my books and poetry to protect me"?

7 What is the soldier on Tom Robinson's "Hope & Glory" carrying?

8 With which musical instrument has Giorgio Moroder had chart success as a performer?

9 Which Spanish town links Frankie Laine and Frank Sinatra?

10 Who were the stars originally lined up for *The Bodyguard* 20 years before the Whitney Houston/Kevin Costner version?

11 Who recorded a reggae version of "Give Peace a Chance" in 1969?

12 In which town was Graham Nash born?

13 Where did Jerry Lee Lewis move to live in 1993?

14 Who released a boxed album set *The Complete Collection and then Some* in 1992?

15 Who sang about "Snoopy vs. The Red Baron" in 1967?

16 When the England cricket team were asked to choose a piece of music to walk on to the pitch to in New Zealand what did Jack Russell choose?

17 Who was Redhead Kingpin's backing group in 1989?

18 Which country do Roxette come from?

19 Who had a 1980 hit with "Captain Beaky"/"Wilfred the Weasel"?

20 What was the Oscar-winning song from the 1987 film *Dirty Dancing*?

Pot Luck 23 (see Quiz 45)
1 The lyrics. 2 "Shout". 3 Columbia. 4 His Voice. 5 The Smiths.
6 A stack of gold ingots. 7 "Not Fade Away". 8 T. Rex. 9 Stewart
Copeland. 10 A Brick Wall. 11 Wilfred Brambell. 12 Tokyo.
13 *Hell Freezes Over*. 14 Donny Osmond. 15 Philadelphia Furies.
16 "The Look of Love". 17 Sonny Bono. 18 "Let The River Run".
19 Iceland. 20 He said members of the audience were talking.

Answers

Quiz 48 2's Company

Answers – see page 254

LEVEL 3

1 Which singing duo appeared in "The Man From U.N.C.L.E." in 1967?

2 What are the members of Alisha's Attic called?

3 How did Everything But the Girl get their name?

4 Which crisis inspired the Style Council's hit "Soul Deep"?

5 What was Clock's first album called?

6 Who said "Sorry I'm a Lady" in 1978?

7 Which duo's song was used as a theme for the 1980 film *Little Darlings*?

8 How are Esther Zaled and Abraham Reichstadt better known?

9 Whose "Shake Your Head" had uncredited backing vocals by Kim Basinger and Ozzy Osbourne?

10 Whose first album was called *Let's Push It*?

11 Which duo had the top-selling single of 1981?

12 Who duetted with Pavarotti singing "Nessun Dorma" on a US late-night TV show in 1996?

13 How were Kevin Parrott and Michael Coleman better known?

14 Who went One Step Further in 1982?

15 Who had a hit with "I'll find My Way Home" in 1981?

16 Up to 1996 who had the most duet partners in the charts?

17 Who took "Surrender Your Love" to No. 7 in 1995?

18 Whose debut album was *1 Polish 2 Biscuits and a Fish Sandwich*?

19 Which country do Jam and Spoon come from?

20 Who had a hit with "Blue Guitar" in 1975?

Answers

Queen (see Quiz 46)
1 Smile. 2 Larry Lurex. 3 *Hot Space*. 4 "Killer Queen". 5 Walt Disney. 6 Wreckage. 7 Astronomy and physics. 8 Ealing College of Art. 9 Mott the Hoople. 10 Kenny Everett. 11 *The Works*. 12 Paul Anka's "Diana". 13 *Queen at the Rainbow*. 14 "You're My Best Friend". 15 Kiki Dee and Supercharge. 16 Royal Ballet. 17 Freddy Mercury. 18 The Cross. 19 Jimmy Nail. 20 *The Miracle*.

Quiz 49 Pot Luck 25

Answers – see page 259

1 What colour is the title on Neil Young's *Harvest* album?

2 Who won Grammys in 1986 for Best Album, Producer and Male Vocalist?

3 Who did Sandie Shaw record "Hand In Glove" with?

4 Which blondes are on the cover of the Stones' *Some Girls* album?

5 What links Nino Tempo and April Stevens with Donny and Marie Osmond?

6 Who does Prince give thanks to on the inner sleeve of *1999*?

7 Whose first album was *First Take* in 1970?

8 Who was executive producer of the Monty Python film *Life Of Brian*?

9 What former Cream star backed Roger Waters on a 1984 tour?

10 Which China Crisis album cover shows a photo of an industrial area?

11 How is the reggae singer Everton Bonner better known?

12 Which organization were the Joy Strings in?

13 Whose music was used by David Puttnam in *The Frog Prince* in 1985?

14 Whose middle names are Peter George St John Le Baptiste de la Salle?

15 Who made a reunion album *Far From Home* in 1994?

16 Who played a lock-keeper in the BBC sitcom "The River" in 1986?

17 Which band is led by Ms Leskanich?

18 Whose father was in the Jim Mac Jazz Band?

19 What does LOD stand for on Billy Ocean's 1979 hit?

20 What was the Oscar-winning song from *The Thomas Crown Affair*?

Answers

Pot Luck 26 (see Quiz 51)
1 Driveway of a stately home. 2 *Poor Me.* 3 Cockney Rebel. 4 Keith Emerson burned a US flag on stage. 5 Jonathan King. 6 "Wee Tom". 7 Plane crash. 8 Christopher Cross. 9 Nigel Planer. 10 Trumpet. 11 Glove. 12 Kylie Minogue. 13 "Kokomo". 14 Jennifer Rush. 15 Frankie Laine. 16 Simon and Garfunkel. 17 "Last Dance". 18 John Lennon. 19 They didn't have one. 20 Sri Lanka.

Quiz 50 In the Family

Answers – see page 260

1   What was the name of Sonny and Cher's daughter born in 1969?

2   Who is the mother of the writer and producer Terry Melcher?

3   Who is John and Michelle Phillips's singing daughter?

4   Who is the sister of the Dakotas' drummer, Tony Mansfield?

5   Who had a daughter called Owen Vanessa in 1967?

6   What is the name of Steve Winwood's brother, who was also in the Spencer Davis Group?

7   Whose brother set up the label Illegal Records?

8   Which father and son had No. 1 hits in 1967 and 1991 respectively?

9   Which second-generation musical group's first hit was "Boys Will Be Boys"?

10 Which musical star was the mother of Larry Hagman, a.k.a. J.R. in "Dallas"?

11 Which father and son were both on the 1987 hit "Hey Matthew"?

12 On which single did Sam Brown's mother Vicki make the Top Ten?

13 Whose sons had a chart hit with "Don't Bring Me Your Heartaches"?

14 Who was born Gary Levitch and is the son of a famous comedian?

15 Who were the first father and daughter to top the charts separately and together?

16 Who was the father of the Wilson sisters in Wilson Phillips?

17 Who was the husband of Beverley Sister Joy?

18 Who is the son of Marnie Nixon who sang for Natalie Wood and Audrey Hepburn in *West Side Story* and *My Fair Lady* respectively?

19 Who is the pop star son of the former Mrs Roy Boulting?

20 Which two brothers were in the Bluebells?

The Beatles (see Quiz 52)

Answers

1 "Ready Steady Go". 2 Bobby Vinton. 3 Leeds University Law Society. 4 "Can't Buy Me Love". 5 *A Spaniard in the Works*. 6 Paul McCartney. 7 Rory Storm and the Hurricanes. 8 Tambourine. 9 40 years. 10 Schoolgirl on a train. 11 Brian Epstein. 12 "Flying". 13 Tony Sheridan. 14 Christ. 15 *The Family Way*. 16 "Something". 17 Barbara Dickson. 18 Peter Sellers' "A Hard Day's Night". 19 "All You Need is Cash". 20 Asteroids.

Quiz 51 Pot Luck 26

Answers – see page 257

LEVEL 3

1 Where is Elton John standing on the album cover of *A Single Man*?

2 What was Adam Faith's autobiography called?

3 Whose debut album was called *The Psychomodo*?

4 Why were the Nice banned from the Royal Albert Hall?

5 Who was Bubblerock on "(I Can't Get No) Satisfaction" in 1974?

6 What was Lord Rockingham XI's follow-up to "Hoots Mon"?

7 How did Jim Croce die?

8 How is Christopher Geppert better known?

9 Who understudied for David Essex in *Evita* and had a No. 1 in 1986 ?

10 What was the first musical instrument Eddy Grant learned?

11 Which item of clothing of Michael Jackson's was sold for £16,500 in 1991?

12 Who had the best-selling UK album in 1988?

13 Which Beach Boys single was co-written by Scott McKenzie?

14 Who was the only female to have one of the Top Ten best-selling singles of the 80s?

15 Who has had more weeks at No. 1 than Bryan Adams with one single?

16 Who had the two best-selling albums of the 70s?

17 What was the Oscar-winning song from the 1978 film *Thank God It's Friday*?

18 Who was guest of honour at the Foyles Literary Lunch to mark Shakespeare's 400th birthday?

19 Who was the drummer with Mungo Jerry on "In The Summertime"?

20 Where was the Seekers' Keith Potger born?

Answers

Pot Luck 25 (see Quiz 49)
1 Orange. 2 Phil Collins. 3 The Smiths. 4 Marilyn Monroe, Brigitte Bardot, Jayne Mansfield. 5 Deep Purple. 6 God. 7 Roberta Flack. 8 George Harrison. 9 Eric Clapton. 10 *Working With Fire and Steel*. 11 Pliers. 12 Salvation Army. 13 Enya. 14 Brian Eno. 15 Traffic. 16 David Essex. 17 Katrina and the Waves. 18 Paul McCartney. 19 Love on Delivery. 20 "Windmills of Your Mind".

Quiz 52 The Beatles

Answers – see page 258

1 On which show were the Beatles first seen live on nationwide TV?

2 Whose record did the Beatles vote a miss on "Juke Box Jury" although it knocked them off the top of the US charts eight weeks later?

3 Which society elected Ringo its vice-president in 1964?

4 What was the first song they sang on "Top of the Pops"?

5 What was John Lennon's second book called?

6 Who was the last Beatle to marry?

7 Who was Ringo drummer with before the Beatles?

8 Which instrument did George Harrison play on "Hey You've Got to Hide Your Love Away"?

9 What did Ringo reply as the Queen asked him, "How long have you been together now?" when she presented them with their MBEs?

10 Which part did Patti Boyd play in *Hard Day's Night*?

11 Who won an album in *Melody Maker* for saying Paul McCartney played lead guitar on "Ticket to Ride"?

12 What was the Beatles' first instrumental release?

13 Who was the first non-Beatle to be credited on a Beatles single?

14 Which word in "The Ballad of John and Yoko" made it subject to radio censorship in the US?

15 Which Hywel Bennett film did Paul McCartney write the score for?

16 Which song did Sinatra say was the greatest love song in the last 50 years?

17 Who first starred in Willy Russell's *John, Paul, George, Ringo and Bert*?

18 What was the first cover version of a Beatles hit to make the charts?

19 What was the name of Eric Idle's TV parody of the Beatles' career?

20 Which new discoveries were named Lennon, McCartney, Harrison and Starr in 1990?

Answers

Quiz 53 Pot Luck 27

Answers – see page 263

LEVEL 3

1 Who drew the album cover for *The Who By Numbers*?

2 Who won a Grammy in 1970 for Best New Artist?

3 Whose pet boa constrictor died in 1977 stopping his plans for his first tour for two years?

4 Where was Duran Duran's video for "Hungry Like the Wolf" shot?

5 What is on the cover of Huey Lewis and the News' *Sports* album?

6 Which fifties pop star used to wear a hearing aid?

7 Which 1985 song won an Ivor Novello award for Elton John and Bernie Taupin?

8 Who was at No. 6 in 1958 with "Mad Passionate Love"?

9 Which Everly Brother has the lower voice?

10 On which Beatles album cover does George Harrison sit on top of the first letter of the title?

11 What is Whitney Houston's character called in *The Bodyguard*?

12 Who did Michael Jackson escort to her 65th birthday party in 1997?

13 Who was lead singer with Rose Royce?

14 What was Manic Street Preachers' first solo single?

15 Which country was Manfred Mann himself from?

16 What was the Oscar-winning song from the 1979 film *Norma Rae*?

17 Who was asked to write the music for the Disney *Tarzan* film?

18 What were Ziggy Marley's backing group called?

19 Who won the Grammy Best Pop Male Vocal Performance in 1961 for "Lollipops and Roses"?

20 Which musical won the Oscar for Best Picture in 1958?

Pot Luck 28 (see Quiz 55)

LEVEL 3

1   Who had a Top Ten hit with Marie Osmond's "Paper Roses" in 1960?

2   Who made a cover version of "Reet Petite" in 1993?

3   Which British artist previously recorded UB40 and Chrissie Hynde's "Breakfast in Bed"?

4   What did Rozalla sing in 1994 that the O'Jays had in 1976 and 1978?

5   Who had the original chart hit with "Caravan of Love"?

6   Who had the first hit with "It's All in the Game" in 1958?

7   Who also had a hit with "When I Fall in Love" between Nat King Cole, the first time, in 1958 and Rick Astley in 1987?

8   Who did Johnny Mathis duet with on "When A Child is Born" five years after his solo hit?

9   Who before Take That took "Could It Be Magic?" into the Top 40?

10 Who joined the Troggs on a rerecording of "Wild Thing" in 1993?

11 Who had a Top Ten single hit with "Twist and Shout" 30 years before Chaka Demus and Pliers' 1993 No. 1?

12 Whose version of "This Old Heart of Mine" got higher in the charts?

13 Who did the cover of "Too Busy Thinking 'Bout My Baby" in 1972?

14 Who had the '95 version of "Always Something There to Remind Me"?

15 Who had a Total Eclipse of the Heart in 1995?

16 Who released the Beach Boys' "I Can Hear Music" in 1973?

17 Who made an EP of "Only Living Boy in New York" in 1993?

18 What was on the others side of KWS's No. 1 "Please Don't Go", a 1979 hit for KC and the Sunshine Band?

19 Who released the Kinks' "Waterloo Sunset" in 1997?

20 Who revived "Hazy Shade of Winter" for the film *Less Than Zero*?

1   What is Paul McCartney holding in his right hand on the cover of *Abbey Road*?

2   Which Madness video featured a van dropping out of a plane?

3   Which James Bond theme did Duran Duran sing?

4   Who was singing "If you'll be my bodyguard" in 1986?

5   What song title was a No. 1 for Frankie Laine and Barbra Streisand?

6   What word begins song titles that end with Cherry and Horses?

7   What was the Move's only No. 1?

8   Which song won the Oscar for the 1965 film *The Sandpiper*?

9   Whose debut album was *Time and a Word*?

10   What are the Beach Boys doing on the album cover of *Pet Sounds*?

11   Which song won a Grammy for Frank Sinatra for Best Pop Male Vocal Performance in 1965?

12   Who had the original UK hit with "Oh No Not My Baby"?

13   Who wrote "Don't Bring Me Down" a hit for the Animals?

14   Who had an album called *Blue Light Red Light*?

15   What was the Oscar-winning song from the 1970 film *Lovers and Other Strangers*?

16   Who was the subject of the biography *He's A Rebel*?

17   Who first played the title role in *Imagine – The John Lennon Story*?

18   Whose son is called Giacomo Luke?

19   How many Oscars was *My Fair Lady* nominated for in 1964?

20   Who felt like Buddy Holly in 1984?

LEVEL 3

1 Who spent Another Weekend in 1988?

2 Who sang about August October in 1970?

3 Where was the A-Bomb on the Jam's 70s double-A-sided record?

4 Which day has been recorded more than any other?

5 What was Earth Wind and Fire's first single?

6 Which year features in a minor Bryan Adams' hit?

7 Who were under April Skies in 1987?

8 Who had a Three Minute Hero in 1980?

9 Who had a 1956 No. 1 with "It's Almost Tomorrow"?

10 Who backed Chris Farlowe on "Out of Time"?

11 Whose second album was subtitled *1990 A New Decade*?

12 Who wrote the English lyric for "Seasons in the Sun"?

13 Whose only No. 1 was "One Day at a Time"?

14 Who turned down the title role in *Midnight Cowboy*?

15 Who had a Morning Dance in 1979?

16 Which song's third line is "If woman can survive"?

17 Which song won the Oscar for Best Song in 1960?

18 What was Status Quo's fourth No. 1 album?

19 Who made a cover version of "Morning Has Broken" in 1992?

20 Who sang "Midnight at the Oasis" in 1974?

Quiz 57 Pot Luck 29

Answers – see page 267

LEVEL 3

1 What is Roger Daltry covered in on *The Who Sell Out* album?

2 Which song says "Check out Guitar George – he knows all the chords"?

3 What was Guns N' Roses' best-selling 80s album?

4 Who swapped autographs and soccer chat with Lech Walesa in 1984?

5 Where was Jumpin' Jack Flash born according to the Stones?

6 Who proposed to Maria Elena Santiago on their first date?

7 What was Madonna's best-selling UK album in the 1980s?

8 Who had the first UK hit with "Will You Still Love me Tomorrow?"?

9 Who were going to Montego Bay in 1986?

10 Which US producer plays guitar on the Stones' "Play With Fire"?

11 Which film had an Oscar nomination for "Let's Hear it For the Boy"?

12 Who was 'another man' in "Get Back"?

13 What are Holland, Dozier and Holland's first names?

14 Which song has the line "tell me will this déjà vu never end"?

15 Who were the first act after the Beatles to have a US hit with "I Want To Hold Your Hand"?

16 Which 30-year-old garment of John Lennon's was sold for £24,200 in 1992?

17 What was the top UK single of 1979?

18 Which song from the 1961 film *Breakfast At Tiffany's* won an Oscar?

19 Which Vanessa Williams song was used to advertise Bisto Gravy?

20 Who played solo recorder on Marvin, Welch and Farrar's "Music Makes My Day"?

Pot Luck 30 (see Quiz 59)

Answers
1 Animal Masks. 2 "Roses are Red". 3 Peggy Lee. 4 Duane Eddy. 5 "Charlie Brown". 6 *Some Girls*. 7 The Tremblers. 8 The Bass Guitar. 9 Yazoo. 10 "The Final Countdown". 11 Chisholm. 12 "Eye of the Tiger". 13 Judge Dread. 14 Jeff Lynne. 15 Toni Braxton. 16 Bobby Brown and Whitney Houston. 17 Pope Paul VI. 18 "Call Me Irresponsible". 19 "Cigarettes and Alcohol". 20 Keith Michell, Captain Beaky and his Band.

265

Quiz 58 Place the Place

Answers – see page 268

LEVEL 3

1. Which Matt Monro hit has a country in the title?

2. In which year did the Beatles hit the Top Ten with "Back in the USSR"?

3. What was U2's second hit of 1988?

4. Where did the Council Come To in 1985?

5. What was the Gibson Brothers' first UK hit?

6. What was Tom Browne in the charts with in 1980 and in 1992?

7. Where did the Bee Gees try to hitch a ride to in "Massachusetts"?

8. Which song has the line "If only you'd started ringing your bell"?

9. Where is Paul Simon "counting the cars" in "America"?

10. Which musical includes a character called Nathan Detroit?

11. Which 1985 chart toppers had a country and continent in their name?

12. Where were Christie after "Yellow River" in 1970?

13. Where was Marty Robbins in 1960?

14. Which Lassie was a 50s hit for Tommy Steele and Freddy Cannon?

15. Where were the Piranhas in 1982?

16. Which city links Ronnie Hilton and Max Bygraves within song titles?

17. Where was Perry Como's 1960 hit?

18. Where were Arrested Development in 1992 and 1993?

19. What was Tony Christie's first solo UK hit?

20. Who were on the "Ventura Highway" in 1972?

1 What have Genesis on their heads on the *Foxtrot* album cover?

2 What was Bobby Vinton's first million-seller?

3 Who co-wrote the songs for Disney's *The Lady and The Tramp*?

4 Who launched his chart career with the instrumental "Rebel Rouser"?

5 Which Coasters hit opens "Fee-fee fi-fi fo-fo fum"?

6 Which Stones album cover has holes in it with movable pictures?

7 Which group did Peter Noone join in 1980?

8 What did Jimmy Page play until Jeff Beck left the Yardbirds?

9 Who had a No. 3 album in 1983 entitled *Nobody's Diary*?

10 What was Europe's best-selling 80s single?

11 What is Spice Girl Mel C's surname?

12 Which Survivor hit was used in *Rocky III*?

13 Whose singles "Big Seven" and "Big Six" were banned by the BBC?

14 Whose first solo album was *Armchair Theatre*?

15 Who was Best New Artist in the 1993 Grammy awards?

16 Who are the parents of Bobbi Kristina?

17 Who did Sonny and Cher have a private audience with in 1966?

18 What was the Oscar-winning song from the 1963 film *Papa's Delicate Condition*?

19 When the England cricket team were asked to choose a piece of music to walk on to the pitch to in New Zealand what did Phil Tufnell choose?

20 Who were responsible for The Trial of Hissing Sid?

Quiz 60 Rod Stewart

Answers – see page 266

LEVEL 3

1 What was Rod's first solo album?

2 What is his birth sign?

3 Which 60s group members were in Rod's class at school?

4 Which football club did he sign with as an apprentice?

5 Why was Rod deported from Spain when he was in his teens?

6 With which group did he make his TV debut?

7 Who was the female vocalist with his Steampacket group?

8 What was the 30-minute documentary about him in 1965 called?

9 Why did his plane have to make a forced landing in 1995?

10 Who is the mother of his daughter who appeared in his "Forever Young" video?

11 Who did he dedicate his album *Vagabond Heart* to?

12 In 1991 it was reported that Rod had been accepted into the Highgate branch of what?

13 Who did he duet with on "Angel" on the Scottish Football Squad's *Easy Easy* album?

14 Which song did he record in 1982 for the Michael Keaton film *Night Shift*?

15 Who played solo guitar on "Infatuation"?

16 Which song was "Do Ya Think I'm Sexy?" said to be "borrowed" from?

17 Who did Rod donate the royalties from the song to?

18 Which album did "Baby Jane" come from?

19 Which single did he release with Sting and Bryan Adams in 1994?

20 Where did he travel on the tour called Worth Leaving Home For?

Answers

Place the Place (see Quiz 58)
1 "From Russia With Love". 2 1976. 3 "Angel of Harlem".
4 Milton Keynes. 5 "Cuba". 6 "Funkin' In Jamaica". 7 San
Francisco. 8 "Winchester Cathedral". 9 The New Jersey Turnpike.
10 *Guys and Dolls.* 11 USA For Africa. 12 San Bernardino.
13 El Paso. 14 Tallahassee. 15 Zambesi. 16 Amsterdam.
17 Delaware. 18 Tennessee. 19 "Las Vegas". 20 America.

Quiz 61 Pot Luck 31

Answers – see page 271

Answers – see page 271

LEVEL 3

1 In what country are the Beatles skiing in *Help!*?

2 Who drew the cartoons on the back cover of "Between The Buttons"?

3 Which singer celebrated his Bar Mitzvah in Minnesota in May 1954?

4 Who was Torn Between Two Lovers in 1977?

5 Who was the first country singer to tour Britain and appear at the London Palladium?

6 What was a hit for the Ronettes, Dave Edmunds and the Ramones?

7 Who was voted Capital Radio's Best Female Singer from 1978–1980?

8 Who wrote "Where Are You Now (My Love)"?

9 Who composed the theme song for *Ghostbusters*?

10 Which ELO album won the British Rock and Pop Best Album award in 1978?

11 What was Def Leppard's best-selling album of the 80s?

12 Which British singer had chart success with "Magic Moments"?

13 Who recorded "I'll Never Fall in Love Again" on an EP in 1990?

14 What was the name of the song from *On Her Majesty's Secret Service*?

15 Who had a 90s hit with "Dedicated to the One I Love"?

16 What was the first Manchester United hit not to have United in the title?

17 Which film did Elvis's "Hard Headed Woman" come from?

18 Who had a hit cover version of the Beatles' "We Can Work It Out"?

19 What is Spice Girl Emma's middle name?

20 Which singer is Whitney Houston's godmother?

Pot Luck 32 (see Quiz 63)

Answers

1 Creedence Clearwater Revival. 2 "Cantare… oh, oh, oh, oh".
3 "Dance to the Music". 4 John Lennon. 5 Bay City Rollers.
6 Jonathan King. 7 "As Time Goes By". 8 *No Parlez*.
9 Declared bankrupt. 10 A pith helmet. 11 Gladys Knight.
12 *Loving You*. 13 Keyboards. 14 Hank Marvin. 15 Don Partridge. 16 Boyz. 17 Elaine Paige. 18 "All Over the World".
19 "Up Where We Belong". 20 Gavin Sutherland.

1 What was on the other side of "Come Outside" in 1975?

2 Who did a cover of Slade's "Merry Xmas Everybody" in 1990?

3 Who said Merry Christmas Darling in 1972 and again in 1990?

4 Who sang "Frosty the Snowman" on the compilation album *A Christmas Gift For You* in 1963?

5 Which Christmas hit was subtitled "Soleado"?

6 What are the Two Little Boys called in Rolf Harris's 1969 Christmas No. 1?

7 Which duo had a hit with "White Christmas" in 1985?

8 Which trio spent Christmas in Vienna in 1993?

9 Who had a *Merry Merry Christmas* album in 1990?

10 For how many consecutive Christmases was Bing Crosby's "White Christmas" in the US charts?

11 Which duo made a *Christmas Collection* in 1990?

12 Who is credited on the label of "Happy Christmas (War is Over)"?

13 Which Christmas No. 1 was from the musical *The Little Match Girl*?

14 Which female was on the *Christmas in Vienna II* album in 1994?

15 What was the Slade Christmas party album called?

16 Who made *The Christmas Album* in 1992?

17 What was on the other side of "My Hometown" in 1985?

18 Which instrumentalist had a 1984 *Christmas* album?

19 Who was in a Winter Wonderland in 1958?

20 What was on the other side of "Bluebottle Blues" in 1956?

Quiz 63 Pot Luck 32

Answers – see page 269

Answers – see page 269

LEVEL 3

1 Whose debut album was *Green River*?

2 What follows "Volare... oh, oh!"?

3 What was Sly and the Family Stone's debut single?

4 Which Beatle looks directly at the camera on the *Rubber Soul* cover?

5 Whose final 70s No. 1 in the UK was "Give A Little Love"?

6 Who wrote "Johnny Reggae"?

7 Which song title links Jason Donovan and Dooley Wilson?

8 What was the title of Paul Young's 1983 million–selling album?

9 Which problem did Cyndi Lauper have in 1983?

10 What is George Harrison wearing on the *Revolver* album cover?

11 Who sang the theme song from *A Licence to Kill* in 1989?

12 In which film did Elvis sing "Teddy Bear"?

13 Which musical instrument did Herbie Hancock play?

14 Who joined Brian May on the 1992 "We Are the Champions"?

15 Which one-man band went into the charts in 1968?

16 Who was Heavy D's backing band?

17 Which female vocalist made an album of Queen songs?

18 What was Françoise Hardy's first hit in English?

19 Which song won an Oscar in *An Officer and a Gentleman*?

20 Who wrote Rod Stewart's "Sailing"?

Pot Luck 31 (see Quiz 61)

Answers

1 Austria. 2 Charlie Watts. 3 Bob Dylan. 4 Mary MacGregor.
5 Slim Whitman. 6 "Baby I Love You". 7 Kate Bush. 8 Tony
Hatch and Jackie Trent. 9 Ray Parker Jnr. 10 *Out Of The Blue*.
11 *Hysteria*. 12 Ronnie Hilton. 13 Deacon Blue. 14 "We Have
All the Time in the World". 15 Bitty McLean. 16 "Come On You
Reds". 17 *King Creole*. 18 Stevie Wonder. 19 Lee. 20 Aretha
Franklin.

1 Whose debut UK album was called *Both Sides*?

2 Who made a TV movie called *Buffalo Girls*?

3 Which group did Kenny Rogers join in 1966?

4 How is Sam Hutt better known?

5 How is Nudie important to country stars?

6 Who was Merle Haggard's album *Same Train, a Different Time* a tribute to?

7 Who were reunited for the *Historic Reunion* album in the late 60s?

8 Which country singer starred in the US soap "Washington"?

9 Who had the 80s country hit "If Drinking Don't Kill Me (Her Memory Will!)"?

10 Who wrote "Crazy", a huge hit for Patsy Cline?

11 Who produced Waylon Jennings's first single?

12 Who made the album *King's Record Shop* in 1987?

13 Who is Johnny Cash's country-singer step-daughter?

14 Which cause did Johnny Cash champion in "Bitter Tears"?

15 What was Dolly Parton's first US country No. 1?

16 What was Alabama's best-selling US 80s album?

17 In which Prison did Johnny Cash record live in 1968?

18 Who wrote the Johnny Cash hit "Busted"?

19 What was Willie Nelson's film debut with Jane Fonda and Robert Redford?

20 Whose debut album was *Elite Hotel*?

Answers

Christmas Records (see Quiz 62)
1 "Christmas in Dreadland". 2 Metal Gurus. 3 The Carpenters. 4 The Ronettes. 5 "When A Child is Born". 6 Joe, Jack. 7 Keith Harris and Orville. 8 Placido Domingo, Jose Carreras and Diana Ross. 9 New Kids on the Block. 10 Ten. 11 Foster and Allen. 12 John and Yoko and the Plastic Ono Band with the Harlem Community Choir. 13 "Mistletoe and Wine". 14 Dionne Warwick. 15 Crackers. 16 Neil Diamond. 17 "Santa Claus is Comin' To Town". 18 Richard Clayderman. 19 Johnny Mathis. 20 "I'm Walking Backwards for Christmas".

Quiz 65 Pot Luck 33

1 Who was the promoter of "Live Aid"?

2 Which group has included Alan Paul, Tim Hauser, Janis Siegel and Cheryl Bentyne among its members?

3 What was the No. 1 produced by Fluck and Law creations in 1986?

4 What is being modelled on the back cover of the Stones' "Some Girls"?

5 Which group with a 1964 No. 1 hit had a girl drummer?

6 Who was lead singer on Python Lee Jackson's "In A Broken Dream"?

7 What was unique about the US Top 5 singles of April 4, 1964?

8 Who was the first female singer to top the UK charts?

9 Whose debut album was *Kimono My House* in 1974?

10 What colour is Paul McCartney wearing on the inside cover of the *Sgt Pepper* album?

11 What was the name of Anthony Hopkins's first – minor – chart venture?

12 Which FA Cup squad featured Tippa Irie and Peter Hunnigale in 1993?

13 How was the Joan Collins Fan Club better known?

14 Who did David Essex duet with on "True Love Ways" in 1986?

15 In which film did Elvis first sing "Return to Sender"?

16 What was the daytime profession of several of the Honeycombs?

17 Who sang the theme for *For Your Eyes Only*?

18 Who formed his own Dark Horse record label in 1974?

19 What was the subtitle of "Arthur's Theme" from the 1982 film?

20 From what was Don Johnson/Barbra Streisand's "Till I Loved You" the love theme?

Quiz 66 Stage Show Songs

LEVEL 3

1   Which song from *Sweet Charity* did Shirley Bassey chart with in 1967?

2   Who duetted with Patti Labelle on the 1986 "On My Own"?

3   What was David Essex's only chart hit from *Evita*?

4   Who took "Memory" into the Top 50 in 1985?

5   Who made the album *Stage Heroes*?

6   Which song from *A Little Night Music* did Judy Collins take into the charts?

7   Which musical flop contained the songs "If You Want to See Palermo Again" and "They're Naked and they Move"?

8   Which musical play did "Hymne A l'Amour" come from?

9   Who took "The Perfect Year" into the charts?

10 Which show has the song "People"?

11 Who sang Peron on the original recording of *Evita*?

12 Who wrote "Wandrin' Star"?

13 What was the Song part of *Song and Dance* in the West End?

14 Who was the main lyricist on the songs from *Phantom of the Opera*?

15 Which show had the song "We're the UFO"?

16 What was on the A side of Shirley Bassey's "Reach For the Stars"?

17 Which Follies song did Liza Minelli chart with in 1989?

18 "Ain't Nobody here But Us Chickens" is in which show?

19 Which *Jesus Christ Superstar* song did Petula Clark release as a single in 1972?

20 Who co-wrote the musical *Tallulah Who?* with Willy Russell?

Answers

Bob Dylan (see Quiz 69)

1 Allen. 2 Chicago. 3 Gerde's Folk City, Greenwich Village.
4 *The Freewheelin' Bob Dylan*. 5 Sheffield. 6 "Mr Tambourine Man". 7 "If You Gotta Go, Go Now". 8 Concert for Bangla Desh.
9 Alias. 10 Accomplice. 11 Bob Dylan. 12 Dave Stewart.
13 Lucky. 14 "The Times They Are A-Changin'".
15 Synagogue. 16 The Band. 17 Six. 18 *Dylan and the Dead*.
19 Michael Bolton. 20 Motorcycle accident.

1   Who won British Rock and Pop Best Band in 1979 and 1980?

2   Who wrote "Eloise"?

3   Which family was Terry Jacks a former member of?

4   Which record label uses the reference number prefix "CAS"?

5   Whose debut album was *Look At Us*?

6   What follows "We don't have to take our clothes off" in Jermaine Stewart's 1986 hit?

7   Which group's career is profiled in *The Great Rock 'n' Roll Swindle*?

8   Who wrote "Jealous Guy"?

9   Which Hungarian had her only chart entry with "Pickin' A Chicken"?

10   Who had the highest chart position with "Hello Dolly"?

11   What relation were Hank and Eddie Cochran, known as the Cochran Brothers?

12   Which school did the teenage Peter Gabriel go to?

13   Who had a one-man show in 1995 called *To The Bone*?

14   What did Chris Rea's "You Can Go Your Own Way" advertise?

15   Who was the Red Hot Chili Peppers' *Working Class Hero* album dedicated to?

16   Who had the original US country hit "Love Can Build a Bridge"?

17   Who has a Gothic mail-order catalogue called *Sanctuary*?

18   Who duetted with Michael Hutchence on "Please (You Got That ...)" on the Inxs album?

19   Who replaced Cliff Richard in *Time* in the West End?

20   Who were once known as the BB5?

Quiz 68 Bob Dylan

Answers – see page 274

LEVEL 3

1   What was Bob Dylan's middle name when he was born?

2   Where did he run away to when he was ten?

3   Where was his first live performance in New York ?

4   Which album was "A Hard Rain's Gonna Fall" first featured on?

5   Where in England did the 1965 Don't Look Back Tour start?

6   Which was the first Dylan composition to top the charts?

7   Which Dylan composition was a 1965 chart hit for Manfred Mann?

8   What was Dylan's only live concert in 1971?

9   Which role did he play in *Pat Garrett and Billy the Kid*?

10   Which record label did he launch in 1979?

11   Who painted the "Saved" sleeve?

12   Who produced his *Knocked Out Loaded* album?

13   What was Dylan's name in the Travelling Wilburys?

14   What was the first Dylan song used in a commercial?

15   What type of building did Dylan buy in 1994?

16   Who did he record "The Basement Tapes" with?

17   By 1970 how many No. 1 albums did Dylan have?

18   Which was the first album made with a credited band?

19   Who did he collaborate with on "Steel Bars"?

20   What stopped his live performances in 1966 for many months?

Stage Show Songs (see Quiz 66)

Answers

1 "Big Spender". 2 Michael McDonald. 3 "Oh What a Circus".
4 Aled Jones. 5 Colm Wilkinson. 6 "Send in the Clowns".
7 *Budgie*. 8 *Piaf*. 9 Dina Carroll. 10 *Funny Girl*. 11 Paul Jones.
12 Lerner and Loewe. 13 "Tell Me on a Sunday".
14 Charles Hart. 15 *Time*. 16 "Climb Every Mountain".
17 "Losing My Mind". 18 "Five Guys Named Moe". 19 "I
Don't Know How to Love Him". 20 Suzi Quatro.

1   What is in the centre of the Eagles's *Greatest Hits* album cover?

2   Who had a hit with "Where Will The Baby's Dimple Be?"?

3   Which group had a hit in 1986 with "Rage Hard"?

4   Which British rocker had a rabies jab after biting a rat on stage?

5   Which soap did Sue Nicholls's "Where Will You Be?" come from?

6   What was John Lennon holding in his right hand on the cover of his book *A Spaniard In The Works*?

7   Who released a live recordings album titled *Arena*?

8   Which building has been "the ruin of many a poor boy"?

9   What did Yazoo change their name to for their releases in the US?

10 Which pianist had the album *I'm Mighty Glad*?

11 Where were the Easybeats formed?

12 Who released the album *In the Hot Seat* in 1994?

13 Who released a single of "The Man I Love" in 1994 with Larry Adler on harmonica?

14 Which product did Desmond Dekker's "Israelites" advertise in 1990?

15 Who named themselves after a favourite song of one of their grannies?

16 What was Levi Stubbs's voice used for in the film *The Little Shop of Horrors*?

17 Who was voted the Face of 1968?

18 What was the first record on the Zang Tumb Tumm label?

19 Which book does the name Heaven 17 come from?

20 Who wrote the children's fantasy *The Point*?

Quiz 70 Big Ballads

LEVEL 3

1   Which ballad was at No. 1 when Queen Elizabeth II was crowned?

2   Which Tony Bennett hit was based on a tune by Borodin?

3   Which ballad gave the first 1964 No. 1 for a female soloist?

4   Who wrote "Make It Easy On Yourself", a hit for the Walker Brothers?

5   Which single held the record for longest time in the Top 50 in 1967?

6   Which Frank Sinatra song won the Oscar for Best Song in 1954?

7   Which album was "Without You" on in June 1971?

8   Which TV series was "She" the theme song for?

9   Which song was nearly called "It's Only Your Lover Returning"?

10 Which ballad by two different singers had the No. 1 spot in 1953?

11 What is the name of the character which Elaine Paige sings in "I Know Him So Well"?

12 Which ballad was a No. 1 for Dave Lee Travis, Bruce Forsyth and Keith Chegwin among others?

13 Who was the woman to take "The Power of Love" to No. 1 in the US?

14 Which 80s Whitney Houston hit was a US No. 1 and a UK No. 8?

15 What was the first single by a woman to enter the charts at No. 1?

16 In which year did "He Ain't Heavy, He's My Brother" first get to No. 1?

17 Which ballad was the best-selling song of Les Reed and Barry Mason?

18 Which film did "Secret Love" come from?

19 In which decade was "Who's Sorry Now" written?

20 Which musical was "No Other Love" from?

Answers

One-Hit Wonders (see Quiz 72)

1 Hedgehoppers Anonymous. 2 Brian and Michael. 3 Charlene. 4 Lee Marvin's "Wandrin' Star". 5 Carol Kidd. 6 Crazy World of Arthur Brown. 7 Overlanders – "Michelle". 8 Kalin Twins, Jerry Keller, Kitty Kallen. 9 Tommy. 10 "Nut Rocker". 11 Floaters. 12 Anita Ward. 13 Tammy Jones. 14 "Don't Cry For Me Argentina". 15 Clive Dunn. 16 Phyllis Nelson – "Move Closer". 17 Canada. 18 Partners in Kryme – "Turtle Power". 19 "When You're Young and In Love". 20 Oran "Juice" Jones.

Quiz 71 Pot Luck 36

Answers – see page 277

LEVEL 3

1 Who had hits with "Scarlett O'Hara" and "Applejack"?

2 Whose first album was called *Everybody Loves a Nut*?

3 Whose 1978 album was called *Captain Paralytic and the Brown Ale Cowboy*?

4 Which band became the first to receive royalties from the USSR?

5 Who won the 1979 British Rock and Pop Best Male Singer award?

6 To whom was Marino Marini saying "Ciao, Ciao" in 1959?

7 Who wrote "Spirit In The Sky"?

8 Whose second album was *Rage in Eden*?

9 Which group had "Groovy Train" in the charts in 1990?

10 What , according to Paul Simon, was "only a motion away"?

11 In which decade did *Grease* open on Broadway?

12 How is William Levise better known?

13 Which solo Madonna song from *Evita* was especially written for the soundtrack?

14 Which country does Shabba Ranks come from?

15 Who sang "I'm Your Puppet" in 1976?

16 Who was Zoot Money's backing group?

17 Which musical instrument does Bonnie Wright play?

18 Who played the piano on Bobby Darin's "Dream Lover"?

19 Why was the Shamen's 1995 concert from Kentish Town Forum unusual?

20 Who was the lead singer with the Sweet Sensations from 1967 to 1970?

Pot Luck 35 (see Quiz 69)

Answers

1 A bird's skull. 2 Rosemary Clooney. 3 Frankie Goes To Hollywood. 4 Ozzy Osbourne. 5 "Crossroads". 6 A Spanner. 7 Duran Duran. 8 The House of the Rising Sun. 9 Yaz. 10 Mrs Mills. 11 Australia. 12 Emerson Lake and Palmer. 13 Kate Bush. 14 Maxell audio tapes. 15 Deep Purple. 16 Audrey II, the man-eating plant. 17 Peter Frampton. 18 "Relax". 19 *A Clockwork Orange*. 20 Nilsson.

1 Who had a 1960s hit with "It's Good News Week"?

2 Who had a hit about artist L. S. Lowrie?

3 Which Ms Duncan, née d'Angelo, had her only hit in 1982?

4 Whose only hit had Clint Eastwood's "I Talk to the Trees" on the other side?

5 Who did Terry Waite duet with on his only chart venture?

6 Which one-hit wonder was seen as the forerunner of Alice Cooper?

7 Who were the first group to take a Beatles cover version to No. 1?

8 Which three 50s one-hit wonders had names beginning with K?

9 Who is Laura's boyfriend in "Tell Laura I Love Her"?

10 Which hit was written by Pyotr Ilyich Tchaikovsky and subsequently arranged by Kim Fowley?

11 Which hit group had an Aquarian, a Libran, a Leo and a Cancerian?

12 Who sang "Ring My Bell" in 1979?

13 Whose only UK hit was "Let Me Try Again"?

14 What was Lena Martell's failed follow-up to "One Day at a Time"?

15 Which one-hit wonder was also known as Corporal Jones?

16 Whose hit was used for an ad for Soft and Gentle anti-perspirant?

17 Which country was Robin Beck from?

18 Who wrote their film-track one-hit wonder in less than three days without seeing the film concerned?

19 What was the only UK hit for the Marvelettes?

20 Which Jones had a 1986 hit with "The Rain"?

1   Who won Grammy Record of the Year for "A Day in Paradise"?

2   How was Benjamin Peay better known?

3   Who was 47 when his fourth child Renée was born?

4   Which Frenchman designed the Beatles' early collarless jackets?

5   Which songwriter's last hit show in the fifties was *Silk Stockings*?

6   Who had an album called *Acid Queen*?

7   Who played bass with the Ronnie Pierson Trio on cruise liners before having chart success?

8   Whose first chart entry was "Hold Me", in the sixties?

9   Who produced the banned Frankie Goes to Hollywood hit "Relax"?

10   How many joint Eurovision winners were there in the only ever tie?

11   Who sang the theme for *The Living Daylights*?

12   Where was Robert Palmer born?

13   Which professional sporting career did M.C. Hammer follow?

14   In which film did Elvis Presley play the role of Chad Gates?

15   Which singer wrote under the name of Frere Manston?

16   Who sang "A Whole New World" from Disney's *Aladdin*?

17   Which country were Rednex from?

18   Which drink did "We Have All the Time in the World" advertise?

19   How is John Henry Deighton better known?

20   Whose first album was *Rabbits On and On*?

Pot Luck 38 (see Quiz 75)

Answers

1   Thunderclap Newman. 2   19. 3   *Back To The Future*.
4   Holiday. 5   Van Morrison. 6   Jonathan King. 7   "Sloop John B".
8   A horse. 9   "Hit and Miss". 10   "When I'm Dead and Gone".
11   Canada. 12   "Nobody Does It Better". 13   "The Last Waltz"
("La Dernière Valse"). 14   Billy Connolly. 15   Don Black.
16   Susan Maughan. 17   "Worzel's Song". 18   Rod Stewart.
19   J.J. Barrie. 20   Tights.

1 Who is the mother of Kurt Cobain's daughter Frances Bean?

2 Which serious injury did Def Leppard's Rick Allen suffer in 1984?

3 Where was he racing at the time?

4 Keith Moon's death was from an overdose from a drug used to combat what?

5 Who had died in the same flat four years previously?

6 Who had the original hit with "Born To Be Wild"?

7 Which film did it come from?

8 Why did Pete Townshend break his first guitar?

9 Who fell off the stage and broke six ribs during his Welcome to My Nightmare tour?

10 How did Marc Bolan's first T. Rex partner die in 1980?

11 Which other one-time T. Rex member died the following year?

12 Who walked off the "Top of the Pops" stage in 1983 after turning up two hours late and being criticized by the producer?

13 Where in his apartment was Jim Morrison found dead?

14 Who left his last message "I need help bad, man" on his manager's answering machine?

15 Whose solo debut album was *Back Street Crawler*?

16 Who said about a record, when a panellist on "Juke Box Jury", "I'd like it at a party if I was stoned"?

17 Who had a Chelsea shop called Too Fast to Live Too Young to Die?

18 Who broke his foot during a Swedish tour by jumping off the top of a moving bus?

19 Which band did Ace Frehley leave after a car accident?

20 Whose real name is James Jewel Osterberg?

Answers

The Stones (see Quiz 76)

1 Walking frame. 2 Ron Wood. 3 Sticky Fingers. 4 The Post Office. 5 Andrew Oldham 6 "I Wanna Be Your Man". 7 There were five panellists. 8 Jagger's brother Chris. 9 Ed Sullivan. 10 Honorary President of the LSE. 11 *Voodoo Lounge*. 12 Darryl Jones. 13 *Aftermath*. 14 Ike and Tina Turner. 15 Dandelion. 16 Allen Klein their representative. 17 Andy Warhol. 18 "Rewind". 19 Ambition, Ideas, Motivation, Success. 20 Broadcast on the Internet.

Quiz 75 Pot Luck 38

Answers – see page 281

1   Who was the first act to take "Something In The Air" to No. 1?

2   How many years did Stevie Wonder wait between his first UK chart entry and his first solo No. 1?

3   Which film uses Huey Lewis's hit "Power Of Love"?

4   What word links song titles by Cliff Richard, Madonna and the Human League?

5   Who released a 60s album called *Hard Nose the Highway*?

6   Who launched a record label called UK?

7   Which Beach Boys hit refers to "My grandpappy and me"?

8   In the Lonnie Donegan song, what was the Stewball?

9   What was the theme tune for "Juke Box Jury" called?

10   What was McGuinness Flint's most successful single?

11   What is the home country of Martha and the Muffins?

12   What is the name of the theme song from *The Spy Who Loved Me*?

13   Mireille Mathieu's only UK hit was a cover of which UK No. 1?

14   Whose 1975 album was Cop Yer Whack of This?

15   Who wrote the lyric for the Oscar-winning "Born Free"?

16   Who wanted to be Bobby's Girl in 1962?

17   What was Jon Pertwee's only UK hit?

18   Who said "I intend to delve deeply into the numerous stains I've left on the tapestry of life" when talking about his autobiography?

19   How is Barry Authors better known?

20   Which product did "Move Over Darling" advertise in 1987?

Quiz 76 The Stones

Answers – see page 282

1   What did Spike Milligan buy 52-year-old Bill Wyman as a wedding present when he married 19-year-old Mandy Smith?

2   Which Stone recorded "Gimme Some Neck" as a solo?

3   What is Bill Wyman's Kensington restaurant called?

4   Who did Keith Richard work for before he became a rock star?

5   Who was known as the sixth Stone?

6   What did the Stones sing on the first "Top of the Pops"?

7   Why was the Stones' appearance on "Jukebox Jury" a first?

8   Who won a Jagger lookalike contest in 1964 under the alias Laurie Yarham?

9   Who said "It took me 17 years to build this show and I'm not going to have it destroyed in a matter of weeks" after Stones fans rioted in the audience?

10   In 1994 Mick Jagger beat Mother Teresa and Carlos the Jackal in a poll to become what?

11   What was the Stones' first No. 1 album on the Virgin label?

12   Who replaced Bill Wyman on bass guitar after he left the group in 1993?

13   What was the first album, composed entirely of Jagger/Richard songs?

14   Which husband-and-wife act joined the Stones on their Rolling Stones '66 tour?

15   What was the name of the daughter of Keith Richard and Anita Pallenberg, born in 1972?

16   Who did the Stones sue in 1970 for "mismanagement of funds"?

17   Who designed the Sticky Fingers record sleeve with a real jeans zip fastener on the front?

18   Which Stones video was the first in the UK to have an 18 certificate?

19   What did AIMS stand for for Bill Wyman's in 1987?

20   Why was a live Rolling Stones concert in 1994 a famous first?

Answers

Born to be Wild (see Quiz 74)

1 Courtney Love. 2 Lost an arm in a car crash. 3 A57 Sheffield-to-Derby road. 4 Alcoholism. 5 Mama Cass. 6 Steppenwolf. 7 *Easy Rider.* 8 His grandmother complained about the noise. 9 Alice Cooper. 10 Choked on a cherry after taking morphine and magic mushrooms. 11 Steve Currie. 12 Thin Lizzy. 13 In a bath. 14 Jimi Hendrix. 15 Paul Kossoff. 16 Marianne Faithfull. 17 Malcolm McLaren. 18 Liam Gallagher. 19 Kiss. 20 Iggy Pop.

1   What is the theme music for *Dr No* called?

2   How is Eunice Waymon better known?

3   Who had a hit in 1961 with "A Hundred Pounds Of Clay"?

4   What word precedes song titles which end Bird, Safari and USA?

5   Who painted the artwork for the cover of *Teaser and the Firecat*?

6   Who wrote "Running Bear"?

7   What was Charlie Rich's biggest hit?

8   Who were Jonathan Richman's backing group?

9   What links "Two Tribes" and "Do They Know It's Christmas"?

10 What did Sammy Davis Jr lose in a 1954 car crash?

11 Which band was Gerry Rafferty in with Billy Connolly?

12 What was the name of the record label established by Queen Latifah?

13 Where is Toyah's home town?

14 Whose first album was *16 Hits From Stars and Garters*?

15 Which is the most southerly point of the US to have a song written about it?

16 Which Tom Waits rail-road song did Rod Stewart record?

17 Which song has the lines "When we called out for another drink, The waiter brought a tray"?

18 Who sang the theme from *Moonraker*?

19 Who was Phil Lynott's father-in-law?

20 How is McKinley Morganfield better known?

Answers

Pot Luck 40 (see Quiz 79)
1 "Take A Look At Me Now". 2 The Pretty Things. 3 Lulu.
4 9 a.m. 5 Johnny Tillotson. 6 Randy Jackson. 7 "La Bamba".
8 Dennis Wilson. 9 *Strictly Ballroom*. 10 The Gibb brothers.
11 Cilla Black. 12 *Abbey Road*. 13 Melbourne. 14 Lucky
Jackson. 15 Elton John. 16 Little Boxes. 17 Jumpin' Jack Flash.
18 Patsy Kensit. 19 Marc Bolan. 20 Robert Palmer.

Quiz 78 Producers

Answers – see page 288

 **LEVEL 3**

1 Which former chart topper produced Cher's "Shoop Shoop Song"?

2 How were the producers Matt Black and Jonathan Moore known?

3 Who was Norrie Paramor's production assistant on "Lily the Pink"?

4 Which Norrie Paramor production was used as the theme music for "Sounds of the Sixties"?

5 Who gave George Martin his first No. 1 hit single?

6 What is Quincy Jones's middle name?

7 Which performers did Quincy Jones tell to "check your egos at the door" before a 1985 recording?

8 Who called his work "little symphonies for the kids"?

9 Who were Mickie Most's first signing as an independent producer?

10 Whose early claim to fame was St Cecilia's "Leap Up and Down (Wave Your Knickers in the Air)"?

11 Where outside the UK did George Martin open his own studio as independent producer?

12 What is producer R.J. Lange's nickname?

13 Who was the first UK producer to have No. 1 hits for CBS?

14 Which pop writer went on to produce Blondie and Pat Benatar?

15 Who started out as a DJ in a Coventry ballroom in the early 70s?

16 What was the first label Gamble and Huff formed?

17 Whose real name was Anthony Instone?

18 Which Beatles album did Phil Spector work on?

19 Who produced "Isn't She Lovely?" for Stevie Wonder?

20 Who co-produced "Ashes to Ashes" with David Bowie?

Beyond the Grave (see Quiz 80)

Answers

1 "I Won't Forget You". 2 Phil Spector. 3 "All Along the Watchtower". 4 "Raining In My Heart". 5 Jackie Wilson. 6 16 – 1. 7 *Double Fantasy*. 8 k. d. lang. 9 1977. 10 "Let's Face the Music and Dance". 11 "The Great Pretender". 12 Eddie Cochran. 13 "Buffalo Soldier". 14 "20th Century Boy". 15 10. 16 "My Way". 17 "We Have All the Time in the World". 18 "You Got It". 19 Three. 20 None.

LEVEL 3

1   What follows in brackets in the Phil Collins hit "Against All Odds"?

2   What group were asking "Don't Bring Me Down" in 1964?

3   Who sang the theme from *The Man With the Golden Gun*?

4   What time is the Rocket Man's zero hour?

5   "Poetry in Motion" was a great success for whom in 1960?

6   Who played bass synthesizer on Whitney Houston's "I Wanna Dance With Somebody (Who Loves me)"?

7   Which 80s No. 1 has a Spanish title meaning "The Goat"?

8   Which Beach Boy died in 1984?

9   Which film had John Paul Young's "Love is in the Air" as its theme?

10 Who wrote the Kenny Rogers/Dolly Parton hit "Islands In The Stream"?

11 Who sang "Something Tells Me" as a TV show theme?

12 Which Beatles album was the best-selling album of 1969?

13 In which city was Jason Donovan born?

14 Which character did Elvis Presley play in *Viva Las Vegas*?

15 Whose nickname was Captain Fantastic?

16 What were made of ticky tacky in the 60s hit?

17 Who was "raised by a toothless bearded hag"?

18 Who played Ray Davies's daughter in *Absolute Beginners*?

19 Who wrote a book of poetry called *The Warlock of Love*?

20 Who was the male half of Vinegar Joe?

Pot Luck 39 (see Quiz 77)

Answers

1 "The James Bond Theme". **2** Nina Simone. **3** Craig Douglas.
4 Surfin'. **5** Cat Stevens. **6** The Big Bopper. **7** "The Most Beautiful Girl". **8** Modern Lovers. **9** Both entered the chart at No. 1. **10** His left eye. **11** Humblebums. **12** Flavor Unit.
13 Birmingham. **14** Kathy Kirby. **15** Key Largo. **16** "Downtown Train". **17** "A Whiter Shade of Pale". **18** Shirley Bassey. **19** Leslie Crowther. **20** Muddy Waters.

Quiz 80 Beyond the Grave

Answers – see page 286

LEVEL 3

1. What was Jim Reeves's first hit after his death?

2. Who produced "Imagine" with John and Yoko, which hit No. 1 in '81?

3. Which 1968 Hendrix hit was re-released 20 years after his death?

4. What was on the flip-side of Buddy Holly's first posthumous No. 1 "It Doesn't Matter Anymore"?

5. Who was shot on stage in 1961, died in 1984 and had a No. 1 hit two years after that?

6. How many No. 1 hits did Elvis have before, then after his death?

7. Which album was "Woman" on?

8. Who duetted with Roy Orbison on the 1992 "Crying"?

9. When did Bing Crosby's "White Christmas" first chart in the UK?

10. Which 90s Top 30 hit for Nat King Cole came back to fame as Torvill and Dean dance music?

11. Which 1987 hit for Freddie Mercury was re-released in 1993?

12. Who was the second artist to reach No. 1 posthumously?

13. What was the second record by Bob Marley to chart after his death?

14. What was the first Marc Bolan and T. Rex single re-released in the 90s?

15. How many albums did Queen have in the Top 100 in December 1991?

16. Which Elvis single was released just before Christmas 1977?

17. Which Louis Armstrong hit was re-released in 1994?

18. What was Roy Orbison's first chart hit after his death?

19. How many singles did John Lennon have in the UK Top Five week beginning January 10, 1981?

20. How many No. 1 hits has Marvin Gaye had since his death?

Answers

Producers (see Quiz 78)
1 Peter Asher. **2** Coldcut. **3** Tim Rice. **4** "Foot Tapper" – The Shadows. **5** The Temperance Seven. **6** Delight. **7** USA For Africa. **8** Phil Spector. **9** The Animals. **10** Jonathan King. **11** Montserrat. **12** Mutt. **13** Mike Smith. **14** Mike Chapman. **15** Pete Waterman. **16** Excel and Gamble. **17** Tony Macaulay. **18** *Let It Be.* **19** Tony Hatch. **20** Tony Visconti.

Quiz 81 Pot Luck 41

Answers – see page 291

1   What was the second UK hit to be sung in Italian?

2   What is Dean Martin's only UK No. 1 hit in his lifetime?

3   Who beat the Beatles for the most gold singles and albums in a year from 1971–72?

4   Which song was turned down by 30 acts before being a hit for the Everlys?

5   Which musical instrument were the Lemon Pipers singing about?

6   Which country is Frances Ruffelle from?

7   How many members of Love Affair performed on "Everlasting Love"?

8   Who was killed in a plane crash in 1986 with five band members?

9   Which album has the tracks "Human Nature" and "Lady In My Life"?

10   What was Humble Pie's first album?

11   In which film did Elvis play the role of Ross Carpenter?

12   Who is known as Soul Brother No. 1?

13   Which folk singer has the middle name Chawdos?

14   What was Charlie Chaplin's best-selling composition of the 60s?

15   Who was manager of Tom Jones and Gilbert O'Sullivan?

16   What did Cliff Adams's "Lonely Man Theme" advertise in 1960?

17   Who produced "Telegram Sam" for T. Rex?

18   Who wrote under the pseudonym Mark Anthony?

19   What was at No. 1 when "Reet Petite" first entered the UK charts?

20   Who had the best-selling album of 1975?

Answers

Pot Luck 42 (see Quiz 83)
1   *Serious Charge.* 2   *Dead End Street.* 3   Eddie Fisher.
4   "Figaro". 5   Paul McCartney and Wings. 6   Led Zeppelin.
7   Both married cousins. 8   Camp Grenada. 9   *Fun in Acapulco.* 10
The Replays. 11   Lionel Bart. 12   Robson and Jerome.
13   *With The Beatles.* 14   *Night Flight to Venus.* 15   Wedding of
Charles and Diana. 16   Des O'Connor. 17   Eric Clapton, Steve
Winwood. 18   *Help!* 19   Petrol. 20   Portuguese.

Quiz 82 Diana Ross

Answers – see page 292

1   Where was Diana Ross born?

2   Who produced her first solo album?

3   Who did Diana Ross introduce as her replacement at her final concert with in the Supremes?

4   What was her second film?

5   Which album was "Chain Reaction" from?

6   Who told Tamla he'd make "I'm Still Waiting" his record of the week if they'd release it as a single?

7   Which single had a pseudo-60s video in black and white?

8   What was her first solo No. 1 album?

9   Who was her single "Missing You" dedicated to?

10   Which hit was intended to ask parents of drug addicts to be understanding about their children ?

11   Where did she broadcast a 1992 Christmas concert from?

12   Who did she duet with on "All of You"?

13   Which record label did she move to after leaving Motown?

14   In which year did she make her first solo British tour?

15   Who was the album *Pops We Love You* dedicated to?

16   What is her fourth child called?

17   What did she open in January 1992?

18   Which Radio 1 DJ did she deputize for in July 1992?

19   Who directed her in *Mahogany*?

20   Which album was "Muscles" on?

Eurovision (see Quiz 84)

1 Switzerland. 2 Rolf Harris. 3 Switzerland. 4 Patricia Bredin.
5 Brotherhood of Man. 6 Spain, France, Netherlands. 7 Dana.
8 Johnny Logan. 9 "Power to All Our Friends". 10 Ken Bruce.
11 "Come What May". 12 Izhar Cohen and Alphabeta.
13 Love City Groove. 14 "A Little Peace". 15 Dublin.
16 Olivia Newton-John. 17 Pearl Carr and Teddy Johnson.
18 Norway. 19 Kenneth McKellar – he wore a kilt. 20 Lynsey de Paul and Mike Moran.

Quiz 83 Pot Luck 42

Answers – see page 289

LEVEL 3

1 Which film was "Living Doll" written for?

2 What was the Kinks' *Greatest Hits* album subtitled?

3 Which of Elizabeth Taylor's husbands had two chart hits in 1953?

4 Which Brotherhood of Man No. 1 title has an operatic title?

5 Who recorded the theme song for *Live and Let Die*?

6 Who had *Presence* at No. 1 in the album charts in 1976?

7 What maritally links Jerry Lee Lewis and Sebastian Bach?

8 Where was Allan Sherman in "Hello Muddah Hello Faddah"?

9 In which film did Elvis play the role of Mike Windgren?

10 Who was Rocky Sharpe's backing group?

11 Who co-wrote "From Russia With Love" with John Barry?

12 Who were top of both the single and album charts in December 1995?

13 What replaced *Please Please Me* at the top of the album charts?

14 What was the first of Boney M's trio of No. 1 albums between 1978 and 1980?

15 Which event of 1981 produced a No. 1 album?

16 Who spent 36 consecutive weeks in the charts with "I Pretend"?

17 Who were in Blind Faith with Rick Grech and Ginger Baker?

18 Which was the first-ever album to go straight to No. 1?

19 What was Georgie Fame's "Get Away" first used to advertise?

20 Which language was Kaoma's "Lambada" sung in?

Answers

Pot Luck 41 (see Quiz 81)
1 "Nessun Dorma". 2 "Memories are Made of This".
3 The Osmonds. 4 "Bye Bye Love". 5 A green tambourine.
6 UK. 7 One. 8 Ricky Nelson. 9 *Thriller*. 10 *As Safe As Yesterday Is*. 11 *Girls! Girls! Girls!* 12 James Brown. 13 Joan Baez.
14 "This Is My Song". 15 Gordon Mills. 16 Strand cigarettes – "You're never alone with a Strand". 17 Tony Visconti. 18 Tony Hatch. 19 "That'll Be The Day". 20 The Stylistics.

291

Quiz 84 Eurovision

Answers – see page 290

LEVEL 3

---

1   Which country won the very first Contest?

2   Who compered the show in the UK the year Sandie Shaw won?

3   Who did Celine Dion represent in the contest?

4   Who was the UK's first-ever Eurovision entrant?

5   Until 1996 who won the Contest by the biggest margin?

6   Who tied with the UK when there were four winners?

7   Who was the first Irish winner?

8   Who was the first artist to win the Contest twice?

9   What did Cliff Richard sing the second time he sang for the UK?

10   Who has done the Radio 2 commentary in the UK in the mid 90s?

11   Under which title did "Après Toi" reach No. 2 in the UK charts?

12   Who were the first Israeli winners?

13   Who performed the UK's first rap entry?

14   How did "Ein Bisschen Frieden" translate at the top of the UK charts?

15   Where did Bucks Fizz have their 1982 win?

16   Who represented the UK the year Abba won?

17   Who were the first duo to represent the UK?

18   Which country broke the Irish run of wins from 1992–1996?

19   Which male singer represented the UK without wearing any trousers?

20   Who represented the UK with "Rock Bottom"?

Answers

Diana Ross (see Quiz 82)

1 Detroit. 2 Ashford and Simpson. 3 Jean Terrell. 4 *Mahogany*. 5 *Eaten Alive*. 6 Tony Blackburn. 7 "Chain Reaction". 8 *One Woman*. 9 Marvin Gaye. 10 "Reach Out and Touch". 11 Vienna. 12 Julio Iglesias. 13 Capitol. 14 1973. 15 Berry Gordy Sr. 16 Ross. 17 Harrods sale. 18 Simon Bates. 19 Berry Gordy. 20 *Silk Electric*.

Quiz 85 Pot Luck 43

Answers – see page 295

LEVEL 3

1 Who co-wrote and produced "Let the Heartaches Begin"?

2 Whose show won Radio Programme of the Year in 1978?

3 Which album won a Grammy in 1973 for Neil Diamond?

4 Who was found dead at Hollywood's Landmark Hotel on the October 4, 1970?

5 Who wrote "The Last Waltz"?

6 Which Donovan hit is sung partly in French?

7 Out of Dave Dee's group who were Trevor Davies and John Dymond?

8 Who won *Melody Maker*'s Instrumentalist of the Year award in 1961?

9 What is on the other side of the Everlys' "Claudette"?

10 Who had a No. 1 with "You Belong To Me" in 1952?

11 Who had most weeks in the UK charts in 1994?

12 Who has had a hit with Delaney and Bonnie and Friends, Tina Turner and Elton John?

13 Who did Annie Lennox duet with on "Why"?

14 What was Julie Covington's second 70s hit?

15 Who had the one-hit-wonder album *Blast* in 1989?

16 What was the Oscar-winning song from *Dick Tracy*?

17 In which film did Elvis Presley play the role of Josh Morgan?

18 How is Angus McKenzie better known?

19 Which album knocked *A Hard Day's Night* off the top of the charts?

20 Which songwriters used the pseudonym Elmo Glick?

Answers

Pot Luck 44 (see Quiz 87)
1 *Led Zeppelin II*. 2 *Double Trouble*. 3 Jeff Lynne. 4 Bert Weedon. 5 Pete Murray. 6 Red. 7 The Bee Gees. 8 George Harrison. 9 Vertigo. 10 Sloopy. 11 Supergrass. 12 Vanessa Paradis – "Joe le Taxi". 13 Midge Ure. 14 World's worst air disaster in 1985. 15 "Save Your Kisses For Me". 16 Whitney Houston. 17 *Aladdin Sane*. 18 "Mull of Kintyre". 19 "She Loves You". 20 *Bringing It All Back Home*.

1 Which Abba hit was rejected as a Eurovision song in 1973?

2 Who co-wrote it with them?

3 What was the orchestra conductor wearing when Abba won the Eurovision Song Contest?

4 Where was *Abba – The Movie* set?

5 Who was Abba's manager and co-writer of many of their hits?

6 What was Abba's only US No. 1?

7 Which city was "Summer Night City" about?

8 What was Abba's publishing company called?

9 To which charity did Abba give all their royalties from "Chiquitita"?

10 What were the surnames of the group members?

11 What was the name of Abba's own studio in Stockholm?

12 Björn and Agnetha were investigated in 1987 about what?

13 Which Stock and Waterman production had a hit with "Dancing Queen" in in 1992?

14 Why were the group barred from touring the USSR in 1982?

15 Who had recorded a solo of "Fernando" before the group recorded it together?

16 A Swedish company also had the name Abba. What did they do?

17 Who produced Frida's solo album *Something's Going On*?

18 Which top Swedish rock 'n' roll band of the 60s was Benny a member of until they folded in 1969?

19 On which label did Abba record all their hits in the 70s and 80s?

20 In which film, set in Australia, did Abba music feature in 1994?

Answers

90s Britpop (see Quiz 88)
1 Jay Darlington. 2 Dina Carroll. 3 Birmingham. 4 Gabrielle.
5 Kicked a microphone across the stage. 6 *(What's the Story)*
Morning Glory?. 7 *Candyfloss and Medicine*. 8 Burnage.
9 *Ugly beautiful*. 10 Indian Emperor. 11 Paul Weller.
12 Someone threw a pair of spectacles at him. 13 Louise.
14 Piano. 15 Blur. 16 Glasgow. 17 *Trainspotting*. 18 Lisa
Stansfield. 19 Leicester. 20 Phil Daniels.

Quiz 87 Pot Luck 44

Answers – see page 293

1 Which Led Zeppelin LP won *Melody Maker*'s LP of the Year award in 1970?

2 In which film did Elvis play the role of Guy Lambert?

3 Who produced the album *Out Of The Blue*?

4 Who had his only Top 10 entry with "Guitar Boogie Shuffle" in 1959?

5 Which DJ was on the panel on the first "Juke Box Jury"?

6 What is the main colour of the *West Side Story* album cover?

7 Which group's first Australian No. 1 was "Spicks and Specks"?

8 Who said, "Paul is really writing for a 14-year-old audience now"?

9 Which label released the first Dire Straits recordings in the UK?

10 Who, according to the McCoys, lives "in a very bad part of town"?

11 Whose debut album was *I Should Coco*?

12 Which was the first French disc in the charts with a wholly French act?

13 Who has had a hit with Visage, Rich Kid and Mick Karn?

14 How did the 60s Top Ten artist Kyu Sakamoto meet his death?

15 What was the best-selling single of 1975?

16 Who had most weeks in the UK charts in 1993?

17 What was the first of David Bowie's trio of No. 1 albums between 1973 and 1974?

18 What was the first UK single to sell more than 2 million copies?

19 What was the previous record holder?

20 Which album knocked *Freewheelin' Bob Dylan* off the top of the charts?

Pot Luck 43 (see Quiz 85)

Answers

1 Tony Macaulay. 2 Noel Edmonds. 3 *Jonathan Livingston Seagull*.
4 Janis Joplin. 5 Les Reed, Barry Mason. 6 "Jennifer Juniper". 7 Dozy, Beaky. 8 Bert Weedon. 9 "All I have to do is dream". 10 Jo Stafford. 11 Mariah Carey. 12 Eric Clapton.
13 Al Green. 14 "Only Women Bleed". 15 Holly Johnson.
16 "Sooner or Later (I Always Get My Man)". 17 *Kissin' Cousins*.
18 Karl Denver. 19 *Beatles For Sale*. 20 Jerry Leiber and Mike Stoller.

1   Who plays keyboards with Kula Shaker?

2   Whose debut album was *So Close*?

3   Where are Ocean Colour Scene based?

4   Who won the Brit Award for Best Newcomer in 1994?

5   How did Jarvis Cocker injure a foot during a Norwegian TV show?

6   Which album won the Best Album award at the 1996 Brit Awards?

7   On which album was Eddi Reader's "Town Without Pity"?

8   In which Manchester suburb were the Gallagher brothers brought up?

9   What was Babybird's debut album?

10 Who was the original Kula Shaker?

11 Who won the Brit award for Best Male Singer in 1995 and 1996?

12 Why did Liam Gallagher walk off stage on a US tour in March 1995?

13 Who left Eternal and went Naked?

14 What is the musical accompaniment on "Forever Love"?

15 Who won the Brit Award for Best Group in 1995?

16 Where is Eddi Reader from?

17 To which film did Blur and Damon Albarn contribute a track in 1996?

18 Who won the Brit Award for Best Female Singer in 1992?

19 Where did Mark Morrison grow up?

20 Which actor spoke on Blur's "Parklife"?

Quiz 89 Pot Luck 45

Answers – see page 299

1 Which band was Eddi Reader in in the late 80s?

2 What was the first of Dire Straits' trio of No. 1 albums between 1985 and 1991?

3 Which two rock rebels died on the same day two years apart in 1969 and 1971?

4 Which performer is credited on the *Variations* album?

5 What was Petula Clark's first No. 1 in 1961?

6 Who did Clyde McPhatter join after leaving the Dominoes in 1953?

7 Who won five Grammys in 1980 including Best Single?

8 What was Boyzone's first No. 1 single?

9 Who had a 60s hit with "Les Bicyclettes de Belsize"?

10 Which song says "Don't hang around 'cause two's a crowd"?

11 What was Elvis Presley's first million-selling record?

12 Who played percussion on the Bee Gees' "You Should Be Dancing"?

13 Who wrote the soundtrack for the film *La Passione*?

14 Who produced Alisha's Attic's album *Alisha Rules the World*?

15 Who had the one-hit wonder album *Turn Back the Clock* in 1988?

16 Who had most weeks in the UK charts in 1989?

17 What was the best-selling single of 1972?

18 Who has had a hit with Fun Boy Three, Vegas and the Specials?

19 What did Gene Pitney's "Town Without Pity" advertise?

20 What was the Oscar-winning song from *Pocahontas*?

Pot Luck 46 (see Quiz 91)
1 Red. 2 "Not the Nine O'Clock News" cast. 3 Jermaine.
4 The Gibb brothers. 5 Six. 6 New Kids on the Block. 7 *Touch*.
8 *Abracadabra*. 9 Dressing Gown. 10 Seal. 11 *Mercury Falling*.
12 Brian Poole. 13 Tina Turner. 14 *Life*. 15 Richey James.
16 *Genesis*. 17 David Sylvian. 18 "Can You Feel the Love Tonight". 19 "We're In This Together". 20 "I Remember You".

1   Who awarded Mark Knopfler an honorary music doctorate in 1993?

2   Which heavy-metal guitarist said, "If it's too loud you're too old"?

3   Who inspired Eric Clapton to write "Layla"?

4   What was Eric Clapton's No. 1 album of 1994?

5   Which guitarist's first two names were Brian Robson?

6   Which album did Mark Knopfler release with Chet Atkins in 1990?

7   Who was guest vocalist on Ted Nugent's *Free For All album*?

8   Who duetted on "Wonderful Land" on the 1993 *Heartbeat* album?

9   Which film soundtrack did Mark Knopfler work on after *Local Hero*?

10 Who asked Hank Marvin to join which band in 1970?

11 Which group has included the guitarists John Williams and Kevin Peek?

12 What did Brian May reputedly make his first guitar from?

13 What type of guitar did Jimi Hendrix use on the *Are You Experienced*? album?

14 Which two acts took "Cavatina", the theme from *The Deer Hunter* into the Top Ten?

15 Where did Jimi Hendrix take part in a fund raising "Guitar In" in 1967?

16 Whose career history album was called *Crossroads*?

17 What did Brian May play at the end of the Concert For Life at Wembley in 1992?

18 What was Jeff Beck's debut solo album called?

19 What honour did Eric Clapton receive in January 1995?

20 What was the debut album by the Brian May Band?

Answers

Elton John (see Quiz 92)

1 Kenneth. 2 Rocket. 3 Bluesology. 4 *Tumbleweed Connection*.
5 Renate Blauer. 6 Officer of Arts and Letters. 7 Lulu. 8
RuPaul. 9 Stage was overcome by crickets. 10 Big Pig Music. 11
Billie Jean King. 12 John Lennon – son Sean. 13 Bernie Taupin.
14 John Reid. 15 Thomas. 16 Throat. 17 Wasn't given VIP
treatment. 18 Beach Boys. 19 The new Mrs Rod Stewart. 20
Tammy Wynette.

Quiz 91 Pot Luck 46

Answers – see page 297

LEVEL 3

1 What is the predominant colour of the *Making Movies* album cover?

2 Who made a comedy album called *Hedgehog Sandwich*?

3 Which Jackson brother suggested "Let's get serious"?

4 Which brothers starred in a weekly TV series in Australia in the 60s?

5 How old is Marie in the Chuck Berry hit "Memphis Tennessee"?

6 Who had most weeks in the UK charts in 1990?

7 On which Eurythmics album cover is Annie Lennox in a black mask?

8 What album and single gave the Steve Miller Band chart success in 1982?

9 What is Nilsson wearing on the album cover of *Nilsson Schmilsson*?

10 Who won the Brit Award for Best Male Singer in 1992?

11 On which album was Sting's "Let Your Soul Be Your Pilot"?

12 Who is the father of Alisha's Attic sisters Karen and Shellie?

13 Who was made a Chevalier des Ordres des Arts et Lettres in February 1996?

14 Which Simply Red album is "Fairground" on?

15 Which founder member of Manic Street Preachers left the group in 1995?

16 What was the first of Genesis's trio of No. 1 albums between 1983 and 1991?

17 Who has had a hit with Robert Fripp and Mick Karn?

18 What was the Oscar-winning song from *The Lion King*?

19 What was Simply Red's song for Euro 96?

20 What was the best-selling single of 1962?

Pot Luck 45 (see Quiz 89)

1 Fairground Attraction. **2** *Brothers In Arms*. **3** Brian Jones and Jim Morrison. **4** Julian Lloyd Webber. **5** "Sailor". **6** The Drifters. **7** Christopher Cross. **8** "Words". **9** Engelbert Humperdinck. **10** "Get Off Of My Cloud". **11** "Heartbreak Hotel". **12** Stephen Stills. **13** Chris Rea. **14** Dave Stewart. **15** Johnny Hates Jazz. **16** Bobby Brown. **17** "I'd Like To Teach the World to Sing". **18** Terry Hall. **19** Miller beer. **20** "Colours of the Wind".

Answers

Quiz 92 Elton John

Answers – see page 298

1 What was Elton's original middle name?

2 Which record label did he launch in 1972?

3 Which soul band did Elton play with when he worked for a music publisher ?

4 Which album reflected Bernie Taupin's influence by the Wild West?

5 Who did Elton John marry in 1984?

6 Which honour did Elton receive from the French government in 1993?

7 Who sang a prospective Eurovision song by John and Taupin in 1969, but it came last in the viewers' poll?

8 Who duetted with Elton on "Don't Go Breaking My Heart" in 1994?

9 Why did Elton cut short an encore in Australia in February 1993?

10 What was the publishing company founded by Elton in 1974?

11 Who did Elton write "Philadelphia Freedom" for?

12 Elton became godfather to which pop star's child in 1975?

13 Who was the album *Sleeping With the Past* dedicated to?

14 Who became Elton's personal manager in 1971?

15 What was the name of Elton's dog which he chose in Battersea Dog's Home because it looked the saddest?

16 On which part of him did he undergo surgery in Australia in 1987?

17 Why did he fly out of Tel Aviv airport just after arriving in 1993?

18 Who sings "Crocodile Rock" on the tribute album *Two Rooms*?

19 Who was Elton dressed like when he appeared in Rod Stewart's Wembley concert in 1991?

20 Who did Elton duet with in "What a Woman Needs" on her *Without Walls* album?

Quiz 93 Pot Luck 47

LEVEL 3

1   Who was the first solo male pianist to reach No. 1 twice?

2   Who first took a cover version of Little Richard's "Good Golly Miss Molly" into the Top Ten?

3   Who plays sitar on "Paint It Black"?

4   What was the first of Prince's three No. 1 albums between 1988 and 1991?

5   Who made his chart debut in 1957 with "School Day"?

6   Which Kraftwerk hit lasted 22.5 minutes in its album version?

7   Who had most weeks in the UK charts in 1991?

8   On which label did Human League record "Don't You Want Me?"?

9   Who made "Modern Sounds in Country and Western Music"?

10   Whose first album was called *Have Twangy Guitar Will Travel*?

11   Who said "Elvis taught white America to get down"?

12   What is Robert Miles's home country?

13   What was U2's first No. 1 album?

14   What is Beck's surname?

15   Who had the one-hit wonder album *Spartacus* in 1991?

16   What was the best-selling single of 1959?

17   How much did the original collarless Beatles suits cost?

18   Who produced Dire Straits' first album?

19   Who joined Ozzy Osbourne on "The Urpney Song" from the TV series "The Dreamstone"?

20   Which TV drama featured the fictional Little Ladies and starred Julie Covington and Rula Lenska?

Pot Luck 48 (see Quiz 95)

Answers

1   "You Don't Have To Say You Love Me". 2   The Boomtown Rats.
3   "Je t'aime... moi non plus". 4   *Miracle*. 5   Carl Perkins.
6   Crowded House. 7   *The Stranger*. 8   "My Cherie Amour".
9   "Jump". 10   Pete Townshend. 11   Roger Moore. 12   Germany, Rumania. 13   Bee Gees – "Massachusetts". 14   "Don't You Want Me?" 15   Michael Jackson. 16   "Can't Help Falling in Love".
17   *Good Morning Vietnam*. 18   Bobbie Gentry. 19   "Silence is Golden". 20   Jim Reeves.

1   What was the best-selling single of 1960?

2   Which song has the lines "Sunshine, yellow orange blossom, laughing faces ev'rywhere"?

3   Who won the Grammy Record of the Year in 1964 for "The Girl From Ipanema"?

4   Who had the album *On the Threshold of a Dream*?

5   Which band did John Fogerty sing with, write for and produce?

6   What was the first Stones No. 1 after Brian Jones left?

7   Who played keyboards with Amen Corner?

8   What was the top-selling album of 1960?

9   On which album did "While My Guitar Gently Weeps" feature?

10   In Des O'Connor's "1-2-3- O'Leary" what does "O Leary" rhyme with?

11   Which band had twins Derv and Lincoln Gordon?

12   Which was the only other album to top the 1966 album charts with *Revolver* and *Aftermath*?

13   Which song beat Cliff's "Congratulations" into second place in the Eurovision Song Contest?

14   Whose version of "This Is My Song" reached No. 2?

15   What was the Beach Boys' first Top Ten hit?

16   Which record got to No. 1 on Glenn Hoddle's ninth birthday?

17   Who had the album *Stand Up*?

18   Which Beatles song features the tune of "Greensleeves"?

19   What replaced "Yellow Submarine"/"Eleanor Rigby" at No. 1?

20   Which album did Dusty Springfield's "Son of a Preacher Man" come from?

Quiz 95 Pot Luck 48

Answers – see page 301

LEVEL 3

1 Which 60s No. 1 was originally called "Io Che No Vivo Senza Te"?

2 Who recorded the album *Tonic For The Troops*?

3 Which record was at No. 1 as Margaret Thatcher was celebrating her 44th birthday?

4 What was the first of Queen's three No. 1 albums between '89 and '91?

5 Whose blue suede shoes were bought by Dan Ackroyd in 1984?

6 Who won the Brit Award for Best International Group in 1994?

7 Which album does Billy Joel's "Just The Way You Are" come from?

8 Who, according to Stevie Wonder, is "as distant as the Milky Way"?

9 Which Van Halen hit says "I get up and nothin' gets me down"?

10 Whose 1980 album *Empty Glass* included the track "Rough Boys"?

11 Which James Bond shares his birthday with Cliff Richard?

12 Which two European countries do Enigma come from?

13 Who said they could not spell the title of their first No. 1 hit?

14 What was the best-selling single of 1981?

15 Who had most weeks in the UK charts in 1992?

16 Which song has the line "Like a river flows surely to the sea"?

17 Which 1988 film featured the 1968 song "What a Wonderful World"?

18 Which country star married the singer Jim Stafford in 1978?

19 Which future No. 1 was on the other side of the Four Seasons' "Rag Doll"?

20 Which country star was a DJ on Texan KGRI in the early 1950s?

Pot Luck 47 (see Quiz 93)

1 Russ Conway. 2 Swinging Blue Jeans. 3 Brian Jones.
4 *Lovesexy*. 5 Chuck Berry. 6 "Autobahn". 7 R.E.M. 8 Virgin.
9 Ray Charles. 10 Duane Eddy. 11 James Brown. 12 Italy.
13 *War*. 14 Hansen. 15 Farm. 16 "Living Doll". 17 £37 10s.
18 Muff Winwood. 19 Billy Connolly and Frank Bruno.
20 "Rock Follies".

Quiz 96 The 70s Revisited

Answers – see page 302 **LEVEL 3**

1 What was the best-selling single of 1971?

2 Who got to No. 1 in 1979 with a hit from a West End show – although he was actually starring in a different one?

3 What was the best single of 1979 in the British Rock and Pop Awards?

4 Which song won Larry Henley and Jeff Silbar the songwriter Grammy Song of the Year?

5 Who wrote and produced "Bright Eyes" for Art Garfunkel?

6 Who had a 70s hit about a Russian priest?

7 Which 70s film was most successful in terms of spin-off chart singles?

8 Which Shadow wrote "You're The One That I Want"?

9 Who had two No. 1s in succession ending in "O"?

10 What sort of outfits did Slim wear?

11 Which album featured Deniece Williams's No. 1 "Free"?

12 Whose album titles usually consisted of their name plus a Roman numeral?

13 Who was the first Continental act to have a No. 1 in 1976?

14 Which police officer was Going In With his Eyes Open?

15 Who were in Wings when "Mull of Kintyre" was recorded?

16 What was Brotherhood of Man's first hit?

17 What is the cause of "D.I.V.O.R.C.E." in Billy Connolly's version?

18 Which song kept repeating "rat tat tat tat tat"?

19 Who were a combination of the Percussions and the Monarchs?

20 What were the combined ages of Althia and Donna when they made "Uptown Top Ranking"?

The 60s Revisited (see Quiz 94)

1 "It's Now or Never". 2 "Colour My World". 3 Stan Getz and Astrid Gilberto. 4 Moody Blues. 5 Creedence Clearwater Revival. 6 "Honky Tonk Women". 7 Blue Weaver. 8 *South Pacific* (soundtrack). 9 *The Beatles*. 10 Mary. 11 The Equals. 12 *The Sound of Music* (soundtrack). 13 "La La La". 14 Harry Secombe. 15 "I Get Around" 16 "Reach Out I'll Be There". 17 Jethro Tull. 18 "All You Need Is Love". 19 All Or Nothing. 20 *Dusty in Memphis*.

Answers

Quiz 97 Pot Luck 49

Answers – see page 307

LEVEL 3

1   Who went to No. 1 with their debut album in November 1995?

2   What was on the A side of Yoko Ono's "Who Has Seen the Wind"?

3   Who did Stephen Stills unsuccessfully audition for in the 60s?

4   Which Carry On actor had a No. 2 with "Be My Girl" in 1957?

5   Who was nicknamed the Prince of Wails?

6   Who won the 1990 Grammy for Best Female Vocal Performance with "Vision of Love"?

7   Which 50s pianist was a qualified chemist?

8   Who worked with Paul McCartney on his Liverpool Oratorio and conducted the orchestra that performed it on the album?

9   Which newscaster's offering won Capital Radio's World's Worst record in 1980?

10 Which American had a 1962 hit with "A Little Bitty Tear"?

11 Who were the first pair of brothers to have separate solo No. 1 hits?

12 Who did Jeff Lynne replace in the Move?

13 Which then current No. 1 might the passengers on the QEII's maiden voyage might have danced to?

14 What was the real first name of the Tremelo "Chip" Hawkes?

15 Who had Jimmy McCulloch topped the charts with in 1969 before he joined Wings?

16 Who had most weeks in the UK charts in 1985 and 1986?

17 What was the best-selling single of 1983?

18 Who had the one-hit wonder album *Tease Me* in 1994?

19 Who was Brian Jones's immediate replacement in the Rolling Stones?

20 What was the first of R.E.M.'s three No. 1 albums between 1991 and 1994?

Answers

Pot Luck 50 (see Quiz 99)

1 Peter Tork. 2 David Whitfield. 3 "Go For It". 4 *Bonnie and Clyde*. 5 Britain. 6 "Red Red Wine". 7 "Another Day in Paradise". 8 "Pasadena". 9 *Sparkle in the Rain*. 10 Manfred Mann's Earth Band. 11 Buster. 12 House fire. 13 Ball. 14 Billy Idol. 15 Mud. 16 "Can't Buy Me Love". 17 Frank Sinatra. 18 "Proud Mary". 19 Peter Green, later of Fleetwood Mac. 20 *A New Flame*.

1 What was the best-selling single of 1988?

2 Which song was based on "She Moved Through The Fair"?

3 Which instrument did Enya play on "Orinoco Flow"?

4 Which film won the Brit Award for best soundtrack in 1988?

5 Yazz's Plastic Population were initially DJs on which radio station?

6 Whose debut album was *Push*?

7 Who was the only Scot in Fairground Attraction?

8 Who followed up a No. 1 with "Superfly Guy"?

9 Where was Tiffany's first live UK performance?

10 Which album did "I Just Can't Stop Loving You" come from?

11 Which song had the line "life, Jim, but not as we know it"?

12 What was Mel and Kim's surname?

13 How was Johann Holzel better known?

14 Which quotation attributed to Joseph Kennedy – father of the assassinated president – provided the title of a 1986 hit?

15 Who won the Eurovision Song Contest for Norway the year their countrymen A-ha had their first UK No. 1?

16 Who wrote "Saving All My Love For You" with Michael Masser?

17 Where was Feargal Sharkey singing "A Good Heart" live on British TV for the first time?

18 What was the 80s best-selling single by a woman?

19 Who joined the Communards on "Don't Leave Me This Way"?

20 Who produced Ultravox's "Quartet" and where?

1   Who was the first Monkee to leave the group?

2   Who had a No. 1 hit in 1954 with "Cara Mia"?

3   What completes the title of the 1984 Wham hit "Young Guns"?

4   Which film featured the music "Foggy Mountain Breakdown"?

5   What country were America formed in?

6   What was Neil Diamond's second UK No. 1 as a writer?

7   What did Phil Collins win the Grammy for Record of the Year for in 1990?

8   Which Temperance Seven hit began "Oh you railway station, oh you Pullman train"?

9   What was the first of Simple Minds' four No. 1 albums between 1984 and 1989?

10 Who took "Blinded By the Light" to No. 1 in the US and No. 6 in the UK?

11 In which film did the Four Tops sing "Loco in Acapulco"?

12 How did Steve Marriott die in 1991?

13 What is Reg Presley's real surname?

14 Who revived Tommy James and the Shondells' "Mony Mony" in 1987?

15 Who had most weeks in the UK charts in 1975?

16 What was the best-selling single of 1964?

17 Who described Elvis's music as "a rancid-smelling aphrodisiac"?

18 Which 1969 hit was about a Mississippi paddle steamer?

19 Who replaced Eric Clapton in John Mayall's Bluesbreakers?

20 What was the first of Simply Red's trio of No. 1 albums between 1989 and 1995?

Pot Luck 49 (see Quiz 97)

Answers

1 Robson and Jerome. 2 "Instant Karma". 3 The Monkees. 4 Jim Dale. 5 Johnnie Ray. 6 Mariah Carey. 7 Winifred Atwell. 8 Carl Davis. 9 Reginald Bosanquet. 10 Burl Ives. 11 Eden Kane, Peter Sarstedt. 12 Carl Wayne. 13 Last Waltz. 14 Len. 15 Thunderclap Newman. 16 Madonna. 17 "Karma Chameleon". 18 Chaka Demus and Pliers. 19 Mick Taylor. 20 *Out Of Time.*

Quiz 100 Last Round 1

Answers – see page 306

LEVEL 3

1   Who was nicknamed the Tycoon of Teen?

2   Who had most weeks in the UK charts in 1970 and 1971?

3   In which film did Elvis play the role of Walter Gulick?

4   How is Patricia Louise Holt-Edwards better known?

5   What was the sixth of Rod Stewart's six No. 1 albums between 1971 and 1976?

6   Which song begins "Almost heaven West Virginia"?

7   What was the best-selling single of 1980?

8   Whose first UK single was "Halfway Down the Stairs"?

9   In which musical will you find Grizabella and Rumpleteazer?

10   Who won the 1965 Grammy for Record of the Year for "A Taste of Honey"?

11   Who sang Norway's 1995 Eurovision winner "Nocturne"?

12   What was the first of Tom Jones's three No. 2 hits between '67 and '68?

13   Which David Bowie Top Thirty hit has only two letters?

14   Which Desmond Dekker hit has a number as its title?

15   Which soccer team had a hit called "We Can Do It"?

16   What was the first of Slade's trio of No. 1 albums between 1973 and 1974?

17   How did the Beach Boy Dennis Wilson meet his death?

18   Who starred as Pink in Alan Parker's 1982 film *The Wall*?

19   Why did the Police dye their hair blond?

20   Which lady provided Kenny Rogers and Little Richard with hit records?

The 80s Revisited (see Quiz 98)

Answers

1 "Mistletoe and Wine". 2 "Belfast Child". 3 Keyboards. 4 *Buster*. 5 Kiss FM. 6 Bros. 7 Eddi Reader. 8 S Express. 9 Shopping centre in Newcastle. 10 *Bad*. 11 "Star Trekkin'". 12 Appleby. 13 Falco. 14 "When the going gets tough the tough get going. 15 Bobbysocks. 16 Gerry Goffin. 17 A jumbo jet. 18 "The Power of Love". 19 Sarah Jane Morris. 20 George Martin in Montserrat.

308

1 How is Norma Eggstrom better known?

2 What was the first of Sweet's three No. 2 hits between 1973 and 1974?

3 Which Who hit has a number as its title?

4 Which song was subtitled "Spurs Are On Their Way to Wembley"?

5 Which song begins "Music is a world within itself with a language we all understand"?

6 Which was Cliff Richard's first hit to go straight to No. 1?

7 Which Scott Fitzgerald hit has only two letters?

8 Who had most weeks at No. 1 in 1958?

9 Which two instrumentalists had 22 weeks at No. 1 before their 20th birthdays?

10 Who was the first woman aged over 50 to have three Top Ten hits?

11 What was the first of the Rolling Stones' five No. 1 albums between 1969 and 1973?

12 What was the best-selling single of 1982?

13 Which 70s band was Stewart Copeland in before joining the Police?

14 Who was the first British woman to have a solo No. 1 album?

15 Who was nicknamed Sassy?

16 What was the first of Abba's eight No. 1 albums between '76 and '82?

17 Who had most weeks in the UK charts in 1966?

18 Who attempted an 80s revival medley called "Golden Shreds"?

19 Which 70s hit do Wayne and Garth mime to in a gay disco in the 1994 film *Wayne's World II*?

20 In which film did Elvis play the role of Rusty Wells?

Answers

Last Round 4 (see Quiz 103)
1 George Harrison. 2 Kirsty MacColl. 3 Jackie Wilson.
4 *Change of Habit*. 5 Wayne Fontana. 6 "1-2-3". 7 Crystal
Palace. 8 Killer Queen. 9 "The Fly". 10 John Travolta an Olivia
Newton-John. 11 *In Through the Out Door*. 12 Elvis Presley.
13 Yes. 14 Gene Pitney. 15 U2. 16 *New Jersey*. 17 "Mull of
Kintyre". 18 Baccara. 19 Frankie Laine. 20 Lollipop lady.

Quiz 102 Last Round 3

Answers – see page 312

LEVEL 3

1 What does KLF stand for in the context of the 1991 chart toppers?

2 Which female singer starred in the TV series "Your Cheatin' Heart" about the Scottish country music scene?

3 Who was nicknamed the Cappuccino Kid?

4 In which film did Elvis play the role of Walter Hale?

5 Who had most weeks in the UK charts in 1964?

6 How is Defosca Ervin better known?

7 What was the first of Darts' three No. 2 hits in 1978?

8 Which No. 1 hit has the shortest title?

9 Which Prince hit has one digit as its title?

10 Which soccer team sang "Blue is the Colour" in 1972?

11 What was the first of T. Rex's trio of No. 1 albums between 1971 and 1972?

12 Which was Slade's first No. 1 to go straight to No. 1?

13 Who had most weeks at No. 1 in 1991?

14 Which instrument does Cozy play?

15 What was the first of Erasure's five No. 1 albums between 1988 and 1994?

16 What was the best-selling single of 1989?

17 Who were the second pair of brothers to have separate solo No. 1 hits?

18 Which song had the line "Teacher leave those kids alone"?

19 Who was the first woman credited an artist on a UK No. 1 album?

20 Who duetted with Bobby Brown on "She Ain't Worth It"?

Answers

Last Round 5 (see Quiz 104)

1 The Four Seasons. 2 Russ Conway. 3 "Bad Moon Rising".
4 Linda McCartney. 5 *Revolver*. 6 "Never Gonna Give You Up".
7 Lee Marvin. 8 Charlie Rich. 9 Twinkle. 10 "007".
11 Coventry City. 12 "Black or White". 13 Charles Aznavour.
14 "D.I.V.O.R.C.E." 15 Alan Partridge a.k.a. Steve Coogan.
16 *The Unforgettable Fire*. 17 "Star Trek". 18 Pope John Paul II.
19 Gary Numan. 20 Dave Dee.

Quiz 103 Last Round 4

Answers – see page 309

LEVEL 3

1 Who had a production company called Handmade Films?

2 Who made the 1994 album *Titanic Days*?

3 Who was nicknamed Mr Excitement?

4 In which film did Elvis play the role of Dr John Carpenter?

5 How is Glyn Ellis better known?

6 Which Gloria Estefan hit has a number as its title?

7 Which soccer team recorded "Glad All Over" in 1990?

8 Who was "dynamite with a laser beam"?

9 What was U2's first No. 1 to go straight to No. 1?

10 Who had most weeks at No. 1 in 1978?

11 What was the eighth of Led Zeppelin's eight No. 1 albums between 1970 and 1979?

12 Who used the code name John Burrows for telephone messages?

13 Which band did the two member of Buggles join in the early 80s?

14 Who was nicknamed the Rockville Rocket?

15 Who named themselves after a US spy plane?

16 What was the first of Bon Jovi's four No. 1 albums between 1988 and 1995?

17 What was the best-selling single of 1977?

18 Who were the first Spanish group to have a No. 1 hit?

19 Who had most weeks in the UK charts in 1953 and 1954?

20 What is Yazz said to have wanted to be rather than a singer?

Last Round 2 (see Quiz 101)
1 Peggy Lee. 2 "Hell Raiser". 3 "5:15". 4 "Ossie's Dream".
5 "Sir Duke". 6 "The Young Ones". 7 "Go". 8 Connie Francis.
9 Hank Marvin, Bruce Welch. 10 Tina Turner. 11 *Let It Bleed*.
12 "Come On Eileen". 13 Curved Air. 14 Kate Bush. 15 Sarah
Vaughan. 16 *Greatest Hits*. 17 Dave Dee, Dozy, Beaky, Mick and
Tich. 18 Marmalade. 19 "YMCA". 20 *Girl Talk*.

311

Quiz 104 Last Round 5

Answers – see page 310

1 Who named themselves after the cocktail lounge in a bowling alley?

2 Who had most weeks in the UK charts in 1959?

3 Which 1969 song was used in a horror scene of metamorphosis in *An American Werewolf in London*?

4 Who was the second female to be credited on a UK No. 1 album?

5 What was the last of the Beatles' seven No. 1 albums between 1963 and 1966?

6 What was the best-selling single of 1987?

7 Which chart topper once starred in "The Streets of San Francisco"?

8 Who was nicknamed the Silver Fox?

9 How was the 60s singer Lynn Ripley better known?

10 Which Musical Youth hit has a number as its title?

11 Which soccer team recorded "Go For It!" in 1987?

12 What was Michael Jackson's first No. 1 to go straight to No. 1?

13 Whose 1974 album was called *A Tapestry of Dreams*?

14 What was the first No. 1 title to be made up of initials?

15 Who released the album *Knowing Me Knowing You* in 1995?

16 What was the first of U2's trio of No. 1 albums between 1984 and 1988?

17 Which new TV series was previewed in the US the same day as "The Monkees"?

18 Whose second album was called *The Rosary*?

19 Who was the first pop star to fly solo round the world?

20 When Eddie Cochran's car was involved in the fateful crash which future pop star was the police cadet called to the scene?

Last Round 3 (see Quiz 102)

Answers

1 Kopyright Liberation Front. **2** Eddi Reader. **3** Paul Weller.
4 *The Trouble With Girls*. **5** Jim Reeves. **6** Big Dee Irwin.
7 "Come Back My Love". **8** "If". **9** "7". **10** Chelsea.
11 *Electric Warrior*. **12** "Cum On Feel the Noize". **13** Bryan Adams. **14** Drums. **15** *The Innocents*. **16** "Ride On Time".
17 Donny and Jimmy Osmond. **18** "Another Brick in the Wall".
19 Diana Ross. **20** Glenn Medeiros.

HOW TO SET UP YOUR OWN
PUB QUIZ

It isn't easy, get that right from the start. This isn't going
to be easy. Think instead of words like; 'difficult', 'taxing'
and 'infuriating'. Consider yourself with damp palms and
a dry throat and then, when you have concentrated on
that, put it out of your mind and think of the recognition
you will receive at your local, imagine all the regulars
lifting you high upon their shoulders dancing and
weaving their way around the pub. Just like they did
when you won the Karaoke competition. It won't help but
it's good to dream every once in a while.

What you will need:

- A good selection of Biros (never be tempted to give
  your own pen up, not even to family members)

- A copy of *The Best Pop Pub Quiz Book Ever!*

- A set of answer sheets photocopied from the back of
  the book

- A good speaking voice and possibly a microphone
  and an amp

- A pub

- At least one pint inside you

- At least one more on your table

- A table

What to do:

Choose your local to start with, there is no need to get halfway through your first quiz and decide you weren't cut out for all this and then find yourself in the roughest pub in Christendom 30 miles and a long run from home.

Chat it through with the landlord and agree on whether you will be charging or not, if you don't then there is little chance of a prize for the winners other than a free pint each and this is obviously at the landlord's discretion – if you pack his pub to bursting then five free pints won't worry him, but if it's only you and a two others then he may be less than unwilling, as publicans tend to be.

If you decide on a payment entry keep it reasonable, you don't want to take the fun out of the quiz; some people will be well aware that they have very little hope of winning and will be reluctant to celebrate the fact by mortgaging their house.

Once location and prize are all sorted, then advertising the event is paramount. Get people's attention – sell sell, sell or, alternatively, stick up a gaudy looking poster on the door of the bogs. Be sure to specify all the details, time, prize and so on – remember you are selling to people whose tiny attention span is being whittled down to nothing by alcohol.

After this it is time for the big night, if you are holding the event in the 'snug' which seats ten or so you can rely on your voice, if not you should get hold of a good microphone and an amplifier so that you can boom out your questions and enunciate the length and breadth of the pub (once again, clear this with the landlord and don't let liquid anywhere near the electrical equipment). Make sure to practice, and get comfortable with the sound of your own voice and relax as much as possible, try not to rely on alcohol too much or "round one" will be followed by "rown' too" which will eventually give way to "runfree". Relax with your voice so that you can handle any queries from the teams, and any venomous abuse from the 'lively' bar area.

When you enter the pub make sure you take everything listed above. Also, make sure you have a set of tie-break questions and that you instruct everybody who is taking part of the rules – and be firm. It will only upset people if you start handing out impromptu solutions and let's face it the wisdom of Solomon is not needed when you are talking pub quiz rules; 'no cheating' is a perfectly healthy stance to start with.

Finally, keep the teams to a maximum of five members, hand out your answer papers and pens and, when everybody is good and settled, start the quiz. It might not be easy and it might not propel you to international stardom or pay for a life of luxury but you will enjoy yourself. No, really.

ANSWERS

Part One

1 _____

2 _____

3 _____

4 _____

5 _____

6 _____

7 _____

8 _____

9 _____

10 _____

11 _____

12 _____

13 _____

14 _____

15 _____

16 _____

17 _____

18 _____

19 _____

20 _____

ANSWERS

Part Two

1 _____

2 _____

3 _____

4 _____

5 _____

6 _____

7 _____

8 _____

9 _____

10 _____

11 _____

12 _____

13 _____

14 _____

15 _____

16 _____

17 _____

18 _____

19 _____

20 _____

ANSWERS

Part Three

1 _____   11 _____

2 _____   12 _____

3 _____   13 _____

4 _____   14 _____

5 _____   15 _____

6 _____   16 _____

7 _____   17 _____

8 _____   18 _____

9 _____   19 _____

10 _____   20 _____

ALSO AVAILABLE

The Best Pub Quiz Book Ever!

Containing over 10,000 questions
and answers, this book is divided
into over 300 quizzes on all of your
favourite subjects. A must for every
Pub Quiz fanatic.

**The Best Football Pub Quiz Book
Ever!**

Containing 6,000 questions and
answers, this book is divided into
over 300 individual quizzes on all of
your favourite soccer subjects.
Essential reading for Pub Quiz
fanatics.

ISBN 1 85868 259 2
£6.99
Available from all good bookshops